GENETIC ALGORITHMS

IN C++

Scott Robert Ladd

M&T BOOKS

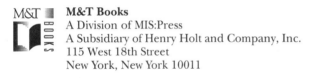

M&T Books
A Division of MIS:Press
A Subsidiary of Henry Holt and Company, Inc.
115 West 18th Street
New York, New York 10011

Library of Congress Cataloging-in-Publication Data

```
Ladd, Scott.
    Genetic algrithms in C++ / Scott Robert Ladd.
       p.   cm.
    ISBN 1-55851-459-7
    1. C++ (Computer program language)  2. Genetic algorithms.
  I. Title.
  Qa76.73.C153L335   1995
  005.1--dc20                                    95-26026
                                                    CIP
```

10 9 8 7 6 5 4 3 2 1

Associate Publisher: Paul Farrell

Development Editor: Michael Sprague

Copy Edit Manager: Shari Chappell

Copy Editors: Melissa Burns

Technical Editor: Don Johnson

Production Editor: Patricia Wallenburg

DEDICATION

For my lovely and talented wife, Maria, who has supported me through tasks and times both mundane and bizarre. Life would not be complete without her.

And to Tessa Maria Ladd, the third daughter who arrived in the midst of chaos and book writing: Thanks for coming!

ACKNOWLEDGMENTS

I greatly appreciate the efforts of my editor, Michael Sprague, in working with me on these projects. In a business where authors and editors are more often adversary than friend, I'm pleased that Michael falls into the latter category.

TABLE OF CONTENTS

Chapter 3

Chapter 4

Chapter 5

Chapter 6

Chapter 7

Chapter 8

CHAPTER 1

THE POWER OF LIFE

Computer programs tend to be static: they begin at point A and go to point B, mindlessly following a specific path. As the basis of most software, deterministic algorithms have proven their efficacy. Yet something fundamental is missing from software: adaptability. Simply put, the vast majority of applications are fixed entities that cannot adjust to situations unforeseen by their programmers. Furthermore, some problems (which I'll introduce later in this book) cannot be easily solved by deterministic programs.

If you're looking for a paradigm of adaptability, look no further than biology. Living things, based on a set of simple underlying chemical principles, have shown remarkable flexibility and adaptability throughout billions of years of changing environments. Implementing biological concepts creates software that evolves solutions. In some cases, a biological algorithm might find solutions that its programmer never envisioned—and that concept allows software to go beyond its human creator's vision.

What makes life a good model for software? The answer to that question lies in understanding the basic principle of biological evolution.

BIOLOGICAL EVOLUTION

In the mid-19th century, Charles Darwin reasoned that immutable species would become increasingly incompatible with their restless environment. The resemblance of offspring to their parents suggested to him that traits pass from one generation to the next; he also noticed slight differences between siblings, which provide a species with a pool of unique individuals who compete for food and mates.

From those observations, Darwin concluded that as the environment changed, organisms best-suited to the new conditions would bear offspring reflecting their successful traits. Darwin named this process *natural selection*, and he believed that it was the central mechanism by which species evolved.

Modern science recognizes evolution as the mechanism that creates biological organization. While evolutionary theory has been refined in the century since Charles Darwin's death, the core concepts remain intact. We can see evolution operating today and in the fossil record of past species; we can see how organisms change to survive in an ever-changing world.

A tiny English moth provides a classic example of natural selection in action. Before the Industrial Revolution, light-colored pepper moths blended with the white lichen on trees, hiding themselves from predaceous birds; dark-colored moths contrasted with the lichen and often became avian meals. But when smoke from England's new coal-fired factories killed the lichens and coated the trees with soot, the light-colored moths became visible targets for birds, while dark-colored moths blended into the new environment. Within a few years the peppered moth population was nearly all dark-colored, having adapted to its new environment through natural selection.

While the survival of individuals determines the characteristics of the next generation, it is the reproductive success of a population as a whole that determines the evolution of a species. Natural selection is limited by the characteristics of a population; while it is often called *survival of the fittest*, natural selection really operates through the survival of the best available organisms. An organism's "fitness" is relative to a changing ecosystem, other species, and other members of its population. What is "best" today (light-colored moths on lichen) may not be "best" tomorrow (dark-colored moths on soot).

Darwin didn't know how characteristics were passed from parent to offspring; he simply saw it happening. The missing element was beyond the science of his time, and nearly a century passed before someone identified the mysterious agents behind evolution. In 1951, biologists Francis Crick and James Watson first described the deoxyribonucleic acid (DNA) molecule—a tiny corkscrew built from surprisingly simple chemicals. DNA encodes the chemical recipes for life's proteins and enzymes, and it packs an amazing amount of information into an incredibly tiny space; if the DNA in a single human cell were straightened out, it would be nearly two feet long.

Biologists are still exploring this most fundamental piece of life's mystery. Each tightly coiled strand of DNA contains genes that define individual parts of an organism's blueprint. Human DNA includes more than 200,000 genes that are responsible for controlling everything from eye color to the potential for developing certain illnesses.

Offspring inherit characteristics through genes received from a parent. Simple organisms such as fungi and bacteria reproduce asexually by duplicating themselves. A single-celled amoeba, for example, creates offspring by splitting into two new organisms that contain identical DNA. Thus, asexual reproduction produces new organisms that differ little from each other or their progenitor.

Most complex organisms reproduce sexually by combining genes from two parents in their offspring. By mixing and matching DNA from two organisms, sexual reproduction increases the variation within a species. The possibilities are almost endless; for example, a human couple can produce more than 7,000,000,000,000 different blueprints for a person.

The collective genetic information in a population constitutes a gene pool. Large gene pools are healthier than small ones because they allow a greater number of genetic combinations. Greater variability means that a larger gene pool is more adaptable and less prone to recessive genetic disorders. A small gene pool leads to inbreeding, increasing the chance that recessive genes will manifest themselves in the offspring of closely related organisms.

Natural selection changes the frequencies of genes in a population, but it doesn't produce new genes. The first life forms began as self-replicating chemicals that bound to each other in mutual cooperation. The first complete organisms resembled an amoeba—and an amoeba clearly does not contain the genes required to evolve into a human being. New characteristics must somehow arise; otherwise, the simple original life forms would never have evolved into the millions of species on Earth today.

A mutation is a random change in an organism's genes. It is highly unlikely that a random genetic change will improve a complex organism that is well-adapted to its environment; most manifest mutations disappear from the population through natural selection. Fortunately, the vast majority of mutations have no effect. Studies of human DNA have found long sequences of "junk genes" that serve no explicit purpose; mutations in junk genes are likely to be meaningless. And sometimes, cells can repair damaged DNA, eliminating many mutations before they are passed along to new cells or offspring.

Natural selection mixes and sifts gene pools, acting on variations produced by reproduction and mutation. Sometimes a gene pool evolves in a straight line, carrying a species from one form to another, as in the earlier example of the peppered moth. In other cases, forces act to divide a gene pool, and natural selection works on the now-separate populations to produce new species.

If a species encounters several open niches, it may quickly diversify in a process known as *adaptive radiation*. When the dinosaurs vanished 65,000,000 years ago, they left unoccupied niches that were exploited by mammals. Through adaptive radiation, a few shrew-like species blossomed into thousands of types ranging from bears to people to whales.

In the 1980s, biologists Niles Eldredge and Stephen Jay Gould introduced a substantial modification in evolutionary theory. They postulated that evolution was not a steady process, moving from species to species continuously. Their review of the fossil record suggested that species remain static until environmental factors force rapid evolution into new forms. Known as *punctuated equilibrium,* this new idea has been hotly debated.

CHAPTER 2

GENETIC ALGORITHMS 101

Based on a few simple mechanisms, life adapts species to uncountable niches in an ever-changing environment. A species can be thought of as life's solution to the problem of exploiting a niche; software, in turn, can simulate natural techniques in the search for solutions to problems. The software universe is far less complex than the biological world, and no piece of software can—or needs—to incorporate all of life's techniques. Whereas living things need to seek flexible roles in variable environments, computer algorithms often need only to find a specific answer to a fixed question.

DEFINING GENETIC ALGORITHMS

The quest to apply evolution to software is not new. The University of Michigan's John Holland defined the concept of *genetic algorithms* in a 1975 paper titled "Adaptation in Natural and Artificial Systems." Reasoning that the robustness of life stemmed from evolution by natural selection, Holland concluded that biology could provide a metaphor for artificial systems. Holland began by codifying the precise mechanisms of biological evolution; he then applied those principles to the development of software.

Computer scientists still debate the precise definition of a genetic algorithm (GA). In the broadest sense, a GA creates a set of solutions that reproduce based on their fitness in a given environment. The process follows this pattern:

1. An initial population of random solutions is created.
2. Each member of the population is assigned a fitness value based on its evaluation against the current problem.
3. Solutions with a higher fitness value are most likely to parent new solutions during reproduction.
4. The new solution set replaces the old, a *generation* is complete, and the process continues at step 2.

That sequence implements, in a most simplistic way, the concept of survival of the fittest. The reproductive success of a solution is directly tied to the fitness value it is assigned during evaluation. In this stochastic process, the least-fit solution has a small chance at reproduction while the most-fit solution may not reproduce at all. The outcome of a genetic algorithm is based on probabilities, just as biological success is grounded in chance.

So how can a random process possibly reach any sort of definitive answer to a question? Look to biology for your answer; living things have evolved flight and millions of other adaptations specific to various niches and environments. Computer programs operate in an environment that is several orders of magnitude simpler than the biological world; the powerful tools of nature should have no trouble finding solutions to relatively trivial problems.

The standard model for a GA solution is an anonymous bit string called a *chromosome* after its biological counterpart. The chromosome must be decoded during evaluation. Where DNA uses the base-4 alphabet, a binary string uses ones and zeros to encode information. During reproduction, the chromosomes of parent solutions combine and undergo mutation in creating the next generation. In the highly idealized universe of silicon, we have fine control over this process.

Let's develop a genetic algorithm for a simple problem and see how these techniques become reality in C++ code.

A PROBLEM TO BE SOLVED

We'll begin with a "blackbox" that returns a single output value for every input value. No one knows what is going on inside the box, but we do know the following facts:

▼ Input to the box is a 32-bit signed integer.

▼ Output from the box is a 32-bit signed integer with a value between 0 and 32.

▼ Only one unknown input value generates an output of 32.

▼ Output values less than 32 may be produced by several different inputs.

▼ There is no obvious correspondence between input values and their outputs. For example, an input of 32 generates an output of 0, while an input of 10 results in an output of 4.

▼ The box cannot be opened or otherwise investigated, other than by feeding it values and examining the associated output.

Our task is to find the input value that produces an output of 32; in other words, we want to maximize the output of the blackbox. For the purposes of this example, I define a Blackbox function with the following prototype:

```
long Blackbox(long x);
```

You have no idea how Blackbox is implemented; it could, for example, be defined in a module for which the source code is missing or lost.

A brute-force approach would test all 4,294,967,296 possible long values. Here's an example of such an algorithm:

```
long n = LONG_MIN;

while (1)
    {
    if (Blackbox(n) == 32L)
        {
        cout << n << " generates 32!";
        break;
        }

    if (n = LONG_MAX)
        {
        cout << "Didn't find 32!"
        break;
        }

    ++n;
    }
```

The problem with a brute-force approach isn't that it won't find the answer; assuming that we have our facts correct, one of the input values will generate an answer of 32. Where brute force falls on its face is in how long it might take to find an answer. The preceding loop might find the answer after a few runs, or after billions of runs. Clearly, a more intelligent solution is required.

PARAMETERS OF A SOLUTION

Let's build a genetic algorithm to maximize the output from Blackbox.

Different programmers implement various ways of mutating chromosomes. A common system sets a probability that any given bit will be changed; a test is performed for each bit to see if its value should be changed. Such a system requires the generation of many random numbers, which can degrade program performance. For example, a population of 50 `long` chromosomes would use 1600 random values during mutation. As we'll see in Chapter 3, the computational overhead of a quality random number generator is substantial.

When I do mutation, I define a probability that a bit in a chromosome will be randomly changed. This requires the generation of one or two random numbers—the first to decide if mutation will take place, and the second to determine the bit that changes. To allow for multiple bit changes within a chromosome, I sometimes implement a looping system such as:

```
while (rand() < MUTE_CHANCE)
    mutate(chromosome);
```

Elaboration

Mutation and crossover are known as *reproduction operators*. Holland also defined another reproduction operator, *inversion*, which reverses a segment of bits within a chromosome. Few researchers have examined inversion seriously, and those that have suggest the use of inversion only when the chromosome size is "large." For now, I'll ignore inversion.

Even if you don't use inversion, you should keep chromosome length in mind when implementing crossover and mutation. In a four-bit chromosome, only 16 possibilities exist; crossover probably won't create any new chromosome variation in such an environment because all possibilities are likely represented in even a small population. Mutation, in turn, has less effect in longer chromosomes; changing one bit in a 256-bit string has less influence than would flipping a bit in a 16-bit chromosome.

Another factor to keep in mind is the population size of a solution set. The larger the population, the longer it will take to process. Smaller populations, however, lack a robust selection of chromosomes. In designing a genetic algorithm, you need to balance the size of the population against the number of generations required to find a solution. For example, a population of 100 chromosomes may find the solution in only 10 generations, but each evaluation cycle may take four times as long as it would for a population of 20 chromosomes that finds the solution in 20 generations. The smaller population is faster by a factor of two.

Population size has another influence on genetic algorithms: it dilutes the influence of high fitness values on reproductive success. In a population of 10 chromosomes, in which one has a fitness of nine and the others a fitness of one, half of all parents will probably be selected from the nine relatively unfit chromosomes, even though the best chromosome is nine times more fit.

Another rule of thumb: evaluating chromosomes and calculating fitness is the most time-consuming component of a genetic algorithm. Your goal should be to reduce the number of fitness evaluations, either by reducing the size of the population or by decreasing the number of generations required to find the solution.

Before getting into the development of code, I'll bring up two more techniques that can enhance the performance of a genetic algorithm. *Elitist selection* always copies of the most-fit chromosome into the next generation. Using elitist selection guarantees that the best solution to a problem survives, ensuring that populations never lose ground on fitness.

Another enhancement is *fitness scaling*. As a population converges on a definitive solution, the difference between fitness values may become very small. That produces a roulette wheel with nearly equal sections, preventing the best solutions from having a significant advantage in reproductive selection. Fitness scaling solves this problem by adjusting the fitness values to the advantage of the most-fit chromosomes.

Windowing is the simplest form of fitness scaling. To implement windowing, begin by computing fitness values as usual, keeping track of the smallest fitness value. Then subtract the minimum value from all fitness values, thus adjusting the fitness array to a zero-base. You might also want to subtract a number slightly smaller than the minimum fitness, just to ensure that all chromosomes have a chance at reproduction.

PARAMETERS

Programming genetic algorithms is largely a matter of "feel." To understand exactly which factors produce the fastest results in a given situation, you need to see what works and how. To aid your exploration, I've defined a set of parameters for solving this chapter's problems. You can set those parameters to a variety of values, learning how different combinations of options affect performance.

Dialog Box

Figure 2.5 shows the Windows dialog box that defines parameters for solving the Blackbox problem.

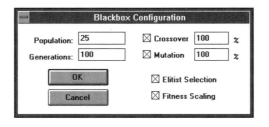

FIGURE 2.5 BLACKBOX CONFIGURATION DIALOG BOX.

Through the dialog box, you can define the population size of the solution set and the number of generations to be run. You can also turn on and off crossover, mutation, elitist selection, and fitness scaling via their checkboxes. Finally, percentage values allow you to set the chance of crossover and mutation. Figure 2.5 shows the dialog box loaded with the default program startup values.

Underlying Code

I created a class, BBOptConfig, to manage parameter values input via the dialog box:

```
class BBOptConfig
    {
    public:
        BBOptConfig
            (
            HINSTANCE inst,
            HWND      parent
            );

        static void DlgInit
            (
            HWND  dlg
            );

        static BOOL DlgStore
            (
            HWND  dlg
            );

        // interrogation
        bool   GetValidity()  { return Valid;     }
        size_t GetPopSize()   { return PopSize;   }
        size_t GetTestSize()  { return TestSize;  }
        bool   GetCrossover() { return Crossover; }
        float  GetCrossProb() { return CrossProb; }
        bool   GetMutate()    { return Mutate;    }
        float  GetMuteProb()  { return MuteProb;  }
        bool   GetScaling()   { return Scaling;   }
        bool   GetElitist()   { return Elitist;   }

    private:
        // parameters
        bool   Valid;
        size_t PopSize;
        size_t TestSize;
        bool   Crossover;
        float  CrossProb;
        bool   Mutate;
        float  MuteProb;
        bool   Scaling;
        bool   Elitist;

        // stored parameter values
        static size_t DefPopSize;
        static size_t DefTestSize;
        static bool   DefCrossover;
        static float  DefCrossProb;
```

```
        static bool    DefMutate;
        static float   DefMuteProb;
        static bool    DefScaling;
        static bool    DefElitist;
    };
```

A BBOptConfig object contains the parameters of a genetic algorithm, which can be retrieved via the various interrogation functions. The static Def... values contain the last set of selected parameters; these are set to default values on program startup:

```
size_t BBOptConfig::DefPopSize   =   25;
size_t BBOptConfig::DefTestSize  =  100;
bool   BBOptConfig::DefCrossover = true;
float  BBOptConfig::DefCrossProb =    1.00F;
bool   BBOptConfig::DefMutate    = true;
float  BBOptConfig::DefMuteProb  =    1.00F;
bool   BBOptConfig::DefScaling   = true;
bool   BBOptConfig::DefElitist   = true;
```

When a BBOptConfig object is instantiated, it creates a dialog box filled with the Def... values. The following code implements the dialog box and error checking:

```
static LPCSTR BBOptConfigDlgName = MAKEINTRESOURCE(DLG_BLACKBOX);

static const char * BBOptConfigDlgErr =
    "Your input is in error!\n\n"
    "Population  must be >= 10.\n"
    "Generations must be > 0.";

BOOL FAR PASCAL __export BBOptConfigDlgProc
    (
    HWND  dlg,
    WORD  message,
    WORD  wParam,
    DWORD lParam
    );

BBOptConfig::BBOptConfig
    (
    HINSTANCE inst,
    HWND      parent
```

```
    )
    {
    DLGPROC thunk
    thunk = MakeProcInstance(FARPROC(BBOptConfigDlgProc),inst);
    int res = DialogBox(inst,BBOptConfigDlgName,parent,thunk);
    FreeProcInstance(thunk);

    if (res)
        Valid = true;
    else
        Valid = false;

    PopSize   = DefPopSize;
    TestSize  = DefTestSize;
    Crossover = DefCrossover;
    CrossProb = DefCrossProb;
    Mutate    = DefMutate;
    MuteProb  = DefMuteProb;
    Scaling   = DefScaling;
    Elitist   = DefElitist;
    }
#pragma argsused
BOOL FAR PASCAL __export BBOptConfigDlgProc
    (
    HWND  dlg,
    WORD  message,
    WORD  wParam,
    DWORD lParam
    )
    {
    switch (message)
        {
        case WM_INITDIALOG:
            BBOptConfig::DlgInit(dlg);
            return TRUE;

        case WM_COMMAND:
            switch (wParam)
                {
                case IDOK:
                    if (TRUE == BBOptConfig::DlgStore(dlg))
                        EndDialog(dlg, 1);

                    break;

                case IDCANCEL:
```

```
                    EndDialog(dlg, 0);
                }

            return TRUE;
        }

    return FALSE;
    }

void BBOptConfig::DlgInit
    (
    HWND   dlg
    )
    {
    char temp[64];

    sprintf(temp,"%u",DefPopSize);
    SetDlgItemText(dlg,IDD_BBOX_POP,temp);

    sprintf(temp,"%u",DefTestSize);
    SetDlgItemText(dlg,IDD_BBOX_GEN,temp);

    sprintf(temp,"%.6g",DefCrossProb * 100.0F);
    SetDlgItemText(dlg,IDD_BBOX_CPROB,temp);

    sprintf(temp,"%.6g",DefMuteProb * 100.0F);
    SetDlgItemText(dlg,IDD_BBOX_MPROB,temp);

    if (DefCrossover)
        SendDlgItemMessage(dlg,IDD_BBOX_CROSS,BM_SETCHECK,1,0L);
    else
        SendDlgItemMessage(dlg,IDD_BBOX_CROSS,BM_SETCHECK,0,0L);

    if (DefMutate)
        SendDlgItemMessage(dlg,IDD_BBOX_MUTE,BM_SETCHECK,1,0L);
    else
        SendDlgItemMessage(dlg,IDD_BBOX_MUTE,BM_SETCHECK,0,0L);

    if (DefScaling)
        SendDlgItemMessage(dlg,IDD_BBOX_FSCALE,BM_SETCHECK,1,0L);
    else
        SendDlgItemMessage(dlg,IDD_BBOX_FSCALE,BM_SETCHECK,0,0L);

    if (DefElitist)
        SendDlgItemMessage(dlg,IDD_BBOX_ELITISM,BM_SETCHECK,1,0);
    else
        SendDlgItemMessage(dlg,IDD_BBOX_ELITISM,BM_SETCHECK,0,0);
```

```
    }

BOOL BBOptConfig::DlgStore
    (
    HWND  dlg
    )
    {
    char temp[64];

    GetDlgItemText(dlg,IDD_BBOX_POP,temp,64);
    size_t psz = abs(atoi(temp));

    GetDlgItemText(dlg,IDD_BBOX_GEN,temp,64);
    size_t gen = abs(atoi(temp));

    if ((psz < 10) || (gen == 0))
        {
        MessageBeep(MB_ICONHAND);
        MessageBox(NULL,BBOptConfigDlgErr,
                   "Configuration Error",MB_OK | MB_ICONHAND);
        return FALSE;
        }

    DefPopSize  = psz;
    DefTestSize = gen;

    GetDlgItemText(dlg,IDD_BBOX_CPROB,temp,64);
    DefCrossProb = fabs(atof(temp)) / 100.0F;

    GetDlgItemText(dlg,IDD_BBOX_MPROB,temp,64);
    DefMuteProb = fabs(atof(temp)) / 100.0F;

    if (SendDlgItemMessage(dlg,IDD_BBOX_CROSS,BM_GETCHECK,0,0L))
        DefCrossover = true;
    else
        DefCrossover = false;

    if (SendDlgItemMessage(dlg,IDD_BBOX_MUTE,BM_GETCHECK,0,0L))
        DefMutate = true;
    else
        DefMutate = false;

    if (SendDlgItemMessage(dlg,IDD_BBOX_FSCALE,BM_GETCHECK,0,0L))
        DefScaling = true;
    else
        DefScaling = false;
```

```
if (SendDlgItemMessage(dlg,IDD_BBOX_ELITISM,BM_GETCHECK,0,0))
    DefElitist = true;
else
    DefElitist = false;

return TRUE;
}
```

Once the constructor completes its work, a `BBOptConfig` object operates as a set of constant values defining the limits of a genetic algorithm. `BBOptConfig` is an example of a class that encapsulates an environment-specific process; any procedure using a `BBOptConfig` object can (and in fact, must) ignore the way in which the parameters are set. Moving `BBOptConfig` to another environment requires changing the class constructor to obtain values using native techniques.

EVOLVING AN ANSWER

Parameters in hand, it's time to write a genetic algorithm for optimizing the output from the `Blackbox` function. For now, I'll keep the implementation of `Blackbox` a secret; while you may have guessed by now what it is doing, I don't want to give away the optimum solution until you've seen how the genetic algorithm performs.

The algorithm begins by creating a `BBOptConfig` object to define the parameters for the run. I then load the parameters into the local variable, to avoid calling functions within the program's many nested loops:

```
BBOptConfig cfg(ThisInstance,MainWdw);

if (!cfg.GetValidity())
    {
    buffer << "Cancelled\r\n";
    return;
    }

const size_t POP_SZ = cfg.GetPopSize();
const size_t GEN_SZ = cfg.GetTestSize();
const bool   cross  = cfg.GetCrossover();
```

```
const float   crate  = cfg.GetCrossProb();
const bool    mutate = cfg.GetMutate();
const float   mrate  = cfg.GetMuteProb();
const bool    elite  = cfg.GetElitist();
const bool    scale  = cfg.GetScaling();
```

I then allocate buffers to hold the population, its children, and fitness values:

```
// allocate population and fitness buffers
long * pop = new long[POP_SZ];

if (pop == NULL)
    ErrorMessage("BB Alloc Failed",ET_CRASH);

long * newpop = new long[POP_SZ];

if (newpop == NULL)
    ErrorMessage("BB Alloc Failed",ET_CRASH);

long * fit = new long[POP_SZ];

if (fit == NULL)
    ErrorMessage("BB Alloc Failed",ET_CRASH);
```

Next, I seed the standard C++ random number generator and define variables:

```
// initialize psuedo-random number generator
srand((unsigned)time(NULL));

// various variables
long bestl, bestf, minf, mask, sel, totf, avgf;
size_t i, g, p1, p2;
char buf[64];
```

The last stage of initialization is the creation of an initial population of random values:

```
// create initial population
for (i = 0; i < POP_SZ; ++i)
    pop[i] = long(rand());
```

The main loop looks like this:

```
// start with generation zero
g = 0;

while (1) // loop breaks in middle
    {
    // display progress
    wsprintf(buf,"%s (loop: %5u of %5u)",AppName,g,GEN_SZ);
    SetWindowText(MainWdw,buf);

    // initialize for fitness testing
    bestf = -1L;
    totf  = 0L;
    minf  = LONG_MAX;

    // fitness testing
    for (i = 0; i < POP_SZ; ++i)
        {
        // call fitness function and store result
        fit[i] = Blackbox(pop[i]);

        // keep track of best fitness
        if (fit[i] > bestf)
            {
            bestf = fit[i];
            bestl = pop[i];
            }

        // keep track of least fit
        if (fit[i] < minf)
            minf = fit[i];

        // total fitness
        totf += fit[i];
        }

    // make sure we have at least some fit values
    if (totf == 0L)
        {
        buffer << "Population has total fitness of ZERO\r\n";
        return;
        }

    // compute average fitness
    avgf = totf / POP_SZ;
```

```
// sum (and maybe scale) fitness values
if (scale)
    {
    // ensures that the least fitness is one
    ++minf;

    // recalculate total fitness to reflect scaled values
    totf = 0L;

    for (i = 0; i < POP_SZ; ++i)
        {
        fit[i] -= minf;   // reduce by smallest fitness
        fit[i] *= fit[i]; // square result of above
        totf   += fit[i]; // add into total fitness
        }
    }

// display stats for this generation
buffer << setw(4) << g
       << " best: " << setw(8) << setbase(16) << bestl
       << " (" << setw(2) << setbase(10) << bestf
       << ") avg. fit = " << setw(2) << avgf
       << " min. fit = "  << setw(2) << minf << "\r\n";

// exit if this is final generation
if (g == GEN_SZ)
    break;

// create new population
for (i = 0; i < POP_SZ; ++i)
    {
    // roulette-select parent
    sel = (long)((float(rand())
                    / float(RAND_MAX)) * float(totf));
    p1  = 0;

    while (sel > fit[p1])
        {
        sel -= fit[p1];
        ++p1;
        }

    // crossover reproduction
    if (cross
    && ((float(rand()) / float(RAND_MAX)) < crate))
        {
```

```
        // roulette-select second parent
        sel = (long)((float(rand())
                    / float(RAND_MAX)) * float(totf));
        p2 = 0;

        while (sel > fit[p2])
            {
            sel -= fit[p2];
            ++p2;
            }

        // mask of bits to be copied from first parent
        mask = 0xFFFFFFFFL << (int)((float(rand())
                                    / float(RAND_MAX))
                                    * 32.0F);

        // new string from two parents
        newpop[i] = (pop[p1] & mask)
                    | (pop[p2] & (~mask));
        }
    else
        // one parent, no crossover reproduction
        newpop[i] = pop[p1];

    // mutation
    if (mutate
    && ((float(rand()) / float(RAND_MAX)) < mrate))
        {
        // select bit to be changed
        mask = 1L << (int)((float(rand())
                            / float(RAND_MAX))
                            * 32.0F);

        // flip the bit
        if (newpop[i] & mask)
            newpop[i] &= ~mask;
        else
            newpop[i] |= mask;
        }
    }

// if elitist selection, replace first item with best
if (elite)
    newpop[0] = best1;

// replace old population with new one
memcpy(pop,newpop,POP_SZ * sizeof(long));
```

```
// increment generation
++g;
}
```

Each generation begins with the fitness testing of each chromosome through calls to Blackbox. The highest fitness is tracked for reporting purposes, while the lowest fitness is determined in case fitness scaling is required. In the unlikely event that the population has a total fitness of zero, the routine stops.

After calculating the average fitness of the population and reporting statistics for the current generation, the algorithm performs fitness scaling (assuming it was selected). To adjust the fitness values, I subtract the minimum fitness value (*windowing*), add one, and then square the result. Adding one gives every chromosome a chance of reproduction, and squaring the windowed fitness value strengthens the reproductive chances of the most-fit chromosomes.

A third loop implements reproduction. Using the roulette wheel technique, the algorithm selects one or two parents (depending on whether or not crossover is enabled). I use one shifted bitmask to implement crossover and another bitmask in mutating a child chromosome. If elitism is enabled, the algorithm automatically copies the best chromosome of the parent generation into the first element of the new population. Then I copy the new population over the old and proceed to the next generation.

Once all generations have run, the routine ends by deleting the various buffers:

```
// delete population and fitness arrays
delete [] pop;
delete [] newpop;
delete [] fit;
```

The output of the preceding routine looks like this, using the default configuration parameters:

```
Pop. Size: 25
```

```
Test Size: 20
Crossover: true (100%)
 Mutation: true (100%)
  Scaling: true
  Elitism: true

    0 best:      7ada (21) avg. fit = 17 min. fit = 16
    1 best:     47ada (22) avg. fit = 19 min. fit = 17
    2 best: 11007ada (23) avg. fit = 20 min. fit = 17
    3 best: 11007ada (23) avg. fit = 20 min. fit = 19
    4 best: 1102789a (24) avg. fit = 21 min. fit = 20
    5 best: 1102789a (24) avg. fit = 22 min. fit = 19
    6 best: 1186785a (28) avg. fit = 22 min. fit = 21
    7 best: 1186785a (28) avg. fit = 25 min. fit = 23
    8 best: 1186785a (28) avg. fit = 26 min. fit = 26
    9 best: 11ce706a (29) avg. fit = 26 min. fit = 25
   10 best: 11ce706a (29) avg. fit = 27 min. fit = 26
   11 best:  1ce784a (30) avg. fit = 27 min. fit = 25
   12 best:  1ce784a (30) avg. fit = 27 min. fit = 25
   13 best:  1ce784a (30) avg. fit = 27 min. fit = 27
   14 best:  1ce784a (30) avg. fit = 28 min. fit = 26
   15 best: 11de7842 (31) avg. fit = 28 min. fit = 27
   16 best: 11de7842 (31) avg. fit = 28 min. fit = 26
   17 best: 11de7842 (31) avg. fit = 29 min. fit = 26
   18 best: 11de7842 (31) avg. fit = 28 min. fit = 28
   19 best: 11de7842 (31) avg. fit = 29 min. fit = 29
   20 best: 11de784a (32) avg. fit = 29 min. fit = 28
```

ANALYSIS

A genetic algorithm is a stochastic process that exhibits variable performance. To aid my analysis of the blackbox optimization algorithm, I created a special version of the preceding code that computes statistics—including performance averages—for 100 runs of the algorithm. I won't present that code here; you'll find it in the Forge application program on this book's source code disk.

With a population of 100 chromosomes and both crossover and mutation enabled, the genetic algorithm doesn't perform very well:

```
Pop. Size: 100
Test Size: 500
```

```
Crossover: true (100%)
 Mutation: true (100%)
   Scaling: false
   Elitism: false

gen   average = 497.43
gen   minimum = 261
gen   maximum = 500

tick average = 5606.19
tick minimum = 3010
tick maximum = 5767
```

Lowering the mutation rate, however, produces faster results:

```
Pop. Size: 100
Test Size: 500
Crossover: true (100%)
 Mutation: true (30%)
   Scaling: false
   Elitism: false

gen   average = 164.49
gen   minimum = 45
gen   maximum = 500

tick average = 1783.97
tick minimum = 494
tick maximum = 5493
```

Since a lower mutation rate speeds the algorithm along, would reducing the crossover rate be advantageous? No. With the crossover rate set to 90%, the algorithm slows considerably:

```
Pop. Size: 100
Test Size: 500
Crossover: true (90%)
 Mutation: true (30%)
   Scaling: false
   Elitism: false

gen   average = 192.94
gen   minimum = 66
gen   maximum = 500
```

```
tick average = 2030.03
tick minimum = 696
tick maximum = 5273
```

Also note that if the mutation rate is too small or if mutation is turned off, the algorithm will run poorly.

Enabling elitist selection improves the speed of the algorithm, ensuring that a solution is found before 400 generations have been run:

```
Pop. Size: 100
Test Size: 500
Crossover: true (100%)
 Mutation: true (100%)
   Scaling: false
   Elitism: true

gen  average = 130.34
gen  minimum = 37
gen  maximum = 392

tick average = 1464.85
tick minimum = 415
tick maximum = 4394
```

Combining a low mutation rate with elitist selection further enhances the algorithm's speed:

```
Pop. Size: 100
Test Size: 500
Crossover: true (100%)
 Mutation: true (30%)
   Scaling: false
   Elitism: true

gen  average = 68.32
gen  minimum = 32
gen  maximum = 152

tick average = 742.59
tick minimum = -1
tick maximum = 1648
```

However, the most dramatic increase in performance comes when fitness scaling is used with mutation and crossover:

```
Pop. Size: 100
Test Size: 500
Crossover: true (100%)
 Mutation: true (70%)
   Scaling: true
   Elitism: false

gen   average = 14.12
gen   minimum = 10
gen   maximum = 18

tick average = 161.48
tick minimum = 120
tick maximum = 220
```

The reason for the stunning increase in the speed of convergence lies with the nature of the problem being solved. Fitness values returned by Blackbox fall into a relatively narrow range, leaving little distinction between different chromosomes. This is known as the *close race* phenomenon. The inclusion of fitness scaling adjusts reproductive success in favor of the chromosomes with the highest fitness.

You should also note the change in mutation rate associated with the advent of fitness scaling. Without scaling, a low mutation rate is advantageous; once fitness testing skews reproductive success, however, a higher mutation rate proves most useful.

Using all four techniques produces an even faster algorithm:

```
Pop. Size: 100
Test Size: 500
Crossover: true (100%)
 Mutation: true (70%)
   Scaling: true
   Elitism: true

gen   average = 13.61
gen   minimum = 10
gen   maximum = 19
```

```
tick average = 155.44
tick minimum = 110
tick maximum = 220
```

Changing the population size also speeds the algorithm along. With a population of 25 and a mutation rate of 85%, the algorithm averages more cycles to find an optimal solution—but processing each generation is so quick that overall performance improves:

```
Pop. Size: 25
Test Size: 500
Crossover: true (100%)
 Mutation: true (85%)
   Scaling: true
   Elitism: true

gen  average = 17.71
gen  minimum = 10
gen  maximum = 34

tick average = 85.13
tick minimum = 50
tick maximum = 165
```

In case you were wondering, the `Blackbox` function compares the input value to a constant, returning the number of bits that match between the two values. Only one value matches all 32 bits in the target:

```
long Blackbox
    (
    long x
    )
    {
    // test value — the speed of light in meters per second
    static const long n =  0x11DE784AL; // 299,792,458;

    long fit  = 0L;
    long mask = 1L;

    // count matching bits
    for (int i = 0; i < 32; ++i)
        {
        if ((x & mask) == (n & mask))
```

```
        ++fit;

    mask <<= 1;
    }

// return fitness between 0 and 32
return fit;
}
```

The genetic algorithm was looking for a single solution among more than 4 million—and it can find it in only a few seconds, testing, on average, only about 500 values.

ONWARD

In optimizing the output of Blackbox, I've demonstrated only the basic principles of genetic algorithms. The next chapters present extensions to the material in this chapter—and in Chapter 3, I'll build a set of reusable components for GA development.

CHAPTER 3

TOOLS FOR SOFTWARE EVOLUTION

In solving the `Blackbox` problem of Chapter 2, I've demonstrated the basic principles of genetic algorithm design. Before expanding on that material, I want to introduce a set of classes that support genetic algorithms.

BOOLEAN VALUES

You'll notice my use of a type named bool, which can take on one of two values, true or false. The C language has always defined logical "true" as a nonzero value, and "false" as zero. The proposed ANSI C++ standard defines the bool type to formalize the return type of logical functions. Instead of defining an operator == function as returning an int, ANSI C++ now uses the bool type.

I've implemented a variety of Boolean types over the years, but none were directly compatible with an ANSI type. Looking over the ANSI document, I realized that I could create a bool class to emulate most of the standard's definition. The class is small and entirely implemented as inline code:

```
enum { false, true };

class bool
    {
    public:
        // constructors
        bool(int b = 0) { Val = (b ? true : false); }

        // assignment
        bool operator = (bool b) { return (Val = b.Val); }

        // conversions
        operator int() const { return Val; }

        // comparisons
        bool operator == (bool b) const { return Val == b.Val; }
        bool operator != (bool b) const { return Val != b.Val; }

        // stream output operator
        friend ostream & operator << (ostream & os, bool b);

    private:
        int Val;
    };

inline ostream & operator << (ostream & os, bool b)
    {
```

```
os << (b ? "true" : "false");
return os;
}
```

Is `bool` really necessary? No, but it will be a part of C++, and using it in my programs brings them closer to compliance with the ANSI standard. And `bool` makes sense as the return type of logical functions, which formerly returned an `int` value. If you are using a compiler that intrinsically supports `bool`, remove any references to the header file **bool.h** from this book's source code.

UNIFORM RANDOM DEVIATES

ALife algorithms depend on random numbers. Unfortunately, the built-in `rand` function is entirely inadequate in circumstances where thousands—or even millions—of random values need to be generated. A run of the algorithm from Chapter 2 may use 100,000 or more random values.

Random Numbers

A *random number* is just that: a number having a value that cannot be predicted in advance of its existence. While the human mind has been known to be unpredictable, it isn't very good at generating a completely unrelated set of numbers. Try creating a list of twenty random integers selected from the range one through one hundred, inclusive. Are those numbers *really* random? Wouldn't it be tedious if you had to generate 1000 or 1,000,000 random numbers?

Computers are supposed to be good at reducing tedious numeric operations. Unfortunately, computers perform calculations via algorithms, and truly random numbers cannot be generated by an algorithm. By definition, an *algorithm* is a specific sequence of operations that produces a predictable output for a given set of parameters. In the case of random numbers, the last thing we want is something predictable!

The best we can do with a computer is create an algorithm that *appears* to generate a random sequence of numbers. The numbers aren't really random—a human with a sharp mind or a calculator could predict the numbers in the sequence by following the algorithm. But the sequence of numbers is very difficult to follow, and a human looking at the values will not be able to see any algorithmic pattern to them. For practical applications, pseudo-random numbers suffice.

Algorithms

In general, a pseudo-random number generator is initialized with a *seed* value that begins the sequence. A set of mathematical operations is performed on the seed, generating a value that is reported as a pseudo-random number. That return value is then used as the next seed value.

Researchers have devoted copious time to inventing and analyzing pseudo–random number generators. The goal of this research has been to produce the most unpredictable sequence of values. Designing a good random number generator involves solving two problems:

▼ **Increasing the size of the repetition cycle:** As the algorithm is applied, the seed will eventually return to its starting value, and the values will start repeating themselves. An algorithm that repeats after generating a million numbers is more useful than a generator that repeats itself every hundred numbers.

▼ **Avoiding predictability:** A random number generator that always returns values with the same last digit is worthless. An algorithm that only generates odd numbers is equally useless.

While there are many fancy and complicated algorithms that generate pseudo-random numbers, one of the most commonly used algorithms is also one of the simplest. First introduced by D. Lehmer in 1951, the *linear congruential* method involves only two mathematical operations. Standard C, as defined by ANSI, uses the following linear congruential generator in implementing the `rand` and `srand` functions:

```
static unsigned long next = 1;

int rand(void)
    {
    next = next * 1103515245 + 12345;
    return ((unsigned int) (next / 65536UL) % 0x32767UL);
    }

 void srand(unsigned int seed)
    {
    next = seed;
    }
```

Why not use the rand function defined by ANSI? Because the ANSI C algorithm is inadequate for many applications. And what's wrong with a linear congruential random number generator? Nothing, so long as your random numbers don't need to be very unpredictable and the repetition of those values is not important to your work. The output of rand is limited, providing values that only lie between 0 and 32,767, inclusive.

In other words, the generator will produce only a few thousand values before repeating itself—a fatal problem for genetic algorithms that rely on vast quantities of random values. Even worse, some mathematically inept compiler vendors try to improve on rand using cut little byte-swapping tricks that only reduce the period of repetition! Statistically, even the best linear congruential generators suffer from convergence in their numeric sequences, and the ANSI generator is not the theoretical best. Furthermore, producing a random floating-point value requires a program to divide the result of a rand call by the constant RAND_MAX.

Uniform Deviates

Uniform deviates are floating-point numbers that fall within a given range, usually 0 and 1. All numbers within the range have a statistically equal probability of being generated upon a call to the deviate generator. The best deviate generators have been thoroughly studied in the computer science literature, and a basic model known as the *Minimal Standard* has passed numerous theoretical tests of its efficacy. Yet even the Minimal Standard can show weaknesses when generating millions of values.

In a 1988 issue of *Communications of the ACM,* Paul L'Ecuyer suggested a variety of algorithms for the production of reliable, long-period random deviates. By combining two generators based on the Minimal Standard, L'Ecuyer creates a routine that avoids the pitfalls of simpler algorithms. The generator, which I use later in my `RandDev` class, produces uniform random deviates between 0.0 and 1.0.

In a nutshell, L'Ecuyer's algorithm uses an approximate factorization, shuffling the result to remove correlation in low-order bits. A single generator of that type will have a repetition period of about 108, which (believe it or not) may not be adequate for some very complex genetic algorithms. Running 1000 generations for a population of 100 chromosomes may require millions of random values. Combining two such generators with a judicious selection of factors gives us a period of approximately 2.3 ¥ 1018, which should be more than effective in genetic algorithms of any practical scope.

A Class

I implemented a uniform deviate generator via a C++ class. C++ classes can often provide a better way of accomplishing a task normally performed via stand-alone functions. Aside from their numerical limitations, `rand` and `srand` have several faults from a software engineering standpoint:

▼ A program must explicitly call `srand` to initialize the `seed`. If `srand` isn't called, the default value of `seed` will be used, and every execution of the program will generate the same sequence of pseudo-random numbers.

▼ Since `srand` and `rand` are two separate functions, `seed` is defined as a global variable. Good programmers avoid global variables, even those that can be hidden using the `static` keyword.

▼ Since there is only one `seed` value, only one sequence of pseudo-random numbers is generated in a program. Often, I like to have separate random number generators for different parts of a program.

▼ The ANSI rand function returns values between 0 and UINT_MAX. In most cases, I want to retrieve random values that are within a specific range, say from 1 to 100.

With the preceding discussion in mind, I defined my RandDev class as follows:

```
class RandDev
    {
    protected:
        // used to set default seed argument from system time
        static long TimeSeed()
            {
            return (long)time(NULL);
            }

    public:
        // constructor
        RandDev
            (
            long initSeed = TimeSeed()
            );

        // set seed value
        void SetSeed
            (
            long newSeed = TimeSeed()
            );

        // get a uniform deviate between 0.0 and 1.0
        float operator () ();

    private:
        long Seed;
    };
```

I defined the TimeSeed function to automatically initialize the constructor's seed parameter with the current system time. You can, of course, supply a specific seed, thus ensuring the creation of identical sequences of values:

```
inline RandDev::RandDev
    (
```

```
long initSeed
)
{
if (initSeed < 0)
    Seed = initSeed;
else
    Seed = -initSeed;
}
```

SetSeed resets the generator using a new seed:

```
inline void RandDev::SetSeed
    (
    long initSeed
    )
    {
    if (initSeed < 0)
        Seed = initSeed;
    else
        Seed = -initSeed;
    }
```

Finally, the operator ( ) function returns the next deviate in the sequence:

```
static const long   IM1 = 2147483563L;
static const long   IM2 = 2147483399L;
static const long  IMM1 = IM1 - 1L;
static const long   IA1 = 40014L;
static const long   IA2 = 40692L;
static const long   IQ1 = 53668L;
static const long   IQ2 = 52774L;
static const long   IR1 = 12211L;
static const long   IR2 =  3791L;
static const long  NTAB =    32L;
static const long  NDIV = 1L + IMM1 / long(NTAB);
static const float RNMX = 1.0F - FLT_EPSILON;
static const float   AM = 1.0F / 2147483563.0F;

float RandDev::operator () ()
    {
    long j, k;
    static long idum2 = 123456789L;
    static long iy    = 0L;
```

```
static long iv[size_t(NTAB)];
float temp;

if (Seed <= 0L)
    {
    if (-Seed < 1L)
        Seed = 1L;
    else
        Seed = -Seed;

    idum2 = Seed;

    for (j = NTAB + 7; j >= 0; --j)
        {
        k = Seed / IQ1;
        Seed = IA1 * (Seed - k * IQ1) - k * IR1;

        if (Seed < 0L)
            Seed += IM1;

        if (j < NTAB)
            iv[size_t(j)] = Seed;
        }

    iy = iv[0];
    }

k = Seed / IQ1;

Seed = IA1 * (Seed - k * IQ1) - k * IR1;

if (Seed < 0L)
    Seed += IM1;

k = idum2 / IQ2;

idum2 = IA2 * (idum2 - k * IQ2) - k * IR2;

if (idum2 < 0L)
    idum2 += IM2;

j  = iy / NDIV;
iy = iv[size_t(j)] - idum2;
iv[size_t(j)] = Seed;

if (iy < 1L)
    iy += IMM1;
```

```
temp = AM * float(iy);

if (temp > RNMX)
    return RNMX;
else
    return temp;
}
```

The primary calculations in RandDev rely on integer math to avoid the performance costs of floating-point arithmetic. If you want an in-depth theoretical explanation of this code, the classic text *Numerical Recipes in C* provides an excellent discussion of random number generators, and I highly recommend that you read that tome for detailed analysis of this topic.

ROULETTE WHEELS

I introduced the concept of roulette wheel selection in Chapter 2. In essence, this technique simulates a gambler's roulette wheel in which the sections represent probabilities that a value will be chosen. In the case of genetic algorithms, each segment of the wheel represents the reproductive chance for a chromosome as reflected by its fitness.

Many applications use roulette wheels, which is an obvious indicator that a class—or in this case, a template—is in order:

```
class RW_Except { };

template < class FType >
    class RouletteWheel
        {
        public:
            // creation constructor
            RouletteWheel
                (
                size_t sz,
                FType * weights = NULL
                );

            // copy constructor
```

```
        RouletteWheel
            (
            const RouletteWheel & rw
            );

        // assignment operator
        void operator =
            (
            const RouletteWheel & rw
            );

        // destructor
        ~RouletteWheel();

        // change the weight of an entry
        FType Change
            (
            size_t i,
            FType weight
            );

        // interrogation function
        size_t GetSize() { return N; }

        float GetWeight
            (
            size_t i
            );

        // retrieve a random index
        size_t GetIndex();

protected:
        // array of weights
        size_t  N;
        FType * W;

        // total weight of all indexes
        FType T;

        // random deviate generator
        RandDev G;

private:
        // internal absolute value of a float
        float AbsVal
            (
```

```
                    FType f
                    )
                    {
                    if (f < 0.0F)
                        return -f;
                    else
                        return f;
                    }

            // internal copy function
            void Copy
                    (
                    const RouletteWheel & rw
                    );
        };
```

By defining `RouletteWheel` as a template, I allow it to support fitness values of any numeric type, as specified by the argument `Ftype`. When created, a `RouletteWheel` must be supplied a pair of parameters identifying an array of `Ftype` fitness values and a number of elements in that array—stored, respectively, in the allocated array `W` and the variable `N`. `T` contains the total of all fitness values in `W`, and `G` is a uniform deviate generator used to "spin" the wheel:

```
template < class FType >
    RouletteWheel<FType>::RouletteWheel
        (
        size_t  sz,
        FType * weights
        )
        {
        size_t i;

        N = sz;
        T = FType(0);
        W = new FType [N];

        if (W == NULL)
            throw RW_Except();

        if (weights == NULL)
            {
            for (i = 0; i < N; ++i)
                {
```

```
            W[i] = FType(1);
            T    += FType(1);
            }
        }
    else
        {
        for (i = 0; i < N; ++i)
            {
            W[i] = AbsVal(weights[i]);
            T    += AbsVal(weights[i]);
            }
        }
    }
```

The constructor copies and sums the array of fitness values; if the pointer is NULL, the constructor creates a new array in which all elements contain an equal weight of one. Note that the constructor does not scale the incoming values; it does, however, use the utility function AbsVal to convert negative weights to positive values.

In general, you'll want to ensure that your weights array contains only positive values and that the sum of all weights is greater than zero.

The destructor simply frees memory allocated to the array of weights:

```
template < class FType >
    RouletteWheel<FType>::~RouletteWheel()
        {
        delete [] W;
        }
```

I've defined the copy constructor and assignment operator as inline functions containing calls to the utility function Copy:

```
template < class FType >
    void RouletteWheel<FType>::Copy
        (
        const RouletteWheel & rw
        )
        {
        T = rw.T;
        N = rw.N;
        W = new FType [N];
```

```
            if (W == NULL)
                throw RW_Except();

            memcpy(W,rw.W,sizeof(FType) * N);
            }

// copy constructor
template < class FType >
    inline RouletteWheel<FType>::RouletteWheel
        (
        const RouletteWheel & rw
        )
        {
        Copy(rw);
        }

// assignment operator
template < class FType >
    inline void RouletteWheel<FType>::operator =
        (
        const RouletteWheel & rw
        )
        {
        delete [] W;
        Copy(rw);
        }
```

The Change function alters a single weight at a given index within the
wheel. This allows dynamic changes to the table:

```
template < class FType >
    FType RouletteWheel<FType>::Change
        (
        size_t i,
        FType weight
        )
        {
        if (i >= N)
            return FType(-1);

        T -= W[i];
        T += weight;

        FType res = W[i];
        W[i] = weight;
```

```
    return res;
    }
```

The interrogation function `GetWeight` returns the weight values for a specified index:

```
template < class FType >
    inline float RouletteWheel<FType>::GetWeight
        (
        size_t i
        )
        {
        return (i < N) ? W[i] : FType(-1);
        }
```

`GetIndex` returns a randomly selected index based on the current weights in `W`:

```
template < class FType >
    size_t RouletteWheel<FType>::GetIndex()
        {
        FType s  = G() * T;
        size_t i = 0;

        while ((i < N) && (s > W[i]))
            {
            s -= W[i];
            ++i;
            }

        return i;
        }
```

The `RouletteWheel` class is an encapsulation of the roulette wheel selection concept I introduced in Chapter 2.

FLOATING-POINT REPRODUCTION

The majority of genetic algorithms work on pure bit strings, converting those strings to the desired types for fitness testing. In Lawrence Davis's book *Handbook of Genetic Algorithms*, he transforms a 44-bit string into two floating-point values via a series of operations. I've seen similar techniques elsewhere, and I find them a bit cumbersome.

In theory, a genetic algorithm should have no knowledge of the format of the data it is modifying; however, natural chromosomes do encode some structure in their sequence. Crossover appears to take place in specific positions along the chromosome. And while mutation doesn't care about the chromosome's structure, it does affect that structure. In context of a computer program, the structure of a chromosome isn't as important as the ability to logically modify its bits through crossover and mutation.

I decided to build tools for the mutation and crossover of encoded floating-point values of types `float` and `double`. The code that follows assumes we are working with 32-bit floats and 64-bit IEEE doubles, which, in my experience, are the norm in C and C++ compilers.

Data Types

Floating-point numbers contain scaled values that may have a fractional part. The `float` and `double` types implement the single-precision and double-precision floating-point formats defined by the Institute of Electrical and Electronic Engineers (IEEE) standard 754-1985. A *float* is a 32-bit value, and a *double* is a 64-bit value. These bits in a floating-point value are divided into three components: a sign bit, an exponent, and a mantissa. Figure 3.1 shows the internal format of the `float` and `double` types. *s* indicates the sign bit *exp* is an abbreviation for exponent.

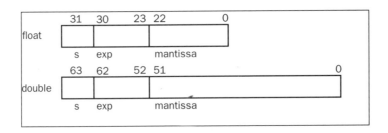

FIGURE 3.1   FORMAT OF IEEE `float` **AND** `double`.

The highest-order bit in a floating-point value is the sign bit. If the sign bit is one, the value is negative; if the sign bit is zero, the value is positive.

In a `float`, the exponent occupies 8 bits and the mantissa uses the remaining 23 bits. A `double` has a 52-bit mantissa and an 11-bit exponent. In addition, the mantissa of `float` and `double` values has an implicit high-order bit of 1.

The mantissa holds a binary fraction greater than or equal to 1 (because of the implied high bit being one) and less than 2. The number of bits in the mantissa affects the accuracy of the floating-point value. A `float` has 6 decimal digits of accuracy, and a `double` (with its longer mantissa) is accurate to 15 decimal digits. Since the mantissa is a binary fraction, it can't always *exactly* reflect a decimal value you've tried to store in it. For example, there is no binary fraction that can exactly represent the values 0.6 or 1/3. Floating-point numbers represent an approximation of a decimal value; this is where rounding errors come from.

The exponent is a binary number representing the number of binary digits the mantissa is shifted left (for a positive actual exponent) or right (for a negative actual exponent). The exponent is a biased value; you calculate the actual exponent value by subtracting a bias value from the exponent stored in the value. The bias for a `float` is 127; the bias for a `double` is 1023. Thus, a `float` value with an exponent of 150 would represent a number with an exponent of 23. The constants `FLT_MIN`, `FLT_MAX`, `DBL_MIN`, and `DBL_MAX` define the minimum and maximum values for floating-point numbers, in the ANSI C header file **float.h**. Borland C++ 4.5 defines those constants as:

```
#define FLT_MIN   1.17549e-38
#define FLT_MAX   3.40282e+38

#define DBL_MIN   2.22507385850720e-308
#define DBL_MAX   1.79769313486232e+308
```

Two other relevant **float.h** constants are `FLT_EPSILON` and `DBL_EPSILON`, which represent the smallest possible difference between two `float` and `double` values.

```
#define FLT_EPSILON   1.19209e-07
#define DBL_EPSILON   2.22044604925031e-16
```

Bestiary

Floating-point numbers can take on some unusual values. It's possible for a floating-point number to represent positive and negative infinity, for example. Or a floating-point value may be in a special format that doesn't represent a valid number. Any routines that randomly change floating-point numbers must avoid generating these unusual values.

A floating-point value represents *infinity* when the bits in the exponent are all one and the bits in the mantissa are all zero. When both the mantissa and exponent are zero, the floating-point number is zero. Infinity—and zero—can have a sign. Positive and negative zero operate identically in calculations and comparisons.

When is a number not a number? When its exponent is all ones and its mantissa contains any set of bits that is not all zeros (which would indicate an infinity). A value in this format is known as a *NaN (not a num*ber). The sign bit for a NaN is irrelevant.

So what is the point of knowing these strange floating-point values? With the exception of Zortech's product, C++ compilers do not support the use and processing of unusual floating-point values. For example, Borland C++ will, by default, generate exceptions when infinities occur in a calculation. What we want to do is avoid the creation of unusual numbers. And in looking at the above, we can see an obvious commonality between the troublesome NaNs and infinities: both types have exponents filled with ones.

Mutation in Parts

A floating-point value contains three components that can be changed during mutation and crossover: the sign bit, exponent, and mantissa. Changing the exponent and sign have the most dramatic affect on a floating-point value, since the change of one bit can dramatically alter the magnitude of a number. Assuming that all bits have an equal chance of mutation, we get the following probabilities that a random bit change will affect a specific component:

	FLOAT	DOUBLE
sign bit	3.1%	1.6%
exponent	25.0%	17.1%
mantissa	71.9%	81.3%

Depending on the application, I've found that those fixed percentages don't always allow for the creation of effective mutations. The exponent, in particular, is so likely to be changed that numbers often fluctuate wildly within a population after mutation. I decided to create a simplified system for the roulette wheel selection of the component to be mutated, allowing me to weight mutation in favor of changing the mantissa.

I create a class named `FloatMutagen`, which defines the parameters of mutation for `float` and `double` types:

```
class FloatMutagen
    {
    public:
        FloatMutagen
            (
            const float & sweight =  5.0,
            const float & eweight =  5.0,
            const float & mweight = 90.0
            );

        float Mutate
            (
            const float & f
            );

        double Mutate
            (
            const double & d
            );

    protected:
        const float TotalW;
```

```
    const float SignW;
    const float ExpW;
};
```

When creating a `FloatMutagen` object, you'll need to supply three floating-point values representing the relative chances of changing the parts of a floating-point number:

```
FloatMutagen::FloatMutagen
    (
    const float & sweight,
    const float & eweight,
    const float & mweight
    )
    : TotalW(sweight + eweight + mweight),
      SignW(sweight),
      ExpW(eweight)
    {
    // intentionally blank
    }
```

The `Mutate` functions use those values in selecting the sections of `float` and `double` values to be mutated:

```
float FloatMutagen::Mutate
    (
    const float & f
    )
    {
    // mask for exponent bits
    static const long FExpt = 0x7F800000L;

    long x, n, mask;

    // choose section to mutate
    float mpick = devgen() * TotalW;

    // copy float to long for manipulation
    memcpy(&x,&f,sizeof(long));

    // if all exponent bits on (invalid #), return original
    if ((x & FExpt) == FExpt)
        return f;
```

```
// mutate
if (mpick < SignW)
    {
    // flip sign
    mask = 0x80000000L;

    if (x & mask)
        x &= ~mask;
    else
        x |= mask;
    }
else
    {
    mpick -= SignW;

    if (mpick < ExpW)
        {
        // mutate exponent while number is valid
        do  {
            n    = x;
            mask = 0x00800000L << int(devgen() * 8.0F);

            if (n & mask)
                n &= ~mask;
            else
                n |= mask;
            }
        while ((n & FExpt) == FExpt);

        x = n;
        }
    else
        {
        // flip bit in mantissa
        mask = 1L << int(devgen() * 23.0F);

        if (x & mask)
            x &= ~mask;
        else
            x |= mask;
        }
    }

// done!
float res;
memcpy(&res,&x,sizeof(float));
return res;
```

```
    }

double FloatMutagen::Mutate
    (
    const double & d
    )
    {
    // mask for exponent bits
    static const long DExpt = 0x7FF00000UL;

    long x[2], n, mask, bit;

    // choose section to mutate
    double mpick = devgen() * TotalW;

    // copy double to pair of longs for manipulation
    memcpy(x,&d,2 * sizeof(long));

    if (mpick < SignW)
        {
        // flip sign
        mask = 0x80000000L;

        if (x[1] & mask)
            x[1] &= ~mask;
        else
            x[1] |= mask;
        }
    else
        {
        mpick -= SignW;

        if (mpick < ExpW)
            {
            // mutate exponent while number is valid
            do  {
                n = x[1];
                mask = 0x00100000L << int(devgen() * 11.0F);

                if (n & mask)
                    n &= ~mask;
                else
                    n |= mask;
                }
            while ((n & DExpt) == DExpt);

            x[1] = n;
```

```
        }
    else
        {
        bit = long(devgen() * 52.0F);

        if (bit > 31L)
            {
            bit -= 32L;
            mask = 1L << (int)bit;

            if (x[1] & mask)
                x[1] &= ~mask;
            else
                x[1] |= mask;
            }
        else
            {
            // flip bit in mantissa
            mask = 1L << (int)bit;

            if (x[0] & mask)
                x[0] &= ~mask;
            else
                x[0] |= mask;
            }
        }
    }

// done
double res;
memcpy(&res,x,sizeof(double));
return res;
}
```

The Mutate functions use a bitmask to examine the bits in a value's exponent, ensuring that any output value is not a NaN or infinity.

My experiments advise me to limit the mutability of the exponent to less than 15%, keeping the sign bit mutation rate at about 2 or 3%. You don't have to take my word for it; the next chapter implements a genetic algorithm for which you can set the weights for each component of floating-point values. That allows you to test my results and explore your own ideas.

Crossover

Floating-point crossover is a simple operation, implemented as two functions named Crossover:

```
float Crossover
    (
    const float & f1,
    const float & f2
    )
    {
    // mask for exponent bits
    static const long FExpt = 0x7F800000L;

    long  l1, l2, lcross, mask;
    float fcross;

    // store values in longs
    memcpy(&l1,&f1,sizeof(long));
    memcpy(&l2,&f2,sizeof(long));

    do  {
        // create mask
        mask  = 0xFFFFFFFFL << size_t(devgen() * 32.0F);

        // generate offspring
        lcross = (l1 & mask) | (l2 & (~mask));
        }
    while ((lcross & FExpt) == FExpt);

    // copy result to float and return
    memcpy(&fcross,&lcross,sizeof(float));

    return fcross;
    }

double Crossover
    (
    const double & d1,
    const double & d2
    )
    {
    // mask for exponent bits
    static const long DExpt = 0x7FF00000L;
```

```
long   l1[2], l2[2], lcross[2], mask, bit;
double fcross;

// store values in longs
memcpy(l1,&d1,sizeof(double));
memcpy(l2,&d2,sizeof(double));

do  {
    // calculate bit position for flip
    bit = size_t(devgen() * 64.0F);

    if (bit > 31) // if flip in high-order word
        {
        // create mask
        mask  = 0xFFFFFFFFL << int(bit - 32L);

        // duplicate low-order word of first parent
        lcross[0] = l1[0];

        // crossover in high-order word
        lcross[1] = (l1[1] & mask) | (l2[1] & (~mask));
        }
    else
        {
        // create mask
        mask  = 0xFFFFFFFFL << int(bit);

        // crossover in low-order word
        lcross[0] = (l1[0] & mask) | (l2[0] & (~mask));

        // duplicate high-order word of first parent
        lcross[1] = l1[1];
        }
    }
while ((lcross[1] & DExpt) == DExpt);

// copy and return
memcpy(&fcross,lcross,sizeof(double));

return fcross;
}
```

Why No Long Double?

What follows is an editorial comment; you can skip it if you like.

I didn't implement the mutation and crossover operations for `long doubles` because I don't use that type in my programs. On a PC, the 80-bit `long double` type represents the internal floating-point format used by the numeric coprocessor. A `long double` has 18 digits of accuracy; it is used internally by the math coprocessor so that the results of calculations can be rounded to produce a very accurate 15 digits of precision in a `double`. The extra three digits in a `long double` provide improved accuracy; they should be viewed *very* suspiciously by a numerical programmer since the coprocessor never means for them to be considered or used.

In my view, current implementations of `long double` are nothing more than frivolous attempts at adding bullets to the compiler advertisement. I'd be far happier if C and C++ compiler vendors would implement a full suite of functions for manipulating `float` values. Double-precision values already exceed the accuracy needs of most scientific and engineering tasks, and for most calculations `float` is more than adequate. Only Symantec/Zortech has spent some effort on understanding the needs of numerical programmers; the market, however, is dominated by the Microsofts and Borlands, which seem to feel that numeric programmers are a small market unworthy of their attention.

And for those folks who wonder why some programmers—including me—stick with dusty old FORTRAN: it's because FORTRAN is *still* the only language that provides full support for single- and double-precision floating-point and complex numbers.

ONWARD

Okay, enough grousing! The tools discussed in this chapter are components of the designs in subsequent chapters, where I implement complex genetic algorithms. In Chapter 4, I'll implement an experimental environment for testing the efficacy of advanced genetic algorithms in solving complex problems.

CHAPTER 4

OPTIMIZATION BY NATURAL SELECTION

With theory and tools in place, it's time to tackle a difficult optimization task.

HUNTING FOR HILLS

Computer scientists often encounter problems that are not amenable to numerical methods of solution. A common problem is finding an input value that produces a minimum or maximum output from a function. It's quite easy to optimize a function that maps a single high or low value; things become quite a bit more difficult when a function generates several such values, as shown in Figure 4.1.

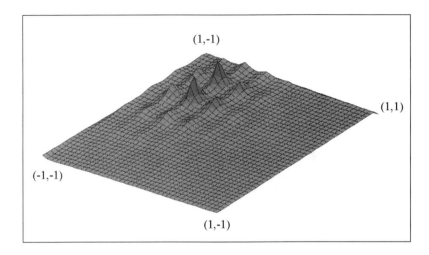

FIGURE 4.1   FUNCTION WITH SEVERAL MAXIMA.

The graph in Figure 4.1 was generated by applying the following formula to the ranges $-1 <= x <= 1$ and $-1 <= y <= 1$:

$$f(x,y) = \frac{1}{(x+0.5)^2 + 2(y-0.5)^2 - 0.3\cos(3\ x) - 0.4\cos(4\ y) + 0.8}$$

How should a program go about finding the maximum for $f(x,y)$? The graph shows several local maxima in the upper quadrant, including two tall spikes in close proximity. Traditional approaches to finding function maxima or minima—a process known as *optimization*—use a variety of techniques that rely on the ability to climb "upward" to a solution. In optimizing $f(x,y)$, most optimization techniques (hill climbing, for example) will become "trapped" on the smaller "hills" unless they begin looking for maxima in just the right place.

A genetic algorithm begins with a set of randomly selected points from which it selects the best performers through fitness testing. Crossover combines the best attributes from the most successful members of the population, and random mutation introduces new characteristics that may produce better solutions. As I'll demonstrate, a genetic algorithm is particularly effective in finding optimal solutions to functions.

CHARACTERISTICS OF A GENETIC ALGORITHM

Chapter 2 introduced genetic algorithms with a simple integer-based example. Now I'll move on to functions that take two floating-point values as arguments. To demonstrate some of the more sophisticated features of genetic algorithms, I created a Configuration dialog box as shown in Figure 4.2.

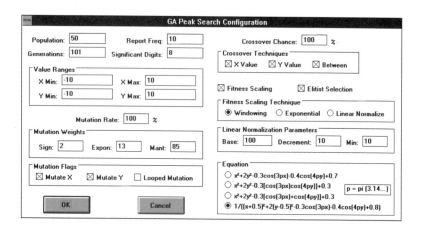

FIGURE 4.2   THE PEAK SEARCH CONFIGURATION DIALOG BOX.

The Peak Search Configuration dialog box contains more than 30 controls that define the techniques and parameters of a genetic algorithm. I'll take you through the dialog box, describing it item by item.

General Parameters

The upper-left quadrant of the dialog box contains controls that define the population size, number of iterations to be performed, the frequency with which results are reported, the number of significant digits displayed, and the ranges of x and y values.

The population size is the most important factor affecting the run time of a genetic algorithm. More chromosomes mean more time spent in fitness calculation, which is the most time-consuming component of most genetic algorithms. And while a large population size provides more chromosomes for testing, it also dilutes the fitness of the best chromosomes.

For example, if we have 10 chromosomes with fitnesses of 10, 8, 5, 1, 1, 1, 1, 1, 1, and 1, the three most-fit chromosomes have a combined 77% chance of reproducing; if another 10 chromosomes of fitness 1 were included in the population, the reproduction probability for the three best would drop to 57%. A balance must be struck between *diversity* (large populations) and *relative fitness* (small populations).

Reporting frequency allows you to run very long tests without overflowing the display buffer. The program can generally show about 250 lines of output; if you run 1000 generations, for example, you should set the report frequency to four or five at a minimum. I've run tests with as many as 25,000 generations, setting the report frequency to 100.

In the real world of science, few calculations involve values of incredible precision; in fact, Heisenberg's Uncertainty Principle guarantees that we'll never know everything "exactly." Scientists work with the concept of significant digits—the number of valid nonzero decimal digits in scientific notation. The accuracy of a result is only as good as the accuracy of the operands used in the calculation.

For example, if you ask C++ to perform these calculations:

```
double a = 1.5;
double b = 2.01;
double c = a * b;
```

the compiler will dutifully assign to c the result of multiplying 1.5 by 2.01, which is 3.015. However, the accuracy of that result must be compared against the accuracy of the numbers used to calculate it. In this case, while b has four decimal digits, we only know the accuracy of a to two decimal places. Unless we know that a is *exactly equal* to 1.5, we cannot assume that c is *exactly equal* to 3.015. It's a case of being sure of our results. If we aren't certain of a's value beyond the second digit, then we cannot be certain, beyond the second decimal place, about the value of any result calculated using a.

It's common in science to know a value to a specific number of decimal places, without certainty that the value is exact. So long as there is doubt about the absolute accuracy of a value, all calculations involving that number are limited to the number of digits we know are exact. In the preceding example, the correct value for c is 3.0, since the least accurate operand used in its calculation (a) had only two digits of accuracy.

Of course, the compiler knows nothing about this. It blithely goes about its business of assigning 3.015 to c. Now, what happens later in the program when another calculation involving c is made?

```
double d = c * 250.0; // assume 250.0 is exact
```

d is assigned the value 3.015 * 250, or 753.75. The error continues to mount! The correct result should be 750, since c is only known reliably to two digits of accuracy (making it 3.0). The problem only grows worse as calculations continue.

I extended the rounding features of C++ to set a specific number of significant digits in a value. Here's the double versions of the SigDig function and a support function named ToNearest that rounds a number at a specific number of significant digits:

```
double ToNearest(double x)
   {
```

```
    double i, f, dummy;

    f = fabs(modf(x,&i));

    if (f == 0.0)
        return i;

    if (f == 0.5)
        {
        if (modf(i / 2.0, &dummy) != 0.0)
            {
            if (x < 0.0)
                i -= 1.0;
            else
                i += 1.0;
            }
        }
    else
        {
        if (f > 0.5)
            {
            if (x < 0.0)
                i -= 1.0;
            else
                i += 1.0;
            }
        }

    return i;
    }

double SigDig
    (
    double x,
    size_t n
    )
    {
    double s, result;

    if (fabs(x) < 1.0E-300)
        result = 0.0;
    else
        {
        if ((n == 0U) || (n > DBL_DIG))
            result = x;
        else
            {
```

```
        s = pow10((int)n - 1 - (int)floor(log10(fabs(x))));
        result = ToNearest(x * s) / s;
        }
    }

    return result;
    }
```

The setting of significant digits in the dialog box will cause numbers to be rounded and truncated at the specified decimal position by SigDig. It also affects the output precision of floating-point numbers. The default of eight digits is usually more than adequate, for the simple reason that most C++ numerical functions have limited precision.

The inexact nature of IEEE floating-point numbers combines with the limitations of C++ functions to produce inexact results. For example, in practical terms, 1.23456E–76 is such a small number that it generates the same result from the sin function as does zero. Since very tiny numbers and zero produce the same result, their fitness as chromosomes is the same, thus preventing a genetic algorithm from distinguishing the two values.

Perhaps it would make sense to convert very tiny numbers to zero automatically, but it might very well be that the function actually *does* produce a peak at a very tiny number and not at zero. In general, a 64-bit IEEE double can only be used to analyze a search grid with a precision of about DBL_EPSILON, and any number smaller than DBL_EPSILON can be considered zero.

The range settings set constraints on the *x* and *y* values being analyzed. Set these ranges to bracket the search area; if you want to find a local maximum instead of a global one, set these values to limit the search to your area of interest.

Mutation Parameters

The mutation parameters define how random changes occur in new populations. I allow you to set the percentage chance of mutation and the relative chances of mutating the various components of a double. The checkboxes let you turn mutation on and off for either the *x* or *y* chromosomes.

Looped mutation is a way of allowing multiple mutations within a chromosome. When the **Looped Mutation** checkbox is selected, the mutation occurs in a loop controlled by a random value. The loop mutates a chromosome until the random value is greater than the mutation chance. The higher the mutation rate, the more mutations will take place. For example, if **Looped Mutation** is selected with a mutation rate of 50%, the three random deviates 0.0715, 0.332, and 0.899 will cause three mutations to take place. The maximum mutation rate with looping is 99%, to prevent infinite loops.

Crossover Parameters

For two-dimensional floating-point GA optimization, I've extended crossover from the model I presented in Chapter 2. The rate of crossover can be set, as can the application of crossover to the *x* and *y* chromosomes. Selecting the **Between** checkbox will simulate nature's ability to randomly select chromosomes from diploid parents. With **Between** set, the *x* and *y* chromosomes of a child may be selected from different parents.

Fitness Scaling

Two checkboxes allow you to turn on and off fitness scaling and elitist selection. When **Fitness Scaling** is on, several other factors come into play. I've defined three forms of fitness scaling: windowed, exponential, and linear normalization. The first two were covered in Chapter 2; linear normalization is something new.

The purpose of fitness scaling is to emphasize the reproductive chances of the most-fit chromosomes in a population. *Linear Normalization* accomplishes this by changing fitness values to reflect a gradation of values. For example, here is a set of fitness values for five chromosomes, as calculated directly by the fitness function:

1: 0.255

```
2: 0.773
3: 0.405
4: 0.928
5: 0.318
```

While chromosome 4 is obviously the most fit, its reproductive chance relative to the entire population is only 35%.

Assuming a base value of 20, a decrement of 8, and a minimum value of 1, linear normalization would assign new fitness values as shown in Table 4.1. For comparison, I've also included the fitness values as scaled by windowing and exponentiation.

TABLE 4.1   FITNESS SCALING EXAMPLE

CHROMOSOME	ORIGINAL FITNESS	SCALED BY WINDOWING	SCALED BY EXPONENTIAL	SCALED BY LINEAR NORM
1	0.255 (10%)	0.000 (0%)	1.575 (13%)	1.00 (3%)
2	0.773 (29%)	0.518 (37%)	3.144 (26%)	12.00 (31%)
3	0.405 (15%)	0.150 (11%)	1.974 (16%)	4.00 (10%)
4	0.928 (35%)	0.673 (48%)	3.717 (31%)	20.00 (53%)
5	0.318 (11%)	0.063 (4%)	1.737 (14%)	1.00 (3%)

Windowing increases the reproductive chances of the strongest chromosomes but eliminates the least-fit chromosome from producing offspring. Exponential fitness scaling (adding one to the original fitness and squaring the result) increases the reproductive capability of less-fit chromosomes, while maintaining the superiority of the best. Linear normalization puts a premium on success, enhancing the reproductive chances of the best chromosomes while maintaining a possibility that the less-fit chromosomes might produce offspring.

Why not have the most-fit chromosome produce all members of the new population? Because the most-fit chromosomes may not have all the components necessary to reach an optimal solution. As discussed in

Chapter 2, crossover mixes the most fit parts of different chromosomes; it may be that a few bits of a less-fit chromosome are essential to create the optimum fitness. And in some cases, we don't want to eliminate the least-fit chromosomes since they may just have an essential piece of the final solution.

What I call exponential fitness scaling is my own—at least, I haven't seen it discussed in the genetic algorithm literature. At first glance, exponential scaling might seem counterproductive in that it "evens out" the reproductive chances within a population. In testing, I've found the exponential method to work quite well, particularly in populations where the fitness is heavily biased toward specific values. To put it another way, when the landscape of a function includes steep approaches to maxima, some values will have dramatically higher fitnesses than their neighbors; exponential scaling can often prevent getting stuck in a suboptimal peak by allowing apparently unfit chromosomes a chance at reproducing.

Equation Selection

The program supports the optimization of four different functions, three classic and one of my own invention. The first three functions come from the work of I.O. Bohachevsky, M.E. Johnson, and M.L. Stein in a 1986 paper analyzing techniques for function optimization. The functions were selected because they generate a "wavy" landscape that contains various configurations of local maxima. Properly, these three functions are known in the genetic algorithm literature as F6, F7, and F8. Functions one through five, developed by K.A. DeJong in 1975, lack several local maxima and are thus less useful than six through eight in testing the effectiveness of optimization algorithms.

Even these three functions suffer from significant problems. To begin with, all three produce a bowl-shaped plot in which the minimum value is located at $x = 0$, $y = 0$. I'm never thrilled with test examples with such easy answers; since the functions produce a minimum instead of a maximum, fitness values need to be adjusted by "flipping" the plot upside down so that the minimum becomes a peak. Otherwise, the most-fit chromosomes will produce the smallest fitness value—zero.

I played around a bit and eventually came up with the equation that produces the plot shown in Figure 4.1. My equation, fourth in the list, is quite tricky to optimize, since it has a broad plain of low maxima punctuated by some very strong peaks. Essentially, I modified equation F6 to offset its maximum away from the origin to a point that is not easily predicted by induction or guesswork.

Implementing the Configuration

I wrapped the dialog box in a class, `GAOptConfig`, as shown here:

```
// genetic algorithm optimization configuration
enum FSAlgor
    {
    FSA_EXPON,
    FSA_WINDOW,
    FSA_LINEAR
    };

class GAOptConfig
    {
    public:
        GAOptConfig
            (
            HINSTANCE inst,
            HWND      parent
            );

        static void DlgInit
            (
            HWND  dlg
            );

        static BOOL DlgStore
            (
            HWND  dlg
            );

        // verify if this object is valid
        bool GetValidity() { return Valid; }

        // interrogate dimensions of test
        size_t GetPopSize()   { return PopSize;   }
```

```
    size_t GetTestSize()  { return TestSize;  }
    size_t GetReptFreq()  { return ReptFreq;  }
    size_t GetSigDigits() { return SigDigits; }

    // interrogate ranges of X and Y
    double GetXMin() { return XMin; }
    double GetXMax() { return XMax; }
    double GetYMin() { return YMin; }
    double GetYMax() { return YMax; }

    // interrogate crossover techniques
    float GetCrossRate() { return CrossRate; }
    bool  GetCrossX()    { return CrossX;    }
    bool  GetCrossY()    { return CrossY;    }
    bool  GetCrossB()    { return CrossB;    }

    // interrogate parameters for mutation
    float GetWtSign()   { return WtSign;   }
    float GetWtExp()    { return WtExp;    }
    float GetWtMant()   { return WtMant;   }
    float GetMuteRate() { return MuteRate; }
    bool  GetMutateX()  { return MutateX;  }
    bool  GetMutateY()  { return MutateY;  }
    bool  GetMuteLoop() { return MuteLoop; }

    // interrogate selection flag
    bool  GetElitist() { return Elitist; }

    // interrogate fitness scaling parameters
    bool    GetFitScale()   { return FitScale;   }
    FSAlgor GetFitAlgor()   { return FitAlgor;   }
    double  GetFitLinBase() { return FitLinBase; }
    double  GetFitLinDec()  { return FitLinDec;  }
    double  GetFitLinMin()  { return FitLinMin;  }

    // interrogate equation #
    size_t GetEquation() { return Equation; }

private:
    // validity flag
    bool   Valid;

    // dimensions of test
    size_t PopSize;
    size_t TestSize;
    size_t ReptFreq;
    size_t SigDigits;
```

```
// ranges of X and Y
double XMin;
double XMax;
double YMin;
double YMax;

// crossover techniques
float CrossRate;
bool  CrossX;
bool  CrossY;
bool  CrossB;

// parameters for mutation
float WtSign;
float WtExp;
float WtMant;
float MuteRate;
bool  MutateX;
bool  MutateY;
bool  MuteLoop;

// selection flag
bool  Elitist;

// fitness scaling
bool    FitScale;
FSAlgor FitAlgor;
double  FitLinBase;
double  FitLinDec;
double  FitLinMin;

// equation selection
size_t  Equation;

// stored parameter values
static size_t  DefPopSize;
static size_t  DefTestSize;
static size_t  DefReptFreq;
static size_t  DefSigDigits;
static double  DefXMin;
static double  DefXMax;
static double  DefYMin;
static double  DefYMax;
static float   DefCrossRate;
static bool    DefCrossX;
static bool    DefCrossY;
```

```
        static bool    DefCrossB;
        static float   DefWtSign;
        static float   DefWtExp;
        static float   DefWtMant;
        static float   DefMuteRate;
        static bool    DefMutateX;
        static bool    DefMutateY;
        static bool    DefMuteLoop;
        static bool    DefElitist;
        static bool    DefFitScale;
        static FSAlgor DefFitAlgor;
        static double  DefFitLinBase;
        static double  DefFitLinDec;
        static double  DefFitLinMin;
        static size_t  DefEquation;
    };

size_t   GAOptConfig::DefPopSize    =     50;
size_t   GAOptConfig::DefTestSize   =    101;
size_t   GAOptConfig::DefReptFreq   =      1;
size_t   GAOptConfig::DefSigDigits  =      8;
double   GAOptConfig::DefXMin       =  -10.0;
double   GAOptConfig::DefXMax       =   10.0;
double   GAOptConfig::DefYMin       =  -10.0;
double   GAOptConfig::DefYMax       =   10.0;
double   GAOptConfig::DefFitLinBase =  100.0;
double   GAOptConfig::DefFitLinDec  =   10.0;
double   GAOptConfig::DefFitLinMin  =   10.0;
float    GAOptConfig::DefWtSign     =    2.0F;
float    GAOptConfig::DefWtExp      =   13.0F;
float    GAOptConfig::DefWtMant     =   85.0F;
float    GAOptConfig::DefMuteRate   =    1.0F;
float    GAOptConfig::DefCrossRate  =    1.0F;
bool     GAOptConfig::DefCrossX     = true;
bool     GAOptConfig::DefCrossY     = true;
bool     GAOptConfig::DefCrossB     = true;
bool     GAOptConfig::DefMutateX    = true;
bool     GAOptConfig::DefMutateY    = true;
bool     GAOptConfig::DefMuteLoop   = false;
bool     GAOptConfig::DefElitist    = true;
bool     GAOptConfig::DefFitScale   = true;
FSAlgor  GAOptConfig::DefFitAlgor   = FSA_WINDOW;
size_t   GAOptConfig::DefEquation   = 3;

static LPCSTR GAOptConfigDlgName = MAKEINTRESOURCE(DLG_GAOPTCFG);

static const char * GAOptConfigDlgErr =
```

```
"Population and Generations must be greater than 9.\n"
"Frequency must be greater than 0 and < generations.\n"
"Significant Digits must be between 1 and 15.\n"
"Minimum values must be < maximums.\n"
"Mutation and Crossover rates must be between 0 and 100%.\n"
"With mutation looping, mutation rate must be < 100%\n"
"Sum of mutation weights must be > 1.";

BOOL FAR PASCAL __export GAOptConfigDlgProc
    (
    HWND   dlg,
    WORD   message,
    WORD   wParam,
    DWORD  lParam
    );

GAOptConfig::GAOptConfig
    (
    HINSTANCE inst,
    HWND      parent
    )
    {
    DLGPROC thunk;
    thunk = MakeProcInstance(FARPROC(GAOptConfigDlgProc),inst);
    int res = DialogBox(inst,GAOptConfigDlgName,parent,thunk);
    FreeProcInstance(thunk);

    if (res)
        Valid = true;
    else
        Valid = false;

    PopSize    = DefPopSize;
    TestSize   = DefTestSize;
    ReptFreq   = DefReptFreq;
    SigDigits  = DefSigDigits;
    XMin       = DefXMin;
    XMax       = DefXMax;
    YMin       = DefYMin;
    YMax       = DefYMax;
    CrossRate  = DefCrossRate;
    CrossX     = DefCrossX;
    CrossY     = DefCrossY;
    CrossB     = DefCrossB;
    WtSign     = DefWtSign;
    WtExp      = DefWtExp;
    WtMant     = DefWtMant;
```

```
    MuteRate    = DefMuteRate;
    MutateX     = DefMutateX;
    MutateY     = DefMutateY;
    MuteLoop    = DefMuteLoop;
    Elitist     = DefElitist;
    FitScale    = DefFitScale;
    FitAlgor    = DefFitAlgor;
    FitLinBase  = DefFitLinBase;
    FitLinDec   = DefFitLinDec;
    FitLinMin   = DefFitLinMin;
    Equation    = DefEquation;
    }

#pragma argsused
BOOL FAR PASCAL __export GAOptConfigDlgProc
    (
    HWND  dlg,
    WORD  message,
    WORD  wParam,
    DWORD lParam
    )
    {
    switch (message)
        {
        case WM_INITDIALOG:
            GAOptConfig::DlgInit(dlg);
            return TRUE;

        case WM_COMMAND:
            switch (wParam)
                {
                case IDOK:
                    if (TRUE == GAOptConfig::DlgStore(dlg))
                        EndDialog(dlg, 1);

                    break;

                case IDCANCEL:
                    EndDialog(dlg, 0);
                }

            return TRUE;
        }

    return FALSE;
    }
```

```
void GAOptConfig::DlgInit
    (
    HWND   dlg
    )
    {
    char temp[64];

    sprintf(temp,"%u",DefPopSize);
    SetDlgItemText(dlg,IDD_GAOPTCFG_POP,temp);

    sprintf(temp,"%u",DefTestSize);
    SetDlgItemText(dlg,IDD_GAOPTCFG_GEN,temp);

    sprintf(temp,"%u",DefReptFreq);
    SetDlgItemText(dlg,IDD_GAOPTCFG_FREQ,temp);

    sprintf(temp,"%u",DefSigDigits);
    SetDlgItemText(dlg,IDD_GAOPTCFG_SIGDIG,temp);

    sprintf(temp,"%.15g",DefXMin);
    SetDlgItemText(dlg,IDD_GAOPTCFG_XMIN,temp);

    sprintf(temp,"%.15g",DefXMax);
    SetDlgItemText(dlg,IDD_GAOPTCFG_XMAX,temp);

    sprintf(temp,"%.15g",DefYMin);
    SetDlgItemText(dlg,IDD_GAOPTCFG_YMIN,temp);

    sprintf(temp,"%.15g",DefYMax);
    SetDlgItemText(dlg,IDD_GAOPTCFG_YMAX,temp);

    sprintf(temp,"%.6g",DefCrossRate * 100.0F);
    SetDlgItemText(dlg,IDD_GAOPTCFG_CPROB,temp);

    if (DefCrossX)
        SendDlgItemMessage(dlg,IDD_GAOPTCFG_CROSSX,
                            BM_SETCHECK,1,0L);
    else
        SendDlgItemMessage(dlg,IDD_GAOPTCFG_CROSSX,
                            BM_SETCHECK,0,0L);

    if (DefCrossY)
        SendDlgItemMessage(dlg,IDD_GAOPTCFG_CROSSY,
                            BM_SETCHECK,1,0L);
    else
        SendDlgItemMessage(dlg,IDD_GAOPTCFG_CROSSY,
                            BM_SETCHECK,0,0L);
```

```
if (DefCrossB)
    SendDlgItemMessage(dlg,IDD_GAOPTCFG_CROSSB,
                       BM_SETCHECK,1,0L);
else
    SendDlgItemMessage(dlg,IDD_GAOPTCFG_CROSSB,
                       BM_SETCHECK,0,0L);

sprintf(temp,"%.6g",DefWtSign);
SetDlgItemText(dlg,IDD_GAOPTCFG_MUTES,temp);

sprintf(temp,"%.6g",DefWtExp);
SetDlgItemText(dlg,IDD_GAOPTCFG_MUTEE,temp);

sprintf(temp,"%.6g",DefWtMant);
SetDlgItemText(dlg,IDD_GAOPTCFG_MUTEM,temp);

sprintf(temp,"%.6g",DefMuteRate * 100.0F);
SetDlgItemText(dlg,IDD_GAOPTCFG_MPROB,temp);

if (DefMutateX)
    SendDlgItemMessage(dlg,IDD_GAOPTCFG_MUTEX,
                       BM_SETCHECK,1,0L);
else
    SendDlgItemMessage(dlg,IDD_GAOPTCFG_MUTEX,
                       BM_SETCHECK,0,0L);

if (DefMutateY)
    SendDlgItemMessage(dlg,IDD_GAOPTCFG_MUTEY,
                       BM_SETCHECK,1,0L);
else
    SendDlgItemMessage(dlg,IDD_GAOPTCFG_MUTEY,
                       BM_SETCHECK,0,0L);

if (DefMuteLoop)
    SendDlgItemMessage(dlg,IDD_GAOPTCFG_MLOOP,
                       BM_SETCHECK,1,0L);
else
    SendDlgItemMessage(dlg,IDD_GAOPTCFG_MLOOP,
                       BM_SETCHECK,0,0L);

if (DefElitist)
    SendDlgItemMessage(dlg,IDD_GAOPTCFG_ELITE,
                       BM_SETCHECK,1,0L);
else
    SendDlgItemMessage(dlg,IDD_GAOPTCFG_ELITE,
                       BM_SETCHECK,0,0L);
```

```
if (DefFitScale)
    SendDlgItemMessage(dlg,IDD_GAOPTCFG_FSCALE,
                        BM_SETCHECK,1,0L);
else
    SendDlgItemMessage(dlg,IDD_GAOPTCFG_FSCALE,
                        BM_SETCHECK,0,0L);

switch (DefFitAlgor)
    {
    case FSA_EXPON:
        SendDlgItemMessage(dlg,IDD_GAOPTCFG_FTEXP,
                            BM_SETCHECK,1,0L);
        break;
    case FSA_WINDOW:
        SendDlgItemMessage(dlg,IDD_GAOPTCFG_FTWDW,
                            BM_SETCHECK,1,0L);
        break;
    case FSA_LINEAR:
        SendDlgItemMessage(dlg,IDD_GAOPTCFG_FTLIN,
                            BM_SETCHECK,1,0L);
    }

sprintf(temp,"%.15g",DefFitLinBase);
SetDlgItemText(dlg,IDD_GAOPTCFG_LNBASE,temp);

sprintf(temp,"%.15g",DefFitLinDec);
SetDlgItemText(dlg,IDD_GAOPTCFG_LNDEC,temp);

sprintf(temp,"%.15g",DefFitLinMin);
SetDlgItemText(dlg,IDD_GAOPTCFG_LNMIN,temp);

switch (DefEquation)
    {
    case 0:
        SendDlgItemMessage(dlg,IDD_GAOPTCFG_EQF6,
                            BM_SETCHECK,1,0L);
        break;
    case 1:
        SendDlgItemMessage(dlg,IDD_GAOPTCFG_EQF7,
                            BM_SETCHECK,1,0L);
        break;
    case 2:
        SendDlgItemMessage(dlg,IDD_GAOPTCFG_EQF8,
                            BM_SETCHECK,1,0L);
        break;
    case 3:
```

```
            SendDlgItemMessage(dlg,IDD_GAOPTCFG_EQCUST,
                              BM_SETCHECK,1,0L);
        }
    }

BOOL GAOptConfig::DlgStore
    (
    HWND  dlg
    )
    {
    char temp[64];

    GetDlgItemText(dlg,IDD_GAOPTCFG_POP,temp,64);
    size_t psz = abs(atoi(temp));

    GetDlgItemText(dlg,IDD_GAOPTCFG_GEN,temp,64);
    size_t gen = abs(atoi(temp));

    GetDlgItemText(dlg,IDD_GAOPTCFG_FREQ,temp,64);
    size_t frq = abs(atoi(temp));

    GetDlgItemText(dlg,IDD_GAOPTCFG_SIGDIG,temp,64);
    size_t sdig = abs(atoi(temp));

    GetDlgItemText(dlg,IDD_GAOPTCFG_XMIN,temp,64);
    double minx = atof(temp);

    GetDlgItemText(dlg,IDD_GAOPTCFG_XMAX,temp,64);
    double maxx = atof(temp);

    GetDlgItemText(dlg,IDD_GAOPTCFG_YMIN,temp,64);
    double miny = atof(temp);

    GetDlgItemText(dlg,IDD_GAOPTCFG_YMAX,temp,64);
    double maxy = atof(temp);

    GetDlgItemText(dlg,IDD_GAOPTCFG_CPROB,temp,64);
    float crate = fabs(atof(temp));

    GetDlgItemText(dlg,IDD_GAOPTCFG_MPROB,temp,64);
    float mrate = fabs(atof(temp));

    GetDlgItemText(dlg,IDD_GAOPTCFG_MUTES,temp,64);
    float msgn = fabs(atof(temp));

    GetDlgItemText(dlg,IDD_GAOPTCFG_MUTEE,temp,64);
    float mexp = fabs(atof(temp));
```

```
GetDlgItemText(dlg,IDD_GAOPTCFG_MUTEM,temp,64);
float mman = fabs(atof(temp));

bool mloop;

if (SendDlgItemMessage(dlg,IDD_GAOPTCFG_MLOOP,
                        BM_GETCHECK,0,0L))
    mloop = true;
else
    mloop = false;

if ((psz < 10)
||  (gen < 10)
||  (frq <  1)
||  (frq > gen)
||  (sdig < 1)
||  (sdig > 15)
||  (mrate > 100.0F)
||  (crate > 100.0F)
||  ((mrate > 99.0F) && (mloop))
||  (minx >= maxx)
||  (miny >= maxy)
||  ((msgn + mexp + mman) < 1.0F))
    {
    MessageBeep(MB_ICONHAND);
    MessageBox(NULL,GAOptConfigDlgErr,
                "Configuration Error",
                MB_OK | MB_ICONHAND);
    return FALSE;
    }

DefPopSize   = psz;
DefTestSize  = gen;
DefReptFreq  = frq;
DefSigDigits = sdig;
DefXMin      = minx;
DefXMax      = maxx;
DefYMin      = miny;
DefYMax      = maxy;
DefCrossRate = crate / 100.0F;
DefMuteRate  = mrate / 100.0F;
DefWtSign    = msgn;
DefWtExp     = mexp;
DefWtMant    = mman;
DefMuteLoop  = mloop;
```

```
if (SendDlgItemMessage(dlg,IDD_GAOPTCFG_CROSSX,
                          BM_GETCHECK,0,0L))
    DefCrossX = true;
else
    DefCrossX = false;

if (SendDlgItemMessage(dlg,IDD_GAOPTCFG_CROSSY,
                          BM_GETCHECK,0,0L))
    DefCrossY = true;
else
    DefCrossY = false;

if (SendDlgItemMessage(dlg,IDD_GAOPTCFG_CROSSB,
                          BM_GETCHECK,0,0L))
    DefCrossB = true;
else
    DefCrossB = false;

if (SendDlgItemMessage(dlg,IDD_GAOPTCFG_MUTEX,
                          BM_GETCHECK,0,0L))
    DefMutateX = true;
else
    DefMutateX = false;

if (SendDlgItemMessage(dlg,IDD_GAOPTCFG_MUTEY,
                          BM_GETCHECK,0,0L))
    DefMutateY = true;
else
    DefMutateY = false;

if (SendDlgItemMessage(dlg,IDD_GAOPTCFG_ELITE,
                          BM_GETCHECK,0,0L))
    DefElitist = true;
else
    DefElitist = false;

if (SendDlgItemMessage(dlg,IDD_GAOPTCFG_FSCALE,
                          BM_GETCHECK,0,0L))
    DefFitScale = true;
else
    DefFitScale = false;

if (SendDlgItemMessage(dlg,IDD_GAOPTCFG_FTEXP,
                          BM_GETCHECK,0,0L))
    DefFitAlgor = FSA_EXPON;
else
    if (SendDlgItemMessage(dlg,IDD_GAOPTCFG_FTWDW,
```

```
                                        BM_GETCHECK,0,0L))
            DefFitAlgor = FSA_WINDOW;
        else
            DefFitAlgor = FSA_LINEAR;

    GetDlgItemText(dlg,IDD_GAOPTCFG_LNBASE,temp,64);
    DefFitLinBase = fabs(atof(temp));

    GetDlgItemText(dlg,IDD_GAOPTCFG_LNDEC,temp,64);
    DefFitLinDec = fabs(atof(temp));

    GetDlgItemText(dlg,IDD_GAOPTCFG_LNMIN,temp,64);
    DefFitLinMin = fabs(atof(temp));

    if (SendDlgItemMessage(dlg,IDD_GAOPTCFG_EQF6,
                        BM_GETCHECK,0,0L))
        DefEquation = 0;
    else
        if (SendDlgItemMessage(dlg,IDD_GAOPTCFG_EQF7,
                            BM_GETCHECK,0,0L))
            DefEquation = 1;
        else
            if (SendDlgItemMessage(dlg,IDD_GAOPTCFG_EQF8,
                                BM_GETCHECK,0,0L))
                DefEquation = 2;
            else
                DefEquation = 3;

    return TRUE;
    }
```

IMPLEMENTATION OF A GENETIC OPTIMIZER

My program implements the four functions listed in the dialog box as inline fitness functions:

```
template <class T>
    inline T sqr(const T & n) { return n * n; }

inline double FitnessF6
    (
    double x,
    double y
```

```
    )
    {
    return  0.7 + sqr(x)
               + 2.0 * sqr(y)
               - 0.3 * cos(3.0 * N_DPI * x)
               - 0.4 * cos(4.0 * N_DPI * y);
    }

inline double FitnessF7
    (
    double x,
    double y
    )
    {
    return  0.3 + sqr(x)
               + 2.0 * sqr(y)
               - 0.3 * (cos(3.0 * N_DPI * x)
                       * cos(4.0 * N_DPI * y));
    }

inline double FitnessF8
    (
    double x,
    double y
    )
    {
    return  0.3 + sqr(x)
               + 2.0 * sqr(y)
               - 0.3 * (cos(3.0 * N_DPI * x)
                       + cos(4.0 * N_DPI * y));
    }

inline double FitnessCust
    (
    double x,
    double y
    )
    {
    return 1.0 / (0.8 + sqr(x + 0.5)
               + 2.0 * sqr(y - 0.5)
               - 0.3 * cos(3.0 * N_DPI * x)
               - 0.4 * cos(4.0 * N_DPI * y));
    }
```

I'll take you through the optimization algorithm step by step, explaining each component as I go along.

The algorithm begins by creating a configuration object and displaying the parameters contained therein:

```
// create configuration and verify it
GAOptConfig gaoc(ThisInstance,MainWdw);

if (!gaoc.GetValidity())
    {
    buffer << "Cancelled\r\n";
    return;
    }

// display parameters for this run
buffer << "\r\n    Equation: ";

switch (gaoc.GetEquation())
    {
    case 0:
        buffer << "f6(x,y) = x2+2y2-0.3cos(3px)"
                  "-0.4cos(4py)+0.7";
        break;
    case 1:
        buffer << "f7(x,y) = x2+2y2-"
                  "0.3[cos(3px)cos(4py)]+0.3";
        break;
    case 2:
        buffer << "f8(x,y) = x2+2y2-"
                  "0.3[cos(3px)+cos(4py)]+0.3";
        break;
    case 3:
        buffer << "f(x,y) = 1/((x+0.5)2+2(y-0.5)2-"
                  "0.3cos(3px)-0.4cos(4py)+0.8)";
    }

buffer << "\r\n  Pop. Size: " << gaoc.GetPopSize();
buffer << "\r\n  Test Size: " << gaoc.GetTestSize();
buffer << "\r\n  Rep. Freq: " << gaoc.GetReptFreq();
buffer << "\r\nSig. Digits: " << gaoc.GetSigDigits();
buffer << "\r\n      X Min: " << gaoc.GetXMin();
buffer << "\r\n      X Max: " << gaoc.GetXMax();
buffer << "\r\n      Y Min: " << gaoc.GetYMin();
buffer << "\r\n      Y Max: " << gaoc.GetYMax();
buffer << "\r\nCrossover %: "
       << gaoc.GetCrossRate() * 100.0F;
buffer << "\r\n    Cross X: " << gaoc.GetCrossX();
buffer << "\r\n    Cross Y: " << gaoc.GetCrossY();
```

```
buffer << "\r\n     Cross B: " << gaoc.GetCrossB();
buffer << "\r\n Mutation %: "
       << gaoc.GetMuteRate() * 100.0F;
buffer << "\r\n    Wt. Sign: " << gaoc.GetWtSign();
buffer << "\r\n    Wt. Expt: " << gaoc.GetWtExp();
buffer << "\r\n    Wt. Mant: " << gaoc.GetWtMant();
buffer << "\r\n    Mutate X: " << gaoc.GetMutateX();
buffer << "\r\n    Mutate Y: " << gaoc.GetMutateY();
buffer << "\r\nMutate Loop: " << gaoc.GetMuteLoop();
buffer << "\r\n     Elitism: " << gaoc.GetElitist();
buffer << "\r\nFit Scaling: " << gaoc.GetFitScale();
buffer << "\r\n  Fit Algor: ";

switch(gaoc.GetFitAlgor())
    {
    case FSA_EXPON:
        buffer << "Exponential";
        break;
    case FSA_WINDOW:
        buffer << "Windowing";
        break;
    case FSA_LINEAR:
        buffer << "Linear Normalization";
        buffer << "\r\nFS Lin Base: "
               << gaoc.GetFitLinBase();
        buffer << "\r\nFS Lin  Dec: " << gaoc.GetFitLinDec();
        buffer << "\r\nFS Lin  Min: " << gaoc.GetFitLinMin();
    }

buffer << "\r\n\r\n";
```

Next, I allocate buffers to hold fitness values and populations of *x* and *y* chromosomes; I also define variables:

```
// store dimensions of test
const size_t POP_SZ  = gaoc.GetPopSize();
const size_t GEN_SZ  = gaoc.GetTestSize();
const size_t EQ_ID   = gaoc.GetEquation();
const size_t SIG_DIG = gaoc.GetSigDigits();

buffer << setprecision(SIG_DIG) << setbase(10);

// create random deviate and mutation objects
RandDev devgen;
FloatMutagen fmute(gaoc.GetWtSign(),
                   gaoc.GetWtExp(),
```

```
                    gaoc.GetWtMant());

// allocate population and fitness arrays
double * x = new double [POP_SZ];

if (x == NULL)
    ErrorMessage("Opt/Param Alloc Failed",ET_CRASH);

double * xnew = new double [POP_SZ];

if (xnew == NULL)
    ErrorMessage("Opt/Param Alloc Failed",ET_CRASH);

double * y = new double [POP_SZ];

if (y == NULL)
    ErrorMessage("Opt/Param Alloc Failed",ET_CRASH);

double * ynew = new double [POP_SZ];

if (ynew == NULL)
    ErrorMessage("Opt/Param Alloc Failed",ET_CRASH);

double * fit = new double [POP_SZ];

if (fit == NULL)
    ErrorMessage("Opt/Param Alloc Failed",ET_CRASH);

double * ptrf = fit - 1;
double * ptrx =  x  - 1;
double * ptry =  y  - 1;

// various variables
double best, lowf, fitn, vf, vx, vy;
size_t i, j, inc, g, ibest, p1, p2;
char buf[64];
```

The initial population contains random values distributed between the specified minimum and maximum values:

```
// calculate ranges
const double rangex = gaoc.GetXMax() - gaoc.GetXMin();
const double rangey = gaoc.GetYMax() - gaoc.GetYMin();

// generate initial X values
for (i = 0; i < POP_SZ; ++i)
```

```
{
x[i] = SigDig(rangex * devgen()
                 + gaoc.GetXMin(),SIG_DIG);
y[i] = SigDig(rangey * devgen()
                 + gaoc.GetYMin(),SIG_DIG);
}
```

The main algorithm is contained within a loop that counts the generations:

```
// do the generations
for (g = 0; g < GEN_SZ; ++g)
    {
    // display progress in app header
    wsprintf(buf,"%s (loop: %u of %u)",AppName,g,GEN_SZ);
    SetWindowText(MainWdw,buf);

    // process generations
    .
    .
    .
    }
```

The first part of processing a generation is calculating fitness values for the population. The following loop calls the selected fitness function for each x–y pair in the population. The loop also tracks the highest and lowest fitness values for both reporting and later fitness scaling:

```
// calculate fitness for x values
best  = DBL_MIN;
lowf  = DBL_MAX;
ibest = 0;

for (i = 0; i < POP_SZ; ++i)
    {
    switch (EQ_ID)
        {
        case 0:
            fit[i] = 1.0 - FitnessF6(x[i],y[i]);
            break;
        case 1:
            fit[i] = 1.0 - FitnessF7(x[i],y[i]);
            break;
        case 2:
```

```
                fit[i] = 1.0 - FitnessF8(x[i],y[i]);
                break;
            case 3:
                fit[i] = FitnessCust(x[i],y[i]);
            }

        fit[i] = SigDig(fit[i],SIG_DIG);

        // track best fitness
        if (fit[i] > best)
            {
            best  = fit[i];
            ibest = i;
            }

        // track lowest fitness
        if (fit[i] < lowf)
            lowf = fit[i];
        }

    // display best solution so far
    if ((g % gaoc.GetReptFreq()) == 0)
        {
        buffer << setw(4) << g << ": (" << x[ibest]
                << "," << y[ibest] << ") fit = "
                << best << "\r\n";
        }
```

To implement linear normalization, the chromosomes must be sorted in descending order of their initial fitness before the algorithm can assign new values from top to bottom. When **Linear Normalization** is selected, I use a shell sort to arrange the x, y, and fit arrays in the required order:

```
    // sort by fitness if linear normalization
    if (FSA_LINEAR == gaoc.GetFitAlgor())
        {
        // shell sort three arrays in order of fitness
        fitn = gaoc.GetFitLinBase();

        for (inc = 1; inc <= POP_SZ / 9; inc = 3 * inc + 1) ;

        for ( ; inc > 0; inc /= 3)
            {
            for (i = inc + 1; i <= POP_SZ; i += inc)
                {
```

```
            vf = ptrf[i];
            vx = ptrx[i];
            vy = ptry[i];

            j  = i;

            while ((j > inc) && (ptrf[j - inc] < vf))
                {
                ptrf[j] = ptrf[j - inc];
                ptrx[j] = ptrx[j - inc];
                ptry[j] = ptry[j - inc];

                j -= inc;
                }

        ptrf[j] = vf;
        ptrx[j] = vx;
        ptry[j] = vy;
        }
    }
}
```

Next comes fitness scaling, in a loop that changes each fitness value
according to the chosen scaling algorithm:

```
    for (i = 0; i < POP_SZ; ++i)
        {
        // fitness scaling
        if (gaoc.GetFitScale())
            {
            switch (gaoc.GetFitAlgor())
                {
                case FSA_EXPON:
                    fit[i] = sqr(fit[i] + 1.0);
                    break;
                case FSA_WINDOW:
                    fit[i] -= lowf;
                    break;
                case FSA_LINEAR:
                    {
                    fit[i] = fitn;

                    if (fitn > gaoc.GetFitLinMin())
                        {
                        fitn -= gaoc.GetFitLinDec();
```

```
                        if (fitn < gaoc.GetFitLinMin())
                            fitn = gaoc.GetFitLinMin();
                        }
                    }
                }
            }
        }
```

Producing a new population requires the selection of parents, who are combined by crossover and then mutated based on the chosen configuration:

```
// create roulette wheel for reproduction selection
RouletteWheel<double> * sel;
sel = new RouletteWheel<double> (POP_SZ,fit);

if (sel == NULL)
    {
    buffer << "Failed to allocate roulette wheel\r\n";
    return;
    }

// if elitist, include best from orig. population
if (gaoc.GetElitist())
    {
    if (FSA_LINEAR == gaoc.GetFitAlgor())
        {
        xnew[0] = x[0];
        ynew[0] = y[0];
        }
    else
        {
        xnew[0] = x[ibest];
        ynew[0] = y[ibest];
        }

    i = 1;
    }
else
    i = 0;

// create new population of x's
for ( ; i < POP_SZ; ++i)
    {
    // create a new x
```

```
p1 = sel->GetIndex();

if (gaoc.GetCrossX()
&& (devgen() <= gaoc.GetCrossRate()))
    {
    p2 = sel->GetIndex();
    xnew[i] = Crossover(x[p1],x[p2]);
    }
else
    xnew[i] = x[p1];

// create a new y
if (gaoc.GetCrossB())
    p1 = sel->GetIndex();

if (gaoc.GetCrossY()
&& (devgen() <= gaoc.GetCrossRate()))
    {
    p2 = sel->GetIndex();
    ynew[i] = Crossover(y[p1],y[p2]);
    }
else
    ynew[i] = y[p1];

// mutate X
if (gaoc.GetMutateX())
    {
    if (gaoc.GetMuteLoop())
        {
        while (devgen() <= gaoc.GetMuteRate())
            xnew[i] = fmute.Mutate(xnew[i]);
        }
    else
        {
        if (devgen() <= gaoc.GetMuteRate())
            xnew[i] = fmute.Mutate(xnew[i]);
        }
    }

// mutate Y
if (gaoc.GetMutateY())
    {
    if (gaoc.GetMuteLoop())
        {
        while (devgen() <= gaoc.GetMuteRate())
            ynew[i] = fmute.Mutate(ynew[i]);
        }
```

```
            else
                {
                if (devgen() <= gaoc.GetMuteRate())
                    ynew[i] = fmute.Mutate(ynew[i]);
                }
            }

        // make sure x & y fit ranges
        if (xnew[i] > gaoc.GetXMax())
            xnew[i] = gaoc.GetXMax();

        if (xnew[i] < gaoc.GetXMin())
            xnew[i] = gaoc.GetXMin();

        if (ynew[i] > gaoc.GetYMax())
            ynew[i] = gaoc.GetYMax();

        if (ynew[i] < gaoc.GetYMin())
            ynew[i] = gaoc.GetYMin();

        // truncate digits
        xnew[i] = SigDig(xnew[i],SIG_DIG);
        ynew[i] = SigDig(ynew[i],SIG_DIG);
        }

    // remove roulette wheel
    delete sel;

    // copy new population
    memcpy(x,xnew,POP_SZ * sizeof(double));
    memcpy(y,ynew,POP_SZ * sizeof(double));
```

After the generation loop ends, the algorithm deletes its buffers and displays its output. With the default parameters, the output will look something like this:

```
Function Optimization (Peak Search)
-----------------------------------

   Equation: 1/((x+0.5)2+2(y-0.5)2-0.3cos(3px)-0.4cos(4py)+0.8)
  Pop. Size: 50
  Test Size: 101
  Rep. Freq: 1
Sig. Digits: 8
      X Min: -10
```

```
        X Max: 10
        Y Min: -10
        Y Max: 10
  Crossover %: 100
      Cross X: true
      Cross Y: true
      Cross B: true
   Mutation %: 100
     Wt. Sign: 2
     Wt. Expt: 13
     Wt. Mant: 85
     Mutate X: true
     Mutate Y: true
  Mutate Loop: false
      Elitism: true
   Fit Scaling: true
     Fit Algor: Windowing

  0: (-0.52349269,1.4340854) fit = 0.45264214
  1: (-0.52349269,5.5870834e-05) fit = 1.1982396
  2: (-0.77349269,3.3389903e-10) fit = 1.2278514
  3: (-0.76568019,5.5870601e-05) fit = 1.2628018
  4: (-0.7174977,1.4181426e-43) fit = 1.4682601
  5: (-0.70592677,5.5870834e-05) fit = 1.5092109
  6: (-0.70592677,5.5870834e-05) fit = 1.5092109
  7: (-0.65048349,1.2885542e-43) fit = 1.5971175
  8: (-0.65112293,2.0928715e-05) fit = 1.5974193
  9: (-0.65112293,2.0928715e-05) fit = 1.5974193
 10: (-0.65112197,5.588631e-05) fit = 1.5975972
 11: (-0.65112247,5.588631e-05) fit = 1.5975974
 12: (-0.65252863,6.089155e-24) fit = 1.5976373
 13: (-0.65252863,6.089155e-24) fit = 1.5976373
 14: (-0.65252863,0.001308991) fit = 1.6041995
 15: (-0.65252863,0.001308991) fit = 1.6041995
 16: (-0.65062648,0.014308266) fit = 1.6546669
 17: (-0.65252857,0.014308266) fit = 1.6551752
 18: (-0.65257166,0.014308266) fit = 1.6551835
 19: (-0.65257166,0.014308266) fit = 1.6551835
 20: (-0.65257166,0.014308266) fit = 1.6551835
 21: (-0.65257166,0.014308266) fit = 1.6551835
 22: (-0.65257166,0.014308266) fit = 1.6551835
 23: (-0.65257166,0.014308266) fit = 1.6551835
 24: (-0.65257166,0.014308266) fit = 1.6551835
 25: (-0.65305793,0.014306664) fit = 1.6552621
 26: (-0.65452085,0.014308265) fit = 1.6554059
 27: (-0.65452085,0.014308265) fit = 1.6554059
 28: (-0.65452085,0.014308265) fit = 1.6554059
```

```
29: (-0.65256773,0.02861653) fit = 1.6780999
30: (-0.65256773,0.02861653) fit = 1.6780999
31: (-0.65256773,0.02861653) fit = 1.6780999
32: (-0.65449439,0.030569565) fit = 1.678632
33: (-0.65449439,0.030569565) fit = 1.678632
34: (-0.65449439,0.030569565) fit = 1.678632
35: (-0.65452754,0.030569616) fit = 1.6786333
36: (-0.65452754,0.030569616) fit = 1.6786333
37: (-0.64524112,0.49106698) fit = 7.7001342
38: (-0.64892061,0.49106698) fit = 7.7494863
39: (-0.65281199,0.4910671) fit = 7.7771032
40: (-0.65281199,0.4910671) fit = 7.7771032
41: (-0.6501175,0.49888723) fit = 7.9227654
42: (-0.6525591,0.49863927) fit = 7.9374947
43: (-0.65354711,0.49881809) fit = 7.9419246
44: (-0.65354711,0.49881809) fit = 7.9419246
45: (-0.65354711,0.49881809) fit = 7.9419246
46: (-0.65354711,0.49881809) fit = 7.9419246
47: (-0.65354711,0.49887103) fit = 7.9421837
48: (-0.65390855,0.49887566) fit = 7.9430377
49: (-0.65390855,0.49887566) fit = 7.9430377
50: (-0.65390855,0.49887566) fit = 7.9430377
51: (-0.65390855,0.49887566) fit = 7.9430377
52: (-0.65390855,0.49887566) fit = 7.9430377
53: (-0.65390855,0.49887566) fit = 7.9430377
54: (-0.65390855,0.49887566) fit = 7.9430377
55: (-0.65390855,0.49887566) fit = 7.9430377
56: (-0.65390937,0.4988759) fit = 7.9430405
57: (-0.65390937,0.4988759) fit = 7.9430405
58: (-0.65390937,0.4988759) fit = 7.9430405
59: (-0.65390937,0.4988759) fit = 7.9430405
60: (-0.65586165,0.49985242) fit = 7.9461068
61: (-0.65586165,0.49985242) fit = 7.9461068
62: (-0.65586165,0.49985242) fit = 7.9461068
63: (-0.65586165,0.49985242) fit = 7.9461068
64: (-0.65586165,0.49985242) fit = 7.9461068
65: (-0.65586165,0.49985242) fit = 7.9461068
66: (-0.65538553,0.49985242) fit = 7.946633
67: (-0.65538553,0.49985242) fit = 7.946633
68: (-0.65538553,0.49985242) fit = 7.946633
69: (-0.6548861,0.49986005) fit = 7.9467513
70: (-0.6548861,0.49986005) fit = 7.9467513
71: (-0.6548861,0.49986005) fit = 7.9467513
72: (-0.6548861,0.49986005) fit = 7.9467513
73: (-0.6548861,0.49986005) fit = 7.9467513
74: (-0.6548861,0.49986005) fit = 7.9467513
75: (-0.6548861,0.49986005) fit = 7.9467513
```

```
 76: (-0.6548861,0.49986005) fit = 7.9467513
 77: (-0.6548861,0.49986005) fit = 7.9467513
 78: (-0.6548861,0.49986005) fit = 7.9467513
 79: (-0.65490136,0.4998591) fit = 7.9467539
 80: (-0.65490136,0.4998591) fit = 7.9467539
 81: (-0.65490116,0.49986011) fit = 7.9467545
 82: (-0.65490116,0.49986011) fit = 7.9467545
 83: (-0.65490116,0.49986011) fit = 7.9467545
 84: (-0.65490116,0.49986011) fit = 7.9467545
 85: (-0.65490116,0.49986011) fit = 7.9467545
 86: (-0.65487088,0.49987451) fit = 7.9467558
 87: (-0.65512932,0.49987513) fit = 7.9467605
 88: (-0.65512932,0.49987513) fit = 7.9467605
 89: (-0.65512932,0.49987513) fit = 7.9467605
 90: (-0.65512932,0.49987513) fit = 7.9467605
 91: (-0.65512932,0.49987513) fit = 7.9467605
 92: (-0.65512932,0.49987513) fit = 7.9467605
 93: (-0.65512932,0.49987513) fit = 7.9467605
 94: (-0.65512932,0.49987657) fit = 7.9467612
 95: (-0.65512932,0.49987657) fit = 7.9467612
 96: (-0.65512932,0.49987657) fit = 7.9467612
 97: (-0.65512932,0.49987657) fit = 7.9467612
 98: (-0.65512932,0.49987657) fit = 7.9467612
 99: (-0.65512932,0.49987657) fit = 7.9467612
100: (-0.65512932,0.49987657) fit = 7.9467612
```

ANALYSIS

With more than 30 factors influencing the performance of the algorithm, my genetic optimizer is difficult to analyze. For the functions F6 through F8, it performs remarkably well, as shown by these output examples:

```
Function Optimization (Peak Search)
-----------------------------------

   Equation: f6(x,y) = x²+2y²-0.3cos(3px)-0.4cos(4py)+0.7
  Pop. Size: 20
  Test Size: 21
  Rep. Freq: 1
Sig. Digits: 8
      X Min: -10
```

```
      X Max: 10
      Y Min: -10
      Y Max: 10
Crossover %: 100
    Cross X: true
    Cross Y: true
    Cross B: true
 Mutation %: 100
   Wt. Sign: 2
   Wt. Expt: 13
   Wt. Mant: 85
   Mutate X: true
   Mutate Y: true
Mutate Loop: false
    Elitism: true
Fit Scaling: true
  Fit Algor: Exponential

   0: (-0.44254005,-4.726122) fit = 2.2250739e-308
   1: (0.010331824,-0.1519475) fit = 0.41941706
   2: (-0.00012594158,-0.15194753) fit = 0.42094459
   3: (0.010560751,-2.6674215e-154) fit = 0.99840368
   4: (-0.00012594158,4.6266576e-39) fit = 0.99999977
   5: (1.4916695e-154,4.6266436e-39) fit = 1
```

Function Optimization (Peak Search)

Equation: $f7(x,y) = x^2+2y^2-0.3[\cos(3px)\cos(4py)]+0.3$

```
   0: (-7.3006952,4.2932582) fit = 2.2250739e-308
   1: (-7.3006952,4.2932582) fit = 2.2250739e-308
   2: (-7.3006952,4.2932582) fit = 2.2250739e-308
   3: (-7.3006952,4.2932582) fit = 2.2250739e-308
   4: (-7.3006952,4.2932582) fit = 2.2250739e-308
   5: (-7.3006952,4.2932582) fit = 2.2250739e-308
   6: (-7.3006952,4.2932582) fit = 2.2250739e-308
   7: (-7.3006952,4.2932582) fit = 2.2250739e-308
   8: (-7.3006952,4.2932582) fit = 2.2250739e-308
   9: (0,0.00010653021) fit = 0.99999971
  10: (0,5.3264666e-05) fit = 0.99999993
  11: (0,5.3264666e-05) fit = 0.99999993
  12: (0,5.3264666e-05) fit = 0.99999993
  13: (0,2.8842959e-24) fit = 1
```

Function Optimization (Peak Search)

```
Equation: f8(x,y) = x²+2y²-0.3[cos(3px)+cos(4py)]+0.3

0: (-5.4749572,-1.7925292) fit = 2.2250739e-308
1: (5.7739816e-06,0.013323638) fit = 1.2954499
2: (5.7739816e-06,0.013323638) fit = 1.2954499
3: (8.5974905e-10,6.0859593e-39) fit = 1.3
```

For the simpler functions, the genetic algorithm quickly zeros in (pun intended) on the optimal value. My custom function presents a more difficult problem, as evidenced by the GA's slower performance. The highest possible fitness value, to 14 decimal places, is 7.94680648572638, which is generated by x and y values such as $x = -0.655009352993422$ and $y = 0.499999998270169$. Several slightly variant x and y pairs generate the maximum fitness due to the limitations in C++ math I discussed earlier in this chapter. For all practical purposes, however, values of $x = -0.65500935$ and $y = 0.5$ yield the peak shown in Figure 4.1.

I've run the algorithm with a variety of parameters, and I present a few examples thereof:

```
Function Optimization (Peak Search)
-----------------------------------

    Pop. Size: 50
   Test Size: 1001
   Rep. Freq: 10
 Sig. Digits: 15
       X Min: -10
       X Max: 10
       Y Min: -10
       Y Max: 10
 Crossover %: 100
     Cross X: true
     Cross Y: true
     Cross B: true
  Mutation %: 100
    Wt. Sign: 2
    Wt. Expt: 13
    Wt. Mant: 85
   Mutate X: true
   Mutate Y: true
 Mutate Loop: false
```

```
     Elitism: true
Fit Scaling: true
  Fit Algor: Exponential


1000: (-0.655006407638930,0.499999780997343) fit =
   7.94680647784851
1000: (-0.655009963894594,0.500000319543856) fit =
   7.94680648520470
1000: (-0.655009147414557,0.500000059853766) fit =
   7.94680648571056
1000: (-0.655009360444216,0.500000144114767) fit =
   7.94680648571228
1000: (-0.655009255459012,0.499999969011235) fit =
   7.94680648574569
1000: (-0.655009268095393,0.500000009665423) fit =
   7.94680648574961
1000: (-0.655009360426982,0.499999962329255) fit =
   7.94680648575332
1000: (-0.655009320489066,0.500000001644545) fit =
   7.94680648575538
1000: (-0.655009355929763,0.500000024927876) fit =
   7.94680648575505
1000: (-0.655009356915107,0.500000001075834) fit =
   7.94680648575636

Function Optimization (Peak Search)
-----------------------------------

  Pop. Size: 50
  Test Size: 1001
  Rep. Freq: 10
Sig. Digits: 15
      X Min: -10
      X Max: 10
      Y Min: -10
      Y Max: 10
Crossover %: 100
    Cross X: true
    Cross Y: true
    Cross B: true
 Mutation %: 100
   Wt. Sign: 2
   Wt. Expt: 13
   Wt. Mant: 85
   Mutate X: true
   Mutate Y: true
```

```
Mutate Loop: false
    Elitism: true
Fit Scaling: true
  Fit Algor: Linear Normalization
FS Lin Base: 100
FS Lin  Dec: 5
FS Lin  Min: 1

1000: (-0.0312499999999999,0.500000001040024) fit =
   3.00621268319913
1000: (-0.6250000000000000,0.500000000007751) fit =
   7.22224299336906
1000: (-0.6562500000000000,0.500000000086154) fit =
   7.94542165924234
1000: (-0.6562500000000000,0.500000000368840) fit =
   7.94542165924234
1000: (-0.6550093543121850,0.499999999864814) fit =
   7.94680648575637

  Fit Algor: Linear Normalization
FS Lin Base: 100
FS Lin  Dec: 10
FS Lin  Min: 10

1000: (-0.656250000000001,0.500000000585619) fit =
   7.94542165924234
1000: (-0.656250000000000,0.499999999905328) fit =
   7.94542165924234

 Mutation %: 75
Mutate Loop: true

 410: (-0.655008500936907,0.499999825115341) fit =
   7.94680648503765
1000: (-0.655009269696162,0.499999999713509) fit =
   7.94680648575005

1000: (-0.656250000000000,0.500000000037419) fit =
   7.94542165924234

 370: (-0.655008594554474,0.499999692783884) fit =
   7.94680648503806
1000: (-0.655009352459260,0.499999999841436) fit =
   7.94680648575637

 250: (-0.655010184091765,0.499999969853140) fit =
   7.94680648513392
```

```
1000: (-0.655009269706068,0.499999999970940) fit =
   7.94680648575005

 300: (-0.655010253605791,0.500000000296741) fit =
   7.94680648502763
1000: (-0.655009355644339,0.500000000558112) fit =
   7.94680648575636

   Fit Algor: Linear Normalization
FS Lin Base: 100
FS Lin  Dec: 20
FS Lin  Min: 10

1000: (-0.655029296875001,0.500000000000227) fit =
   7.94680612798538
1000: (-0.655029296875000,0.500000000061553) fit =
   7.94680612798538
1000: (-0.656250000000000,0.500000000004932) fit =
   7.94542165924234

Function Optimization (Peak Search)
-----------------------------------

   Pop. Size: 50
   Test Size: 1001
   Rep. Freq: 10
Sig. Digits: 15
      X Min: -10
      X Max: 10
      Y Min: -10
      Y Max: 10
Crossover %: 100
    Cross X: true
    Cross Y: true
    Cross B: true
 Mutation %: 75
   Wt. Sign: 2
   Wt. Expt: 13
   Wt. Mant: 85
   Mutate X: true
   Mutate Y: true
Mutate Loop: true
    Elitism: true
Fit Scaling: true
  Fit Algor: Exponential

 900: (-0.655010219853847,0.499999993577163) fit =
```

```
   7.94680648508117
1000: (-0.655009171110619,0.499999993840233) fit =
   7.94680648572636

 650: (-0.655008872066805,0.499999775435237) fit =
   7.94680648544092
1000: (-0.655009200519759,0.499999978417123) fit =
   7.94680648573432

 340: (-0.655009492402470,0.499999881521376) fit =
   7.94680648570925
1000: (-0.655009352063164,0.499999999841051) fit =
   7.94680648575637

1000: (-0.655029297426161,0.499999998410855) fit =
   7.94680612796561

 840: (-0.655010240902514,0.500000046199952) fit =
   7.94680648504353
1000: (-0.655008785822952,0.500000039676606) fit =
   7.94680648546313

Mutation %: 90

1000: (-0.656250035857743,0.499999940199481) fit =
   7.9454215791826

1000: (-0.655029297109007,0.499999983822875) fit =
   7.94680612797643

1000: (-0.655014079211159,0.500003860492379) fit =
   7.94680643406111

 880: (-0.655008618723124,0.500000057105490) fit =
   7.94680648526378
1000: (-0.655008655553562,0.500000082843425) fit =
   7.94680648530361

Mutation %: 50

 420: (-0.655009313396401,0.499999931875535) fit =
   7.94680648574508
1000: (-0.655009352901700,0.499999995726068) fit =
   7.94680648575633

 360: (-0.655009199718026,0.499999740520832) fit =
   7.94680648559230
```

```
1000: (-0.655009352993422,0.499999998270169) fit =
    7.94680648575637

1000: (-0.65502929687796,0.499999997718153) fit =
    7.94680612798527

 470: (-0.655010258739175,0.499999999683997) fit =
    7.94680648501929
1000: (-0.655009262079612,0.49999999822487) fit =
    7.94680648574884

Mutation %: 37.5

1000: (-0.655014038327128,0.500000000665673) fit =
    7.94680646601443

 730: (-0.655008784219406,0.499999892579644) fit =
    7.94680648544036
1000: (-0.655009269468793,0.499999999025829) fit =
    7.94680648575001

Mutation %: 25

 670: (-0.655009763424218,0.500000048182403) fit =
    7.94680648560031
1000: (-0.655009350884128,0.500000000094468) fit =
    7.94680648575636

 130: (-0.655009137532498,0.500000477096368) fit =
    7.94680648523167
1000: (-0.655009359662996,0.500000000594756) fit =
    7.94680648575634

 490: (-0.655008775128453,0.500000014911066) fit =
    7.94680648545498
1000: (-0.655009269659827,0.500000000007973) fit =
    7.94680648575005

1000: (-0.65625000000523,0.499999996166444) fit =
    7.94542165924114

1000: (-0.65625000000576,0.499999998896825) fit =
    7.94542165924105

   Fit Algor: Percentage of Best
 Mutation %: 25
Mutate Loop: true
```

```
 200: (-0.655009543834759,0.499999639599556) fit =
    7.94680648544832
1000: (-0.655009354220356,0.499999999931377) fit =
    7.94680648575637

 680: (-0.655008997640147,0.500000481028751) fit =
    7.94680648515172
1000: (-0.655009269206187,0.500000000547323) fit =
    7.94680648574998

 850: (-0.655010227871641,0.499999938268446) fit =
    7.94680648506062
1000: (-0.655009239296073,0.499999999708460) fit =
    7.94680648574463

 250: (-0.655009238972157,0.499999503773208) fit =
    7.94680648522233
1000: (-0.655009269709048,0.499999999998672) fit =
    7.94680648575005

 920: (-0.655009463444309,0.499999804328323) fit =
    7.9468064856643
1000: (-0.655009449590658,0.499999995463863) fit =
    7.94680648574802

  Fit Algor: Exponential
 Mutation %: 100
Mutate Loop: false

1000: (-0.655029336239088,0.500000133917966) fit =
    7.94680612653362

 270: (-0.655009391502467,0.499999966947987) fit =
    7.94680648575276
1000: (-0.655009341265022,0.499999990109242) fit =
    7.94680648575603

 750: (-0.655009709538472,0.499999995573024) fit =
    7.94680648564232
1000: (-0.655009349207150,0.499999993657152) fit =
    7.94680648575627

 590: (-0.655009530826613,0.500000381306026) fit =
    7.94680648541974
1000: (-0.655009394826101,0.500000011031314) fit =
    7.94680648575458
```

```
Function Optimization (Peak Search)
-----------------------------------

   Pop. Size: 50
   Test Size: 1001
   Rep. Freq: 10
  Sig. Digits: 15
       X Min: -10
       X Max: 10
       Y Min: -10
       Y Max: 10
 Crossover %: 100
     Cross X: true
     Cross Y: true
     Cross B: true
  Mutation %: 25
    Wt. Sign: 2
    Wt. Expt: 13
    Wt. Mant: 85
    Mutate X: true
    Mutate Y: true
 Mutate Loop: true
     Elitism: true
  Fit Scaling: true
   Fit Algor: Linear Normalization
 FS Lin Base: 100
 FS Lin  Dec: 10
 FS Lin  Min: 1

1000: (-0.655029296875029, 0.500000000000249)   fit =
  7.94680612798538
1000: (-0.007812499999999,-6.09111846222457e-74) fit =
  1.18615322939853
1000: (-0.656250000000001, 0.500000000000000)   fit =
  7.94542165924234


 FS Lin  Min: 10

 680: (-0.655009076959701,0.499999999774684) fit =
  7.94680648568757
1000: (-0.655009269707095,0.499999999905651) fit =
  7.94680648575005

1000: (-0.00781249999999999,0.500000000007436) fit =
  2.914930112758
```

I show several runs for a variety of parameter settings, for each run showing the cycle on which the maximum fitness was first reported to 10 significant digits and the best value generated after 1000 generations. If you're looking for six to eight digits of precision, the peak is usually found in a few hundred generations. Being a stochastic process, the genetic algorithm doesn't always produce identical performance. Reducing the influence of chance will be one of the topics I cover in Chapter 6, where I further analyze genetic algorithm performance and parameter selection.

ONWARD

I suggest that you play a bit with the configuration, selecting a variety of parameters to gain a feel for how they affect performance.

Genetic algorithms can do more than optimize a function. In Chapter 5, I look at the use of genetic algorithms in the development of optimum strategies, and I'll show how scientists are using genetic algorithms to explore some of the mysterious aspects of the universe.

CHAPTER 5

THE PRISONER'S DILEMMA

G enetic algorithms are not limited to optimizing functions; they also provide a powerful tool for machine learning and theoretical biology.

THE DILEMMA DEFINED

Here's the situation: the authorities have arrested you and an accomplice for a crime. Once in jail, you aren't allowed to communicate with your partner. The prosecutor brings you to his office and offers you the following deal: "We have substantial evidence against both of you. If you cooperate with your partner and claim innocence, we'll convict you anyway and throw you in jail for a couple of years. But if you defect to us, admitting your guilt and testifying against your friend, we'll set you free and give him a long sentence. But if both of you plead guilty, we'll put both of you behind bars for a year." The prosecutor then tells you he's made the same offer to your accomplice.

You don't know what your accomplice will do, and you want to minimize your own sentence. What will you do? In the case of a single crime, the best choice may be to choose defection, guaranteeing no more than a year in jail. Take the scenario a step further, however, and assume that you've been arrested for a crime spree, with separate trials being held for each indictment. Can a more effective strategy be developed, based on the outcomes of previous trials, to produce the smallest sentence for yourself for the crime spree?

The situation I've outlined is the so-called *Prisoner's Dilemma*, a classic piece of game theory. From a theoretical standpoint, the Prisoner's Dilemma is an elegant and simple tool for investigating strategies and competition. Beyond the realm of criminal activity, the quandary posed by the Prisoner's Dilemma is applicable to evolutionary biology, stock prices, and other situations where interconnected actions can be chosen based on past history.

Many researchers—particularly those investigating genetic and evolutionary algorithms—have implemented the Prisoner's Dilemma in software. In general, they use a payoff scheme based on the chart in Table 5.1.

For example, if Player 1 chooses to defect while Player 2 cooperates, the former scores 5 points (for going free) while the latter earns nothing (for a long jail sentence). The object of an iterated game of the Prisoner's Dilemma is to maximize one's score over a series of competitions with other players.

TABLE 5.1   PRISONER'S DILEMMA PAYOFF

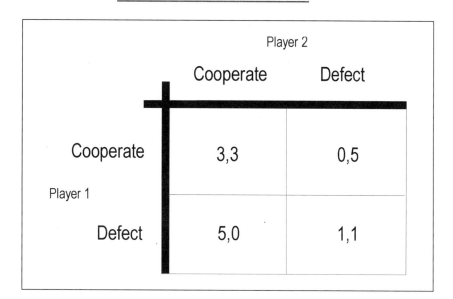

SIMULATED EVOLUTION

Kristian Lindgren, a physicist at the Chalmers University of Technology in Copenhagen, examined the dynamics of the Prisoner's Dilemma through a genetic algorithm. Beginning with a random selection of strategies, Lindgren's program began a series of competitions, with each strategy competing against all others in the population. Those that scored the highest became the progenitors of future generations, and the cycle was repeated.

In Lindgren's simulation, as in most genetic implementations of the Prisoner's Dilemma, a strategy is essentially a binary string wherein a zero-bit represents "cooperate" (C) and a one-bit indicates a choice to "defect" (D). While the computer will store the strategies in binary bits, the strategies will be displayed for people as strings of Cs and Ds, output from low- to high-order bit.

A two-bit strategy can be one of DD, CD, DC, or CC (corresponding to the binary values 00, 10, 01, and 11). A simple way of comparing a pair of two-bit strategies would be to apply the matrix in Table 5.1. For example, to compare CD to CC:

```
          3 + 5 = 8
Player 1: C   D
Player 2: C   C
          3 + 0 = 3
```

In that comparison, CD would earn 8 points while CC receives only 3 points. In a population of CCs and CDs, the CD string would have the higher fitness due to its greater score; using a roulette wheel for selection of parents, CD would be more likely to parent new strings that would be CC.

That algorithm, however, isn't really a strategy. A strategy involves choosing an action based on history. In Lindgren's genetic implementation, each element of a strategy is a reaction to a given history, as opposed to being a fixed action. For example, the CD strategy will cooperate if the opponent's last action was to defect and to defect if the opponent previously cooperated. In other words, the CD strategy complements the last action of its opponent; DD always defects, CC always cooperates, and DC (known as "tit-for-tat") always copies the previous action of its opponents.

Lindgren's model creates an initial population of two-bit strategies. In each iteration of the simulation, each strategy accumulates a fitness value through a round-robin contest with each of the other strategies in its population. The cumulative fitness values provide a relative fitness for each strategy, defining their reproductive chances. In each new generation, Lindgren allowed for the possible mutation of one bit in each new strategy; he also incorporated the ability of strategies to double their length, allowing them to examine even longer histories. For example, a CDDC strategy would cooperate if both it and its opponent defected on the last round; it would defect if it cooperated and the opponent defected.

It might seem, at first, that Lindgren's process would eventually evolve a single strategy that defeats all others and dominates the population. But that *isn't* what happens; instead, the simulation shows interesting dynamics, as the relative abundance of different strategies changes within a population. While one strategy might dominate for a while, no strategy ever takes permanent control of the population; often, two strategies will fight it out, their populations rising and falling as each attempts to dominate. Why?

In the genetic algorithms presented so far, fitness is determined against a fixed external environment, such as a function that always returns the same value for the same strategy. In the Prisoner's Dilemma, the population of strategies represents the fitness landscape. Such an environment is always changing based on the results of past competitions; each new generation represents a different mix of strategies against which fitness is calculated. You might expect such an environment to evolve into anarchy—and you'd be wrong.

In a classic run of his program, Lindgren discovered that periods of relative stasis were punctuated by intervals of variation and population diversity. While one or two strategies might dominate for a while, the dynamics of the population would suddenly enter a near chaotic time that mixed a variety of strategies. The chaos eventually led to a new population dominated by a few strategies, which would last until the next episode of chaos.

What Lindgren saw in his output was a primitive analogy to biological evolution: mass extinction, adaptive stasis, coevolution, and punctuated equilibrium. From a simple premise came a mathematical model of evolution and natural selection. As Claus Emmeche put it in his 1992 book, *The Garden in the Machine*:

> For paleobiologists, there is an important moral to this story: they no longer need to search for or invent "external catastrophes" like volcanoes or meteors crashing to Earth in order to explain violent changes in an ecological system. Even though the biological interpretations of Lindgren's model can be debated, it demonstrates that stochastic dynamic systems can exhibit immensely varied behavior based purely on their inherent factors.

Lindgren's work, and that of others, may put to rest the persistent criticism that punctuated equilibrium is a return to the discarded theory of catastrophism. Perhaps rapid evolution arises from the very complexity of the interactions in an ecosystem—and while cataclysms perturb living systems, the real source of change is the living system itself.

COOPERATIVE DYNAMICS

Lindgren's work is largely unreported in the United States, perhaps because it is focused on the simulation of biological evolution and not on computer science. Better known is the work of Robert Axelrod, a political scientist at the University of Michigan. He created a tournament in which his colleagues provided a variety of strategies for the Prisoner's Dilemma for mutual competition.

While some of the submitted strategies were devilishly complex and convoluted, a very simple strategy won. Game theorist Anatol Rapoport submitted "Tit-for-Tat," a strategy that begins with a cooperative response and then repeats the previous move of its opponent. In a round-robin tournament, Tit-for-Tat scores well in general by minimizing its vulnerability to "defecting" strategies—and it can take advantage of a cooperative partner.

Interestingly, Tit-for-Tat's success allowed it to control the population mix; strategies that bog down in defect-defect conflicts tended to score low, while cooperative strategies scored well against Tit-for-Tat. In the end, Tit-for-Tat helped evolve what Axelrod termed "a more congenial environment," wherein the population tends toward mutual cooperation.

Axelrod's work from the 1970s is a base for today's research into the development of altruism. Several interesting mathematical models have emerged from the work of three European scientists: Martin Nowak of Oxford University, Robert May of the Imperial College in London, and Karl Sigmund of the University of Vienna. Sigmund is a mathematician, Nowak is a zoologist, and May is an evolutionary biologist. Their most recent effort involved a tournament in which strategies choose their actions on the score earned in the previous round rather than on the opponent's previous move. Probabilities influence the selection of actions, allowing for "mistaken" moves that reflect the uncertainties in real life.

Once again, punctuated equilibrium appeared as the population rapidly changed. Populations would often settle on generally cooperative or defective behavior, only to change suddenly to the opposite strategy. And while versions of Tit-for-Tat would sometimes do well in a cooperative environment, a new strategy named *Pavlov* would often dominate the population. Pavlov sticks with a move so long as the reward is high and switches moves when it receives a low payoff. Pavlov sticks with what works but changes its actions abruptly when it loses.

Nowak and company reached the conclusion that cooperation can emerge in any population where the members recognize each other's behavior and remember past actions. They have also experimented with noniterated two-dimensional "spatial games" in which the Prisoner's Dilemma is played out visually, on a grid, using techniques similar to those used for cellular automata. Pockets of cooperation and defection arise, with cooperation having the advantage among cells that must coexist with their neighbors. That, of course, makes sense, in that communal organisms—people, prairie dogs, lions, and so on—seem to have evolved altruism.

The Prisoner's Dilemma is a fruitful tool for examining the evolution of strategies, and the preceding experiments are not the only ones to have been devised. In Chapter 7, I'll describe yet another version of the Prisoner's Dilemma using finite state machines; for now, let's look at an implementation via genetic algorithm.

DESIGNING A PRISONER'S DILEMMA SIMULATION

I designed a modified form of Lindgren's Prisoner's Dilemma for the Forge application. For this genetic algorithm, I defined chromosomes as 32-bit integers.

Each chromosome is mapped as follows:

Bits	Decription
0	Initial move (fixed)
1–2	Move 2, 2-bit strategy
3–6	Move 3, 4-bit strategy
7–14	Move 4, 8-bit strategy
15–31	Move 5, 16-bit strategy
32	Not used

The initial move may or may not be used, depending on a configuration setting. The other moves select an action based on the previous moves of the opponent's strategy; the number of moves defined by a strategy is its level, which ranges between two and five. Following is an example of two level-three strategies in competition.

Strategy **C DC CDDC** (Player 1) will begin by cooperating; strategy **D CC DCCC** (Player 2) will defect on its first move. For the second move, Player 1 cooperates because Player 2 previously defected, and Player 2 always cooperates on the second move. The third, and last, move is based on the previous two moves of the opponent, such that Player 1 chooses to defect while Player 2 continues to cooperate. The final moves are **CCD** for Player 1 and **DCC** for Player 2, for a total of 8 points each.

These calculations can be performed by a series of bit shifts and logical operations, with a 0-bit representing defection and a 1-bit indicating cooperation. Also, you can set the first move to "random," which causes the program to ignore the fixed first move bit and select an initial act for each contest.

Configuration of a Prisoner's Dilemma simulation is accomplished via the same system used in other chapters of this book: a configuration object is created to display a dialog box in which the parameters of a run can be entered. The simulation then interrogates the configuration object—in this case, a `PDOptConfig`—to obtain parameters. For the Prisoner's Dilemma, the dialog box is shown in Figure 5.1.

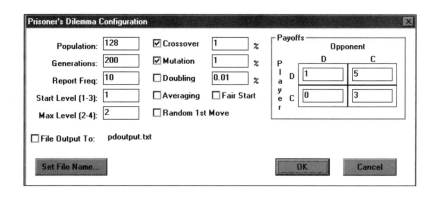

FIGURE 5.1   PRISONER'S DILEMMA CONFIGURATION DIALOG BOX.

The meaning of the parameters is as follows:

Population   The number of strategies to be tested.

Generations   The number of generations to be run in this simulation.

Report Frequency   How often the simulation should report on the strategies it has tested.

Start Level   The number of moves in the initial population of strategies.

Max Level   The maximum level to which strategies can mutate.

Crossover   The checkbox enables one-point crossover during reproduction; the text box contains a percentage chance of crossover occurring.

Mutation   The checkbox enables single-bit mutations during reproduction; the text box contains a percentage chance of mutation occurring.

Doubling   The checkbox enables doubling during reproduction; the text box contains a percentage chance of doubling occurring. When a strategy doubles, it copies its highest level into a new level twice. For example, when the strategy **D DC** doubles, it becomes the strategy **D DC DCDC**.

Averaging   Enabling **Averaging** alters fitness values after competition by dividing them by the number of contests that
occurred. This divides the strategy's total fitness by the
number of contests it engaged in.

Fair Start   Instead of creating a completely random population
of initial strategies, **Fair Start** creates an equal number
of all strategies; it may also change the population size
to an exact multiple of the number of available strategy strings. For example, if Population is set to 100 and
the level is two, setting **Fair Start** will set the number
of strategies to **128**, each representing one of the 128
possible three-bit strategies. Only available with starting levels one and two, since higher levels have a very
large number of possible strategies.

Random 1st   The first move encoded in a strategy is replaced by a
random action for each contest.

Payoffs   Defines the payoff amounts for combinations of cooperation and defection.

File Output   The Prisoner's Dilemma is most interesting when run
for thousands—or tens of thousands—of generations.
Since output to a window is limited in length to about
32,000 characters, I allow a file to record every generation's population. The name of the file can be
changed with the **Set File Name...** button.

The Configuration dialog box is implemented using the same techniques
shown in Chapter 4 for the genetic optimization. I'll give the class definition here to clarify data types and interrogation functions:

```
class PDOptConfig
    {
    public:
        PDOptConfig
            (
            HINSTANCE inst,
            HWND      parent
```

```
        );

    static void DlgSetFileName
        (
        HWND   dlg
        );

    static void DlgInit
        (
        HWND   dlg
        );

    static BOOL DlgStore
        (
        HWND   dlg
        );

    // verify if this object is valid
    bool GetValidity() { return Valid; }

    // interrogate dimensions of test
    size_t GetPopSize()  { return PopSize;  }
    size_t GetTestSize() { return TestSize; }
    size_t GetReptFreq() { return ReptFreq; }
    size_t GetStartLvl() { return StartLvl; }
    size_t GetMaxLevel() { return MaxLevel; }

    // interrogate operator parameters
    bool  GetCrossover() { return Crossover; }
    float GetCrossRate() { return CrossRate; }
    bool  GetMutation()  { return Mutation;  }
    float GetMuteRate()  { return MuteRate;  }
    bool  GetDoubling()  { return Doubling;  }
    float GetDblRate()   { return DblRate;   }
    bool  GetAveraging() { return Averaging; }
    bool  GetFairStart() { return FairStart; }
    bool  GetRandom1st() { return Random1st; }

    // interrogate payoff amounts
    double GetPayoffDD() { return PayoffDD; }
    double GetPayoffDC() { return PayoffDC; }
    double GetPayoffCD() { return PayoffCD; }
    double GetPayoffCC() { return PayoffCC; }

    // interrogate output file information
    bool         GetFileOut()  { return FileOut; }
    const char * GetFileName() { return FileName; }
```

```
private:
    // validity flag
    bool    Valid;

    // dimensions of test
    size_t PopSize;
    size_t TestSize;
    size_t ReptFreq;
    size_t StartLvl;
    size_t MaxLevel;

    // interrogate operator parameters
    bool  Crossover;
    float CrossRate;
    bool  Mutation;
    float MuteRate;
    bool  Doubling;
    float DblRate;
    bool  Averaging;
    bool  FairStart;
    bool  Random1st;

    // payoff amounts
    double PayoffDD;
    double PayoffDC;
    double PayoffCD;
    double PayoffCC;

    // interrogate output file information
    bool FileOut;
    char FileName[256];

    // stored parameter values
    static size_t DefPopSize;
    static size_t DefTestSize;
    static size_t DefReptFreq;
    static size_t DefStartLvl;
    static size_t DefMaxLevel;
    static bool   DefCrossover;
    static float  DefCrossRate;
    static bool   DefMutation;
    static float  DefMuteRate;
    static bool   DefDoubling;
    static float  DefDblRate;
    static bool   DefAveraging;
    static bool   DefFairStart;
```

```
        static bool   DefRandom1st;
        static double DefPayoffDD;
        static double DefPayoffDC;
        static double DefPayoffCD;
        static double DefPayoffCC;
        static bool   DefFileOut;
        static char   DefFileName[256];
    };
```

The implementation code for PDOptConfig is very similar to that of other configuration classes in previous chapters.

IMPLEMENTATION

The algorithm begins by creating a configuration object and displaying its contents:

```
    // create configuration and verify it
    PDOptConfig pdoc(inst,wdw);

    if (!pdoc.GetValidity())
        {
        buffer << "Cancelled\r\n";
        return;
        }

    // open output file (if required)
    ofstream * fout = NULL;

    if (pdoc.GetFileOut())
        {
        fout = new ofstream (pdoc.GetFileName());

        if (fout == NULL)
            {
            buffer << "Memory allocation failed\r\n";
            return;
            }
        }

// display parameters
    size_t POP_SZ  = pdoc.GetPopSize();
```

```
size_t GEN_SZ  = pdoc.GetTestSize();
size_t s;

switch (pdoc.GetStartLvl())
    {
    case  1: s =      8U; break;
    case  2: s =    128U; break;
    case  3: s = 32768U; break;
    default: s =      2U;
    }

if (pdoc.GetFairStart() && (POP_SZ % s))
    POP_SZ = (POP_SZ / s + 1) * s;

buffer << "\r\n Population: " << POP_SZ;
buffer << "\r\n  Test Size: " << GEN_SZ;
buffer << "\r\nReport Freq: " << pdoc.GetReptFreq();
buffer << "\r\nStart Level: " << pdoc.GetStartLvl();

buffer << "\r\n  Crossover: " << pdoc.GetCrossover();
if (pdoc.GetCrossover())
    buffer << " (" << pdoc.GetCrossRate() * 100.0F << "%)";

buffer << "\r\n   Mutation: "<< pdoc.GetMutation();
if (pdoc.GetMutation())
    buffer << " (" << pdoc.GetMuteRate() * 100.0F << "%)";

buffer << "\r\n   Doubling: " << pdoc.GetDoubling();
if (pdoc.GetDoubling())
    {
    buffer << " (" << pdoc.GetDblRate() * 100.0F << "%)";
    buffer << "\r\n Max. Level: " << pdoc.GetMaxLevel();
    }

buffer << "\r\n  Averaging: " << pdoc.GetAveraging();
buffer << "\r\n Fair Start: " << pdoc.GetFairStart();
buffer << "\r\n Random 1st: " << pdoc.GetRandom1st();
buffer << "\r\n  Payoff DD: " << pdoc.GetPayoffDD();
buffer << "\r\n  Payoff DC: " << pdoc.GetPayoffDC();
buffer << "\r\n  Payoff CD: " << pdoc.GetPayoffCD();
buffer << "\r\n  Payoff CC: " << pdoc.GetPayoffCC();
buffer << "\r\nFile Output: " << pdoc.GetFileOut();

if (pdoc.GetFileOut())
    buffer << " (" << pdoc.GetFileName() << ")";

buffer << "\r\n\r\n" << dec;
```

```
if (fout != NULL)
   {
   (*fout) << "\n Population: " << pdoc.GetPopSize();
   (*fout) << "\n  Test Size: " << pdoc.GetTestSize();
   (*fout) << "\nReport Freq: " << pdoc.GetReptFreq();
   (*fout) << "\nStart Level: " << pdoc.GetStartLvl();

   (*fout) << "\n  Crossover: " << pdoc.GetCrossover();
   if (pdoc.GetCrossover())
      (*fout) << " (" << pdoc.GetCrossRate()*100.0F << "%)";

   (*fout) << "\n   Mutation: "<< pdoc.GetMutation();
   if (pdoc.GetMutation())
       (*fout) << " (" << pdoc.GetMuteRate()*100.0F << "%)";

   (*fout) << "\n   Doubling: " << pdoc.GetDoubling();
   if (pdoc.GetDoubling())
      {
      (*fout) << " (" << pdoc.GetDblRate()*100.0F << "%)";
      (*fout) << "\n Max. Level: " << pdoc.GetMaxLevel();
      }

   (*fout) << "\n  Averaging: " << pdoc.GetAveraging();
   (*fout) << "\n Fair Start: " << pdoc.GetFairStart();
   (*fout) << "\n Random 1st: " << pdoc.GetRandom1st();
   (*fout) << "\n  Payoff DD: " << pdoc.GetPayoffDD();
   (*fout) << "\n  Payoff DC: " << pdoc.GetPayoffDC();
   (*fout) << "\n  Payoff CD: " << pdoc.GetPayoffCD();
   (*fout) << "\n  Payoff CC: " << pdoc.GetPayoffCC();
   (*fout) << "\nFile Output: " << pdoc.GetFileOut();

   if (pdoc.GetFileOut())
      (*fout) << " (" << pdoc.GetFileName() << ")";

   (*fout) << dec << "\n\n";
   }
```

Then I define variables and allocate buffers to hold the strategy population and associated fitness values:

```
// create random deviate and mutation objects
RandDev devgen;

// allocate population and fitness arrays
Chromosome * pop = new Chromosome [POP_SZ];
```

```
if (pop == NULL)
    {
    buffer << "Memory allocation failed\r\n";
    return;
    }

Chromosome * newpop = new Chromosome [POP_SZ];

if (newpop == NULL)
    {
    buffer << "Memory allocation failed\r\n";
    return;
    }

size_t * lvl = new size_t [POP_SZ];

if (lvl == NULL)
        {
        buffer << "Memory allocation failed\r\n";
        return;
        }

size_t * newlvl = new size_t [POP_SZ];

if (newlvl == NULL)
    {
    buffer << "Memory allocation failed\r\n";
    return;
    }

double * fit = new double [POP_SZ];

if (fit == NULL)
    {
    buffer << "Memory allocation failed\r\n";
    return;
    }
```

Next, you'll find several constants defining bitmasks and strategy lengths (in number of bits). I also define variables:

```
// shifts for move selection
    static const int shift[4] = { 1, 3, 7, 15 };

    // level masks
```

```
static const Chromosome lmask[5] =
    {
    0x00000001UL,
    0x00000007UL,
    0x0000007FUL,
    0x00007FFFUL,
    0x7FFFFFFFUL
    };

static const float  lbits[5]  = { 1.0F, 3.0F, 7.0F, 15.0F,
31.0F };
static const size_t lbitsn[5] = { 1, 3, 7, 15, 31 };

// strategy masks
static const Chromosome smask[5] =
    {
    0x00000001UL,
    0x00000006UL,
    0x00000078UL,
    0x00007F80UL,
    0x7FFF8000UL
    };

static const int sbits[5] = { 1, 2, 4, 8, 16 };

// various variables
size_t g, i, j, k, l, p1, p2, pl, ps;
Chromosome strati, stratj, tempi, tempj, bit, m, vb;
char buf[64];
RouletteWheel<double> * rw;

// mask off low bit if start is random
if (pdoc.GetRandom1st())
    vb = 0xFFFFFFFEUL;
else
    vb = 0xFFFFFFFFUL;
```

How I generate the initial population depends on the **Fair Start** setting. For a fair start, I create equal numbers of every possible strategy; otherwise, each member is selected randomly:

```
// generate initial population
k = 0;

if (pdoc.GetFairStart())
```

```
        {
    for (i = 0; i < POP_SZ / s; ++i)
        {
        for (m = 0; m < s; ++m)
            {
            pop[k] = m;
            lvl[k] = pdoc.GetStartLvl();
            ++k;
            }
        }
    }
else
    {
    for (i = 0; i < POP_SZ; ++i)
        {
        pop[i] = Chromosome(devgen() * float(s));
        lvl[i] = pdoc.GetStartLvl();
        }
    }
```

The generation loop begins by displaying the status of the test in the Forge program title bar:

```
// do the generations
for (g = 0; g < GEN_SZ; ++g)
    {
    // display progress in app header
    wsprintf(buf,"Forge (loop: %u of %u)",g,GEN_SZ);
    SetWindowText(wdw,buf);
    .
    .
    .
```

I'll break down the contents of the generation loop here, step by step. First, competition occurs between strategies in a round-robin tournament:

```
// calculate fitness for x values
for (i = 0; i < POP_SZ; ++i)
    fit[i] = 0.0;

for (i = 0; i < POP_SZ; ++i)
    {
    for (j = i + 1; j < POP_SZ; ++j)
```

```
{
// compete
l = (lvl[i] < lvl[j]) ? lvl[i] : lvl[j];

// level 1
if (pdoc.GetRandom1st())
    {
    strati = (devgen() > 0.5F) ? 1 : 0;
    stratj = (devgen() > 0.5F) ? 1 : 0;
    }
else
    {
    strati = pop[i] & 1UL;
    stratj = pop[j] & 1UL;
    }

// levels 2 through 5
for (k = 0; k < l; ++k)
    {
    // select my move
    bit   = pop[i] & (1UL << int(shift[k]
                                  + stratj));
    tempi = (strati << 1) | (bit >> int(shift[k]
                                  + stratj));

    // select his move
    bit   = pop[j] & (1UL << int(shift[k]
                                  + strati));
    tempj = (stratj << 1) | (bit >> int(shift[k]
                                  + strati));

    strati = tempi;
    stratj = tempj;
    }

// compete
if (pdoc.GetRandom1st())
    {
    k = 1;
    m = 2;
    }
else
    {
    k = 0;
    m = 1;
    }
```

```
for (; k <= 1; ++k)
    {
    if (strati & m)
        {
        if (stratj & m)
            {
            fit[i] += pdoc.GetPayoffCC();
            fit[j] += pdoc.GetPayoffCC();
            }
        else
            {
            fit[i] += pdoc.GetPayoffCD();
            fit[j] += pdoc.GetPayoffDC();
            }
        }
    else
        {
        if (stratj & m)
            {
            fit[i] += pdoc.GetPayoffDC();
            fit[j] += pdoc.GetPayoffCD();
            }
        else
            {
            fit[i] += pdoc.GetPayoffDD();
            fit[j] += pdoc.GetPayoffDD();
            }
        }

    m <<= 1;
    }
}

// scale fitness to number of bits tested
if (pdoc.GetAveraging())
    fit[i] /= float(1+(pdoc.GetRandom1st() ? 0 : 1));
}
```

Then the program displays the current population, using a keyed binary tree (see the appendices) to count the number of each strategy in the populations:

```
// display results
if ((fout != NULL) || ((g % pdoc.GetReptFreq()) == 0))
    {
    if ((g % pdoc.GetReptFreq()) == 0)
```

```
    buffer << "\r\nGeneration " << g << "\r\n";

if (fout != NULL)
    (*fout) << "\nGeneration " << g << "\n";

BinaryTreeKeyed < CData, size_t > tree;

for (i = 0; i < POP_SZ; ++i)
    {
    CData d(lvl[i],(pop[i] & vb));

    try {
        j = tree.LookUp(d);
        ++j;
        tree.Insert(d,j);
        }
    catch (TreeEx & ex)
        {
        if (ex.WhatsWrong() == BTX_NOTFOUND)
            tree.Insert(d,1);
        else
            throw;
        }
    }

BinaryTreeKeyedIterator < CData, size_t > iter(tree);

while (1)
    {
    try {
        CData d(iter.GetKey());

        if ((g % pdoc.GetReptFreq()) == 0)
            buffer << setw(5) << (*iter) << ": ";

        if (fout != NULL)
            (*fout) << setw(5) << (*iter) << ": ";

        m = 1UL;

        for (j = 0; j < lbitsn[d.Level]; ++j)
            {
            if ((j == 0) && pdoc.GetRandom1st())
                {
                m <<= 1;
                continue;
                }
```

```
                         if ((g % pdoc.GetReptFreq()) == 0)
                             buffer << ((d.Chrom & m) ? 'C' : 'D');

                         if (fout != NULL)
                             (*fout) << ((d.Chrom & m) ? 'C' : 'D');

                         if ((j == 0) || (j == 2)
                         || (j == 6) || (j == 14))
                             {
                             if ((g % pdoc.GetReptFreq()) == 0)
                                 buffer << ' ';

                             if (fout != NULL)
                                 (*fout) << ' ';
                             }

                         m <<= 1;
                         }

                     if ((g % pdoc.GetReptFreq()) == 0)
                         buffer << "\r\n";

                     if (fout != NULL)
                         (*fout) << "\n";

                     ++iter;
                     }
                 catch (TreeEx & ex)
                     {
                     if (ex.WhatsWrong() == BTX_NOTFOUND)
                         break;
                     else
                         throw;
                     }
                 }
             }
```

I create a roulette wheel based on the fitness values and select parents.
The crossover, mutation, and doubling operators may or may not change
any offspring, based on the percentage chance defined by the parameter
object:

```
    // create new generation
    rw = new RouletteWheel<double> (POP_SZ,fit);
```

```
if (rw == NULL)
    {
    buffer << "Failed to allocate roulette wheel\r\n";
    return;
    }

for (i = 0; i < POP_SZ; ++i)
    {
    // select a parent
    p1 = rw->GetIndex();

    // crossover
    if (pdoc.GetCrossover()
    && (devgen() < pdoc.GetCrossRate()))
        {
        // get second parent
        p2 = rw->GetIndex();

        // find longer of two strings
        if (lvl[p1] >= lvl[p2])
            {
            l  = lvl[p2];
            pl = p1;
            ps = p2;
            }
        else
            {
            l  = lvl[p1];
            pl = p2;
            ps = p1;
            }

        // create crossover bitmask
        m = lmask[l] >> int(devgen() * lbits[l]);

        // combine for new child
        newpop[i] = (pl & (~m)) | (ps & m);
        newlvl[i] = lvl[pl];
        }
    else
        {
        newpop[i] = pop[p1];
        newlvl[i] = lvl[p1];
        }

    // doubling
```

```
if (pdoc.GetDoubling()
&& (newlvl[i] < pdoc.GetMaxLevel())
&& (devgen()  < pdoc.GetDblRate()))
    {
    bit        = newpop[i] & smask[newlvl[i]];
    newpop[i] |= (bit <<  sbits[newlvl[i]]);
    newpop[i] |= (bit << (sbits[newlvl[i]] * 2));
    ++newlvl[i];
    }

// mutation
if (pdoc.GetMutation()
&& (devgen() < pdoc.GetMuteRate()))
    {
    m = 1UL << int(devgen() * lbits[newlvl[i]]);

    if (newpop[i] & m)
        newpop[i] &= (~m);
    else
        newpop[i] |= m;
    }

newpop[i] &= lmask[newlvl[i]];
    }

delete rw;
```

Finally, the loop replaces the old generation with the new one before moving on to the next iteration of the loop. Once all generations have been completed, the program frees its buffers, restores the application title, and exits:

```
// copy new generation
memcpy(pop,newpop,POP_SZ * sizeof(Chromosome));
memcpy(lvl,newlvl,POP_SZ * sizeof(size_t));
    }

// remove arrays
delete [] fit;
delete [] newlvl;
delete [] lvl;
delete [] newpop;
delete [] pop;
delete    fout;
```

```
// restore window text
SetWindowText(wdw,"Forge");
```

ANALYSIS

Running this version of the Prisoner's Dilemma showed many results that run parallel to Lindgren's research. Points to ponder include:

▼ When doubling, keep the population size high so that incoming "doubled" children don't overwhelm the smaller chromosomes.

▼ Too much mutation eliminates the value of selection by fitness.

▼ Too little mutation, on the other hand, limits diversity such that the population never evolves at all.

▼ Smaller populations tend to become dominated by a single strategy—usually one that predominantly defects.

▼ Longer runs with large populations show more interesting behavior than do short runs with small populations.

An analysis of a long run illustrates how populations change with time. I began with an example using the following parameters:

```
Population: 512
  Test Size: 5001
Report Freq: 100
Start Level: 2
  Crossover: true (1%)
   Mutation: true (1%)
   Doubling: false
  Averaging: false
 Fair Start: true
  Payoff DD: 1
  Payoff DC: 5
  Payoff CD: 0
  Payoff CC: 3
```

Within a few hundred generations strategies, such as **D DD DDDD** dominate the population. But at about Generation 1700, things begin to change. Here's what generation 1705 looks like:

```
Generation 1705
   142: D DD DDDD
     6: C DD DDDD
    10: D CD DDDD
   103: D DC DDDD
     5: C DD CDDD
     1: D DC CDDD
    18: D DD DCDD
     3: C DD DCDD
     1: D CD DCDD
    16: D DC DCDD
     7: D CD CCDD
     9: D DD DDCD
     3: C DD DDCD
    14: C DD DCCD
     3: D DD DDDC
     1: D DC DDDC
     1: C DD CDDC
     4: C DC CDDC
     2: D DD DCDC
     5: C DD DCDC
    36: D DC DCDC
     2: C DC DCDC
     1: C DD CCDC
     1: D CD CCDC
     2: C DC CCDC
    14: D DD DDCC
    21: C DD DDCC
     1: C CD DDCC
     4: D DD DCCC
    71: C DD DCCC
     4: D CD DCCC
     1: C DC DCCC
```

D DD DDDD is still strong, but **D DC DDDD** is nearly as strong, and **C DD DCCC** isn't far behind. By generation 1715, **D DD DDDD** is no longer the majority strategy; **D DC DDDD** has taken over. **D DC DCDC** is gaining population, as are **C DD DCCC** and **C DD DDCC**:

```
Generation 1715
  96: D DD DDDD
   2: C DD DDDD
 109: D DC DDDD
   6: D CC DDDD
   3: D DD CDDD
   1: D CD CDDD
   2: D DC CDDD
  24: D DD DCDD
  14: C DD DCDD
   5: D CD DCDD
   1: C CD DCDD
   3: D DC DCDD
   1: D DD CCDD
   5: D DD DDCD
   1: C DD DDCD
   2: D DC DDCD
   7: C DD DCCD
   1: D CD CCCD
   5: D DD DDDC
   2: D DC DDDC
   1: C CD CDDC
  24: C DD DCDC
  50: D DC DCDC
   2: C DC DCDC
  15: C DD CCDC
   3: C CD CCDC
   3: C DC CCDC
   7: D DD DDCC
  67: C DD DDCC
   1: C DD CDCC
  48: C DD DCCC
   1: D DC CCCC
```

By generation 1720, **D DC DDDD** is still the leading strategy, and **C DD DDCC** has gained considerably, accompanied by an increase in population for any strategy ending with **DCDC**. The lessening influence of **D DD DDDD** is allowing the diversity of the population to increase:

```
Generation 1720
  87: D DD DDDD
   7: C DD DDDD
 126: D DC DDDD
   2: C DC DDDD
  20: D CC DDDD
```

```
12: D DD CDDD
 1: C DD CDDD
 1: D CC CDDD
21: D DD DCDD
19: C DD DCDD
 4: D CD DCDD
 4: D DC DCDD
 1: C CC DCDD
 1: D DD CCDD
 3: D DD DDCD
 4: C DD DDCD
 2: D DC DDCD
 1: C CD CDCD
 1: D CC CDCD
 1: C DD DCCD
 1: C CD DCCD
 1: D CC DCCD
 1: C CD CCCD
 4: D DD DDDC
 5: C DC DDDC
 3: C CC DDDC
 3: D DD CDDC
18: C DD DCDC
48: D DC DCDC
 3: C DC DCDC
 8: C DD CCDC
 3: D CC CCDC
 1: C CC CCDC
 4: D DD DDCC
70: C DD DDCC
 1: C CD DDCC
 1: D DD CDCC
17: C DD DCCC
 1: D DC DCCC
 1: C CC DCCC
```

Another 34 generations pass, and we see **D DC DDDD** reach the peak of its strength. **C DD DCDD** is now the second-most prominent strategy, and most others make only a relatively small contribution to the overall population. The population is also less diverse now:

```
Generation 1754
26: D DD DDDD
35: C DD DDDD
 8: D CD DDDD
```

```
    5: C CD DDDD
  264: D DC DDDD
   21: C DC DDDD
    1: D DD CDDD
    4: D DC CDDD
    5: D DD DCDD
   86: C DD DCDD
    2: D CD DCDD
    1: C CD DCDD
    5: D DC CCDD
    4: C DC CCDD
    3: D DD DDCD
    1: D CD DDCD
    2: D DC DDCD
    1: D CC DDCD
    1: C DD CDCD
    4: D DC DDDC
    3: C DC DDDC
    3: D DD CDDC
    4: C DD DCDC
    1: C CD DCDC
    4: D DD CCDC
    6: C DD DDCC
    1: D CC DDCC
    2: C DD DCCC
    7: D DC DCCC
    1: C CC DCCC
    1: C DD CCCC
```

D DC DDDD's days as the dominant strategy, however, are numbered. The number of **C DD DDDD** strategies grows quickly through generation 1791. **D DD DDDD** is only a minor player now, and **C DD DCDD** has lost considerable ground:

```
Generation 1791
    9: D DD DDDD
  255: C DD DDDD
    8: C CD DDDD
  115: D DC DDDD
   10: C DC DDDD
    7: D CC DDDD
    1: D CC CDDD
    1: D DD DCDD
   38: C DD DCDD
    4: D DC DCDD
```

```
 1: D DD CCDD
 1: C DD CCDD
 1: C DD DDCD
 3: D DC DDCD
 3: D DC CCCD
 1: D CC CCCD
 1: D DD DDDC
15: C DD DDDC
28: D DC DDDC
 1: D DD CDDC
 1: D DC CDDC
 1: D CC DCDC
 1: C CD CCDC
 1: C DC DCCC
 4: D CC DCCC
 1: C CD CCCC
```

But **C DD DDDD** cannot hold on to its position as top strategy, either. By generation 1840, **D DD DDDD** and **D DC DDDD** have again risen in number:

```
Generation 1840
 114: D DD DDDD
 139: C DD DDDD
   3: C CD DDDD
 117: D DC DDDD
   3: C DC DDDD
   1: C CC DDDD
  13: D DD CDDD
   5: C DD CDDD
   1: C DC CDDD
  53: D DD DCDD
   3: D CD DCDD
  15: D DC DCDD
   1: C DC DCDD
   2: C DD DDCD
   1: D DD CDCD
   3: D DC DCCD
   1: D DD CCCD
   8: D DD DDDC
  14: C DD DDDC
   4: D CD DDDC
   4: D DC DDDC
   1: C CC DDDC
   3: D DD DCDC
```

```
1: D CD CDCC
1: C DD DCCC
1: D CD DCCC
```

By generation 1870, **D DD DDDD** is dominant again:

```
Generation 1870
175: D DD DDDD
 18: C DD DDDD
 45: D CD DDDD
 55: D DC DDDD
  1: C DC DDDD
  3: D CC DDDD
  3: D DD CDDD
  1: C CD CDDD
112: D DD DCDD
  1: C DD DCDD
  5: D CD DCDD
 17: D DC DCDD
  1: D DD CCDD
 30: D DD DDCD
  2: D CD DDCD
  3: D DC DDCD
 14: D DC DCCD
  1: C CC DCCD
 19: D CD DDDC
  2: D DD DCCC
  2: C DD DCCC
  1: C DC DCCC
  1: D CD CCCC
```

D DD DDDD goes on to have a commanding presence of 392 members—more than 75% of the population in generation 1958. Even that strength of presence doesn't make **D DD DDDD** immune from competition; the strategies **D DD DDDC** and **D DD DCDD** challenge it within another hundred generations, and **D DD DDDD** never regains more than 50% of the population. In this case, though, the population change may be due more to genetic drift than to competition, since the three strategies play (and score) the same against each other.

For 170 generations, between generations 1700 and 1870, the population wildly fluctuates before settling into a period of relative peace. Such rapid population changes occur sporadically; the generations

137

around 4900 experience another episode similar to the preceding one. Lindgren often ran his simulations for tens of thousands of generations, and it's important to realize that your results depend on both random chance and the point in time at which you examine the population.

ONWARD

A strength of genetic algorithms is their ability to solve problems without actually knowing what the problem is. Chapter 6 examines how genetic algorithms can solve a problem for a blind artist.

CHAPTER 6

TRAVAILS OF THE TRAVELING ARTIST

G enetic algorithms are particularly well-suited to solving problems for which we have incomplete information. In Chapter 2, for example, a genetic algorithm found an optimal output value from a "blackbox" without any knowledge of how the blackbox actually worked internally.

THE TRAVELING SALESMAN GOES BLIND

Like the Prisoner's Dilemma, the Traveling Salesman Problem (TSP) is a classic problem in game theory. The theoretical salesman has several cities he must visit; his quandary is in ordering his visits so that he will travel the least total distance over his journey. Problems such as this crop up in endeavors ranging from the optimization of scheduled delivery routes to the construction of computer networks.

A similar problem is the search for a *simple closed path*, where you are looking for a shortest route between points that never crosses itself. If you know all the distances involved, numerous algorithms can find a quick and accurate solution to the salesman's dilemma. Selecting one point as an anchor, for example, you can determine the optimal path by calculating the angles to the other points and sorting the angles in ascending order to obtain the order in which the points should be visited.

The TSP is more difficult to solve. A search of all possible pathways is guaranteed to find the right answer—but, like all brute-force approaches, this one could be very computationally expensive. Backtracking and other techniques can reduce the scope of the search under favorable conditions, but they are simply refinements of an exhaustive search. Computer science has yet to find an especially efficient deterministic algorithm for solving very large TSP-like problems.

Now consider the *blind* version of the problem, where the distances between points are unknown. Such a situation would arise, for example, if you were testing a blackbox circuit with varying resistances (i.e., distances) on different electronic pathways. Finding the path that produces the optimal (least resistive) output can't be done with traditional methods that rely on knowing the properties of path segments.

Perhaps a genetic algorithm might be the right tool.

New Crossover Techniques

For the purpose of demonstration, I'll explain genetic algorithm mixing techniques using an eight-city TSP. The cities will be labeled A through H, and a chromosome is a permutation list of the cities representing the salesman's itinerary. For example, the chromosome GFH-BACDE would symbolize a journey from G to F to H, and so on, ending in city E. Whatever techniques we use for mixing and mutating, each city must be represented once (and only once) in a given chromosome. That presents a challenge we didn't have to solve in previous algorithms, where anonymous bit strings could be shifted and mixed without regard for maintaining any particular combination of bits. Also, the individual letters in the chromosome carry unique meanings (each represents a city); these distinct components of a chromosome can be thought of as *alleles*.

Previous chapters demonstrated one-point crossover, where a pair of chromosomes reproduce by copying complementary portions of their genome to offspring. Here is an example of one-point crossover performed on a pair of eight-bit binary chromosomes and showing the two offspring produced when the crossing point is set to bit 3. The vertical bar represents the position of crossover:

	PARENTS	OFFSPRING
#1	010|01110	010|00010
#2	110|00010	110|01110

Another type of crossover uses two points to generate offspring from the combined bits of parent chromosomes:

	PARENTS	OFFSPRING
#1	01|001|110	01|000|110
#2	11|000|010	11|001|010

For binary strings, such crossover techniques work well, but look at what happens when one- and two-point crossover are applied to a list of letters representing the order of travel between cities:

	PARENTS	**OFFSPRING**
#1	ABC|DEFGH	ABC|BACDE
#2	GFH|BACDE	GFH|BACDE

	PARENTS	**OFFSPRING**
#1	AB|CDE|FGH	AB|HBA|FGH
#2	GF|HBA|CDE	GF|CDE|CDE

Something is amiss; crossover, when applied to permutation strings, produces entirely unacceptable results by eliminating some alleles while duplicating others. Clearly, the traveling salesman does not want to make repeat visits to cities C, D, and E while missing cities A, B, and H altogether.

Such problems can be avoided by implementing different types of crossover. Beginning in the mid-1980s, several researchers described reordering operators that preserve the internal consistency of permutation chromosomes. These new crossover techniques involve considerably more processing than is required for one- and two-point crossover, but the extra effort allows us to ensure that offspring are always a valid permutation.

Partially matched crossover (PMX) arose in an attempt to solve the blind TSP. In the blind TSP, fitness is entirely based on the ordering of the cities in a chromosome, and, as such, we need to maintain valid permutations during reproduction. PMX is a modified form of two-point crossover, and it begins by selecting two points, 2 and 5, in this case, for its operation:

Parent 1: AB\|CDE\|FGH

Parent 2: GF\|HBA\|CDE

The PMX algorithm notes that the H allele in Chromosome 2 will replace the C allele in Chromosome 1, so it exchanges Chromosome 1's H to a C and Chromosome 2's C to an H. The same process is accomplished for the other two alleles being swapped, and the end result is two offspring with these encodings:

Offspring 1: EDIHBAIFGC

Offspring 2: GFICDEIHBA

Each offspring is a new permutation, shuffling some alleles while preserving a section of a parent organism.

Order crossover (OX) involves the removal of some alleles and the shifting of others. Given the crossover points and parent chromosomes as in the PMX demonstration, OX would remove the incoming alleles like so (a dash represents a blank allele):

Offspring 1: – —IHBAIFG –

Offspring 2: GFICDEI– – –

Then, beginning after the second crossover point, OX shifts alleles to the left (wrapping around the end of the chromosome if necessary), filling empty alleles and leaving an opening for the swapped-in section:

Offspring 1: BAI– – —IFGH

Offspring 2: DEI– – —IGFC

To finish the process, OX exchanges the alleles within the crossover boundaries, finishing the two offspring:

Offspring 1: BAICDEIFGH

Offspring 2: DEIHBAIGFC

Where PMX preserves the absolute position of a city allele within chromosomes, OX preserves the order of cities in the permutation.

Cycle crossover (CX) works in an entirely different fashion, by swapping a specific set of cities between chromosomes. For comparison, I'll use the same two chromosomes I used earlier in demonstrating PMX and OX:

Parent 1: ABCDEFGH

Parent 2: GFHBACDE

In generating offspring, CX begins with the first cities of the two parent chromosomes:

Offspring 1: G– – – – – – –

Offspring 2: A– – – – – – –

A search of Parent 1 finds the just-introduced G allele in position 7. Another swap occurs:

Offspring 1: G– – – – –D–

Offspring 2: A– – – – –G–

The search-and-swapping process continues until the allele first replaced in Parent 1—the A—is found in a swap between chromosomes. CX then fills the remaining empty alleles from corresponding elements of the parents. The final offspring look like this:

Offspring 1: GECBAFDH

Offspring 2: ABHDECGE

In Chapter 2, I mentioned the *inversion* operator, which reverses a sequence of alleles. Here we can implement it, for inversion does preserve the nature of a permutation while reordering its elements. Here are two examples of inversion applied to the test chromosomes:

ABC|DEFGH|I inverts to ABCHGFED

G|IFHB|IACDE inverts to GBHFACDE

In the case of a permutation chromosome, a mutation changing only one allele would create duplicate alleles and lose others. To solve this problem, I define *mutation* as the swapping of two alleles within the chromosome. For example, swapping the A and E alleles in ABCDEFGH would produce the offspring EBCDAFGH.

DESIGN

All three crossover variations were studied in the context of the traveling salesman problem, and I've presented them here in order of their effectiveness. My TSP implementation allows you to experiment with the four preceding operators and mutation, selecting their application and probability. Figure 6.1 shows the configuration box I designed for the application of a genetic algorithm to a ten-city blind TSP.

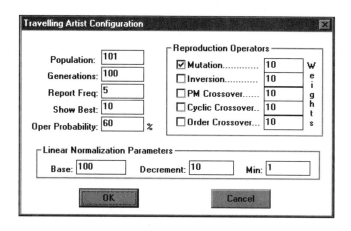

FIGURE 6.1   TRAVELING ARTIST CONFIGURATION DIALOG BOX.

I've renamed the scenario the Traveling Artist Problem to honor my talented wife, Maria, who takes me on long excursions through the Colorado mountains in search of art shows in which we display her works. As such, the ten cities I've selected for this test are real municipalities in the San Juan mountains of Colorado: Alamosa, Cortez, Creede, Durango, Gunnison, Lake City, Montrose, Pagosa, Salida, and Silverton.

Here is a description of the elements in the dialog box:

Population The number of strategies to be tested. Several reproduction operators require two parents, and elitist selection copies the best chromosome of the parent generation into the offspring. Thus, the population should be an odd number.

Generations The number of generations to be run in this simulation.

Report Frequency How often the simulation should report on the strategies it has tested.

Show Best Determines the number of chromosomes shown for each reported generation.

Oper Probability The probability that *any* of the reproduction operators will apply to a given pair of offspring.

Mutation The checkbox enables single-bit mutations during reproduction; the text box contains a percentage chance of mutation occurring.

Inversion The checkbox enables inversion during reproduction; the text box contains a percentage chance of inversion occurring.

PM Crossover The checkbox enables partially matched crossover (PMX) during reproduction; the text box contains a percentage chance of PMX occurring.

Cycle Crossover The checkbox enables cycle crossover (CX) during reproduction; the text box contains a percentage chance of CX occurring.

Order Crossover The checkbox enables order crossover (OX) during reproduction; the text box contains a percentage chance of OX occurring.

Linear Normalization Parameters For the Traveling Artist Problem, I always use linear normalization to scale fitness values, since the relative difference in fitness between chromosomes may not be high. In the group, you can define the base value, decrement, and minimum fitness allowed.

Following the pattern I've set in previous chapters, I've defined a class (TAOptConfig) to encapsulate the Traveling Artist configuration dialog box; I'll give the class definition here for information purposes:

```
class TAOptConfig
    {
    public:
        TAOptConfig
            (
            HINSTANCE inst,
            HWND        parent
            );

        static void DlgInit
            (
            HWND   dlg
            );

        static BOOL DlgStore
            (
            HWND   dlg
            );

        // verify if this object is valid
        bool    GetValidity()   { return Valid; }

        // interrogate dimensions of test
        size_t GetPopSize()     { return PopSize;   }
        size_t GetTestSize()    { return TestSize;  }
        size_t GetReptFreq()    { return ReptFreq;  }
        size_t GetShowBest()    { return ShowBest;  }

        // interrogate operator parameters
        float   GetOperChance() { return OperChance; }
        bool    GetMutation()   { return Mutation;  }
        bool    GetInversion()  { return Inversion; }
        bool    GetPMX()        { return PMX;       }
        bool    GetCX()         { return CX;        }
        bool    GetOX()         { return OX;        }
        float   GetWeightM()    { return WeightM;   }
        float   GetWeightI()    { return WeightI;   }
        float   GetWeightP()    { return WeightP;   }
```

```
        float   GetWeightC()     { return WeightC;    }
        float   GetWeightO()     { return WeightO;    }

        // interrogate fitness scaling parameters
        double GetFitLinBase() { return FitLinBase; }
        double GetFitLinDec()  { return FitLinDec;  }
        double GetFitLinMin()  { return FitLinMin;  }

    private:
        // validity flag
        bool    Valid;

        // dimensions of test
        size_t PopSize;
        size_t TestSize;
        size_t ReptFreq;
        size_t ShowBest;

        // operator parameters
        float   OperChance;
        bool    Mutation;
        bool    Inversion;
        bool    PMX;
        bool    CX;
        bool    OX;
        float   WeightM;
        float   WeightI;
        float   WeightP;
        float   WeightC;
        float   WeightO;

        // fitness scaling parameters
        double  FitLinBase;
        double  FitLinDec;
        double  FitLinMin;

        // stored parameter values
        static size_t DefPopSize;
        static size_t DefTestSize;
        static size_t DefReptFreq;
        static size_t DefShowBest;
        static float  DefOperChance;
        static bool   DefMutation;
        static bool   DefInversion;
        static bool   DefPMX;
        static bool   DefCX;
        static bool   DefOX;
```

```
        static float  DefWeightM;
        static float  DefWeightI;
        static float  DefWeightP;
        static float  DefWeightC;
        static float  DefWeightO;
        static double DefFitLinBase;
        static double DefFitLinDec;
        static double DefFitLinMin;
    };
```

The implementation code for `TAOptConfig` is very similar to that of other configuration classes in previous chapters.

IMPLEMENTATION

The Traveling Artist algorithm begins by creating a configuration object and displaying its contents:

```
// create configuration and verify it
TAOptConfig taoc(inst,wdw);

if (!taoc.GetValidity())
    {
    buffer << "Cancelled\r\n";
    return;
    }

// display parameters
buffer << "\r\n      Population: " << taoc.GetPopSize();
buffer << "\r\n       Test Size: " << taoc.GetTestSize();
buffer << "\r\n      Report Freq: " << taoc.GetReptFreq();
buffer << "\r\n        Show Best: " << taoc.GetShowBest();
buffer << "\r\nOper Probability: " << taoc.GetOperChance();

if (taoc.GetMutation())
    buffer << "\r\n        Mutation: " << taoc.GetWeightM();

if (taoc.GetInversion())
    buffer << "\r\n        Inversion: " << taoc.GetWeightI();

if (taoc.GetPMX())
    buffer << "\r\nPart Match Cross: " << taoc.GetWeightP();
```

```
if (taoc.GetCX())
    buffer << "\r\n Cycle Crossover: " << taoc.GetWeightC();

if (taoc.GetOX())
    buffer << "\r\n Order Crossover: " << taoc.GetWeightO();

buffer << "\r\n    Fitness Base: " << taoc.GetFitLinBase();
buffer << "\r\n    Fitness  Dec: " << taoc.GetFitLinDec();
buffer << "\r\n    Fitness  Min: " << taoc.GetFitLinMin();
buffer << dec << "\r\n";
```

These data arrays define the names of cities and the distances between them:

```
// data arrays
static const size_t CSZ = 10 * sizeof(size_t);

const size_t POP_SZ = taoc.GetPopSize();

static const char * cityName[10] =
    {
    "Alamosa   ", "Cortez    ",
    "Creede    ", "Durango   ",
    "Gunnison  ", "Lake City",
    "Montrose  ", "Pagosa    ",
    "Salida    ", "Silverton"
    };

static const double distance[10][10] =
{
{   0.0,220.0, 90.0,155.0,133.0,123.0,182.0, 89.0,105.0,141.0},
{220.0,  0.0,135.0, 55.0,173.0,117.0,124.0,122.0,222.0, 85.0},
{ 90.0,135.0,  0.0, 92.0, 69.0, 34.0, 95.0, 56.0, 98.0, 57.0},
{155.0, 55.0, 92.0,  0.0,145.0, 84.0,116.0, 68.0,184.0, 54.0},
{133.0,173.0, 69.0,145.0,  0.0, 60.0, 72.0,125.0, 70.0, 91.0},
{123.0,117.0, 34.0, 84.0, 60.0,  0.0, 61.0, 76.0,106.0, 33.0},
{182.0,124.0, 95.0,116.0, 72.0, 61.0,  0.0,134.0,137.0, 66.0},
{ 89.0,122.0, 56.0, 68.0,125.0, 76.0,134.0,  0.0,142.0, 73.0},
{105.0,222.0, 98.0,184.0, 70.0,106.0,137.0,142.0,  0.0,139.0},
{141.0, 85.0, 57.0, 54.0, 91.0, 33.0, 66.0, 73.0,139.0,  0.0}
};
```

After that, I define variables and allocate buffers for populations and fitness values:

```
// create working buffers
    CityChrom * pop = new CityChrom [POP_SZ];

    if (pop == NULL)
        {
        buffer << "Memory allocation failed\r\n";
        return;
        }

    CityChrom * newpop = new CityChrom [POP_SZ];

    if (newpop == NULL)
        {
        buffer << "Memory allocation failed\r\n";
        return;
        }

    double * fit = new double [POP_SZ];

    if (fit == NULL)
        {
        buffer << "Memory allocation failed\r\n";
        return;
        }

    // pointers for shell sort
    CityChrom * ptrp = pop - 1;
    double    * ptrf = fit - 1;

    // define variables
    size_t g, i, j, k, l, n, s, t, p1, p2, inc;
    double vf;
    char buf[64];
    CityChrom vp;
    RouletteWheel<double> * rw;
    RandDev devgen;

    // create roulette wheel for operator selection
    double operwt[5];

    if (taoc.GetMutation())
        operwt[0] = taoc.GetWeightM();
    else
        operwt[0] = 0.0;

    if (taoc.GetInversion())
        operwt[1] = taoc.GetWeightI();
```

```
else
    operwt[1] = 0.0;

if (taoc.GetPMX())
    operwt[2] = taoc.GetWeightP();
else
    operwt[2] = 0.0;

if (taoc.GetCX())
    operwt[3] = taoc.GetWeightC();
else
    operwt[3] = 0.0;

if (taoc.GetOX())
    operwt[4] = taoc.GetWeightO();
else
    operwt[4] = 0.0;

RouletteWheel<double> ow(5,operwt);
```

To create the initial population, I needed a technique for generating random permutations of the city list. I fell back on an ancient technique known as the *Josephus Permutation*. Most algorithm texts skip explaining just where the Josephus Permutation got its name, but I dislike leaving something named without explaining where the name came from. You can skip the quick history lesson in the next few paragraphs if you want and proceed to the next block of code, but it is an interesting, if tragic, tale.

In 67 a.d., a band of Jewish rebels was pursued by a Roman army to the cliff-top town of Jotapata. The Roman army, under the command of General Vespasian, laid siege to Jotapata, finally breaching its walls after 47 days. The brilliant rebel commander, a young rabbi named Josephus, disappeared into the warrens beneath the city, where the town's leaders were hiding.

When the Romans found the warrens, they didn't attack immediately; instead, Vespasian declared his desire to meet with Josephus. The other Jewish leaders would have nothing of it, and, in one account, Josephus suggested mass suicide orchestrated in an unusual manner. Organized into a circle, Josephus chose a number at random and counted around the circle from his position to choose the first person to die. Once that person was gone, the same number of counts was made on the new circle, choosing the next person for death. Repeating the process led to the survival of one person—Josephus.

It is no odd occurrence that Josephus was the lone survivor of this episode; historians suspect him of selecting the count number carefully, so as to save his own life and eliminate the others without explicitly betraying them. And upon surrendering to Vespasian, Josephus claimed to be a prophet with a vision of Vespasian as emperor (and himself as a free man).

The traitor's prediction came true, and he was later freed by Vespasian to write a long (and heavily biased) history of Rome's wars in Judea; in 70 a.d., Josephus observed the utter destruction of Jerusalem. I've heard that the conversion of Josephus from rebel hero to imperial general was a model for the transformation of Darth Vader in *Star Wars* from Jedi warrior to Dark Lord of the Galactic Empire.

History and science fiction aside, Josephus's technique for counting around the circle can be easily adapted to generate permutations from a list. For example, if we have a list of cities labeled A through H, a permutation can be generated by selecting a starting point and a count. In this example, I'll start with the sixth city, F, and a count of five. Counting five cities to the right of F (and assuming the list is circular with H adjoining to A) brings us to C, the first city in our permutation. Withdrawing C from the list, and counting another five cities will locate the second member of the permutation, H. Repeating this process until the last city is selected produced the permutation CHFEGBDA.

By selecting the starting point and count at random, a program can generate a set of different permutations. I've done that in this routine to create the initial population of itineraries for the Traveling Artist Problem:

```
// create initial population with Josephus permutation
for (i = 0; i < POP_SZ; ++i)
    {
    int plist[10];
```

```
memset(plist,0,CSZ);

s = size_t(devgen() *  8.0) + 1;
j = size_t(devgen() * 10.0);

k = 0;

while (1)
    {
    pop[i][k] = j;
    plist[j]  = 1;

    if (k == 9)
        break;

    for (l = 0; l < s; ++l)
        {
        do  {
            ++j; if (j > 9) j = 0;
            }
        while (plist[j] == 1);
        }

    ++k;
    }
}
```

The main generation loop begins by displaying progress information in the application's title bar:

```
// main program loop
    g = 0;

    while (1)
        {
        // display progress in app header
        wsprintf(buf,"Forge (loop: %u of %u)", g,
                    taoc.GetTestSize());
        SetWindowText(wdw,buf);
        .
        .
        .
```

Fitness testing is quick, being a simple summation of distances drawn from a table:

```
// fitness testing
for (i = 0; i < POP_SZ; ++i)
    {
    fit[i] = 0.0;

    for (j = 1; j < 10; ++j)
        fit[i] += distance[pop[i][j-1]][pop[i][j]];
    }
```

Next, I sort the population in descending order of fitness in preparation for linear normalization (and to find the most-fit chromosome):

```
// shell sort in preparation for linear normalization
for (inc = 1; inc <= POP_SZ / 9; inc = 3 * inc + 1) ;

for ( ; inc > 0; inc /= 3)
    {
    for (i = inc + 1; i <= POP_SZ; i += inc)
        {
        vf = ptrf[i];
        memcpy(vp,ptrp[i],CSZ);

        j  = i;

        while ((j > inc) && (ptrf[j - inc] > vf))
            {
            ptrf[j] = ptrf[j - inc];
            memcpy(ptrp[j],ptrp[j - inc],CSZ);

            j -= inc;
            }

        ptrf[j] = vf;
        memcpy(ptrp[j],vp,CSZ);
        }
    }
```

After each round of fitness tests, the best chromosomes are displayed:

```
// report information
if (( g == taoc.GetTestSize())
|| ((g % taoc.GetReptFreq()) == 0))
    {
    buffer << "\r\nGeneration " << g << "\r\n";
```

```
buffer << "Best: " << cityName[pop[0][0]];

for (i = 1; i < 10; ++i)
    buffer << "->" << cityName[pop[0][i]];

buffer << "\r\n";

for (i = 0; i < taoc.GetShowBest(); ++i)
    {
    buffer << setw(5) << fit[i] << ": ";

    for (j = 0; j < 10; ++j)
        buffer << setw(2) << pop[i][j];

    buffer << "\r\n";
    }
}
```

Then I scale the fitness values in preparation for reproduction:

```
// exit, if necessary
if (g == taoc.GetTestSize())
    break;

// fitness scaling (linear normalization)
fit[0] = taoc.GetFitLinBase();
i      = 1;

while (1)
    {
    if (fit[i-1] <= taoc.GetFitLinDec())
        break;

    fit[i] = fit[i-1] - taoc.GetFitLinDec();

    ++i;
    }

for (; i < POP_SZ; ++i)
    fit[i] = taoc.GetFitLinMin();
```

As in past genetic algorithms, a roulette wheel decides the chances of reproduction. In this loop, a switch statement and random number select the operation to be performed on a pair of offspring:

```
// automatic elitist selection
memcpy(newpop[0],pop[0],CSZ);

// generate new population
rw = new RouletteWheel<double> (POP_SZ,fit);

if (rw == NULL)
    {
    buffer << "Failed to allocate roulette wheel\r\n";
    return;
    }

for (i = 1; i < POP_SZ; i += 2)
    {
    // get parents
    p1 = rw->GetIndex();

    do  {
        p2 = rw->GetIndex();
        }
    while (p2 == p1);

    // duplicate parents
    memcpy(newpop[i],   pop[p1],CSZ);
    memcpy(newpop[i+1],pop[p2],CSZ);

    // skip rest of loop if no operator picked
    if (devgen() > taoc.GetOperChance())
        continue;

    // pick an operator
    switch (ow.GetIndex())
        {
        case 0: // mutation
            for (n = 0; n < 2; ++n)
                {
                // pick indexes
                j = size_t(devgen() * 10.0F);

                do  {
                    k = size_t(devgen() * 10.0F);
                    }
                while (k == j);

                // swap city indexes
                t = newpop[i+n][k];
                newpop[i+n][k] = newpop[i+n][j];
```

```
            newpop[i+n][j] = t;
            }

    break;

case 1: // inversion
    for (n = 0; n < 2; ++n)
        {
        // pick indexes
        j = size_t(devgen() * 9.0F);

        do  {
            k = size_t(devgen() * 10.0F);
            }
        while (k <= j);

        // calculate length
        s = (k - j + 1) / 2;

        // reverse codes
        for (l = 0; l < s; ++l)
            {
            t = newpop[i+n][k];
            newpop[i+n][k] = newpop[i+n][j];
            newpop[i+n][j] = t;

            ++j;
            --k;
            }
        }

    break;

case 2: // partially matched crossover
    j = size_t(devgen() * 9.0F);

    do  {
        k = size_t(devgen() * 10.0F);
        }
    while (k <= j);

    // swap cities
    for (n = j; n <= k; ++n)
        {
        if (pop[p1][n] != pop[p2][n])
            {
            s = TAFindCity(newpop[i+1],
```

```
                                      pop[p1][n]);
                    t = newpop[i+1][n];
                    newpop[i+1][n] = newpop[i+1][s];
                    newpop[i+1][s] = t;

                    s = TAFindCity(newpop[i],pop[p2][n]);
                    t = newpop[i][n];
                    newpop[i][n] = newpop[i][s];
                    newpop[i][s] = t;
                    }
               }

          break;

     case 3:
          // cycle crossover
          j = size_t(devgen() * 10.0F);
          t = pop[p1][j];

          while (1)
               {
               newpop[i][j]   = pop[p2][j];
               newpop[i+1][j] = pop[p1][j];

               if (newpop[i][j] == t)
                    break;

               j = TAFindCity(pop[p1],newpop[i][j]);
               }

          break;

     case 4:
          // order crossover
          j = size_t(devgen() * 9.0F);

          do  {
               k = size_t(devgen() * 10.0F);
               }
          while (k <= j);

          if ((j == 0) && (k == 9))
               {
               memcpy(vp,newpop[i],CSZ);
               memcpy(newpop[i],newpop[i+1],CSZ);
               memcpy(newpop[i+1],vp,CSZ);
               break;
```

```
        }

if (k == 9)
    n = 0;
else
    n = k + 1;

// shift and fill
do  {
    while (1)
        {
        s = TAFindCity(pop[p2],newpop[i][n]);

        if ((s < j) || (s > k))
            break;

        // shift members
        if (n == 9)
            l = 0;
        else
            l = n + 1;

        while (1)
            {
            if (l == 0)
                newpop[i][9] = newpop[i][0];
            else
                newpop[i][l-1] =
                            newpop[i][l];

            if (l == k)
                break;

            if (l == 9)
                l = 0;
            else
                ++l;
            }
        }

    while (1)
        {
        s = TAFindCity(pop[p1],
                    newpop[i+1][n]);

        if ((s < j) || (s > k))
            break;
```

```
                    // shift members
                    if (n == 9)
                        l = 0;
                    else
                        l = n + 1;

                    while (1)
                        {
                        if (l == 0)
                            newpop[i+1][9] =
                                        newpop[i+1][0];
                        else
                            newpop[i+1][l-1] =
                                        newpop[i+1][l];

                        if (l == k)
                            break;

                        if (l == 9)
                            l = 0;
                        else
                            ++l;
                        }
                        }

                if (n == 9)
                    n = 0;
                else
                    ++n;
                }
            while (n != j);

            for (n = j; n <= k; ++n)
                {
                newpop[i][n]   = pop[p2][n];
                newpop[i+1][n] = pop[p1][n];
                }

            break;
            }
        }

    // delete, copy and loop
    delete rw;
```

The main loop ends by copying the new generation over the old one. Once all generations have been completed, the simulation ends by freeing dynamic memory and restoring the application's title:

```
        .
        .
        .
    memcpy(pop,newpop,10 * CSZ);

    ++g;
    }

// delete buffers
delete [] fit;
delete [] newpop;
delete [] pop;

// restore window text
SetWindowText(wdw,"Forge");
```

ANALYSIS

Here is an annotated run of the Traveling Artist Problem that produces output such as this (vertical ellipses replace many redundant entries):

```
        Population: 201
        Test Size: 100
       Report Freq: 1
         Show Best: 10
 Oper Probability: 0.6
          Mutation: false
         Inversion: true
 Part Match Cross: true
  Cycle Crossover: true
  Fitness Scaling: true
     Fitness Base: 100
     Fitness  Dec: 10
     Fitness  Min: 1


Generation 0
Best: Gunnison ->Montrose ->Salida   ->Alamosa  ->Creede
```

```
        ->Lake City->Silverton->Durango  ->Cortez    ->Pagosa
702:  4 6 8 0 2 5 9 3 1 7
702:  4 6 8 0 2 5 9 3 1 7
702:  4 6 8 0 2 5 9 3 1 7
717:  8 0 2 4 6 9 3 7 5 1
717:  8 0 2 4 6 9 3 7 5 1
797:  1 3 5 7 9 2 6 0 8 4
797:  1 3 5 7 9 2 6 0 8 4
797:  1 3 5 7 9 2 6 0 8 4
801:  7 9 1 3 5 8 2 6 4 0
816:  0 3 6 9 4 8 5 2 7 1

Generation 1
Best: Alamosa   ->Salida    ->Montrose ->Gunnison ->Creede
        ->Lake City->Silverton->Durango  ->Cortez    ->Pagosa
681:  0 8 6 4 2 5 9 3 1 7
702:  4 6 8 0 2 5 9 3 1 7
702:  4 6 8 0 2 5 9 3 1 7
717:  8 0 2 4 6 9 3 7 5 1
816:  0 3 6 9 4 8 5 2 7 1
820:  4 6 5 0 8 7 9 3 1 2
824:  9 1 3 5 7 0 4 8 6 2
824:  9 1 3 5 7 0 4 8 6 2
824:  9 1 3 5 7 0 4 8 6 2
824:  9 1 3 5 7 0 4 8 6 2
```

An inversion has produced the first improvement in generation 1 by reversing the order of the first four cities.

The overall population improves, but the best chromosome remains the same for the next 20-some generations:

```
Generation 2
Best: Alamosa   ->Salida    ->Montrose ->Gunnison ->Creede
        ->Lake City->Silverton->Durango  ->Cortez    ->Pagosa
681:  0 8 6 4 2 5 9 3 1 7
702:  4 6 8 0 2 5 9 3 1 7
717:  8 0 2 4 6 9 3 7 5 1
769:  8 0 2 3 7 9 4 6 5 1
816:  0 3 6 9 4 8 5 2 7 1
824:  9 1 3 5 7 0 4 8 6 2
835:  0 4 8 3 9 6 5 7 2 1
835:  0 4 8 3 9 6 5 7 2 1
835:  0 4 8 3 9 6 5 7 2 1
846:  2 4 6 8 0 3 7 1 9 5
```

```
Generation 3
Best: Alamosa  ->Salida    ->Montrose ->Gunnison ->Creede
      ->Lake City->Silverton->Durango  ->Cortez   ->Pagosa
 681:    0 8 6 4 2 5 9 3 1 7
 681:    0 8 6 4 2 5 9 3 1 7
 681:    0 8 6 4 2 5 9 3 1 7
 702:    4 6 8 0 2 5 9 3 1 7
 717:    8 0 2 4 6 9 3 7 5 1
 816:    0 3 6 9 4 8 5 2 7 1
 835:    0 4 8 3 9 6 5 7 2 1
 846:    2 4 6 8 0 3 7 1 9 5
 846:    2 4 6 8 0 3 7 1 9 5
 846:    2 4 6 8 0 3 7 1 9 5

Generation 4
Best: Alamosa  ->Salida    ->Montrose ->Gunnison ->Creede
      ->Lake City->Silverton->Durango  ->Cortez   ->Pagosa
 681:    0 8 6 4 2 5 9 3 1 7
 681:    0 8 6 4 2 5 9 3 1 7
 681:    0 8 6 4 2 5 9 3 1 7
 681:    0 8 6 4 2 5 9 3 1 7
 694:    0 8 6 4 2 5 9 3 7 1
 703:    0 8 6 4 2 7 1 3 9 5
 717:    8 0 2 4 6 9 3 7 5 1
 846:    2 4 6 8 0 3 7 1 9 5
 853:    7 0 3 6 1 5 2 9 4 8
 853:    7 0 3 6 1 5 2 9 4 8

Generation 5
Best: Alamosa  ->Salida    ->Montrose ->Gunnison ->Creede
      ->Lake City->Silverton->Durango  ->Cortez   ->Pagosa
 681:    0 8 6 4 2 5 9 3 1 7
 681:    0 8 6 4 2 5 9 3 1 7
 681:    0 8 6 4 2 5 9 3 1 7
 681:    0 8 6 4 2 5 9 3 1 7
 694:    0 8 6 4 2 5 9 3 7 1
 754:    0 8 6 4 9 5 2 3 7 1
 846:    2 4 6 8 0 3 7 1 9 5
 853:    7 0 3 6 1 5 2 9 4 8
 853:    7 0 3 6 1 5 2 9 4 8
 853:    7 0 3 6 1 5 2 9 4 8
  .
  .
  .
```

In generation 25, a mutation or inversion swapped two entries in the best chromosome, reducing the journey by 41 kilometers:

```
Generation 25
Best: Alamosa   ->Salida    ->Gunnison ->Montrose ->Creede
         ->Lake City->Silverton->Durango  ->Cortez    ->Pagosa
  640:   0 8 4 6 2 5 9 3 1 7
  681:   0 8 6 4 2 5 9 3 1 7
  835:   0 9 3 5 2 4 8 6 1 7
  853:   3 1 5 2 4 6 8 9 0 7
  897:   8 0 3 7 6 9 2 1 5 4
  900:   7 3 0 8 6 9 2 1 5 4
  903:   6 8 0 2 4 7 1 5 3 9
  903:   6 8 0 2 4 7 1 5 3 9
  903:   6 8 0 2 4 7 1 5 3 9
  906:   6 3 1 0 2 5 9 4 7 8
  .
  .
  .
```

In generation 35, another swap gains us another 23 kilometers, reducing the journey to only 617 kilometers:

```
Generation 35
Best: Alamosa   ->Salida    ->Gunnison ->Montrose ->Creede    ->
      Lake City->Silverton->Cortez    ->Durango  ->Pagosa
  617:   0 8 4 6 2 5 9 1 3 7
  640:   0 8 4 6 2 5 9 3 1 7
  760:   0 8 4 6 2 3 9 5 1 7
  898:   4 9 5 6 8 7 0 3 1 2
  899:   0 7 4 1 2 3 9 5 6 8
  937:   1 5 8 4 3 7 6 9 0 2
  958:   1 8 6 5 7 0 4 9 2 3
  961:   3 1 6 7 8 9 0 5 2 4
  964:   0 5 2 3 1 4 6 7 8 9
  969:   1 0 3 8 4 5 9 2 7 6

  .
  .
  .
```

An inversion flips the order of the last three in generation 76, leaving us with a trip of only 605 kilometers:

```
Generation 76
Best: Alamosa   ->Salida    ->Gunnison ->Montrose ->Creede    ->
      Lake City->Silverton->Pagosa    ->Durango  ->Cortez
```

```
 605:  0 8 4 6 2 5 9 7 3 1
 617:  0 8 4 6 2 5 9 1 3 7
 617:  0 8 4 6 2 5 9 1 3 7
 617:  0 8 4 6 2 5 9 1 3 7
 670:  0 8 4 7 3 1 9 5 2 6
 670:  0 8 4 7 3 1 9 5 2 6
 697:  0 8 4 7 3 1 9 5 6 2
 725:  0 8 4 7 3 1 5 9 2 6
1051:  7 1 5 0 6 3 2 4 9 8
1051:  7 1 5 0 6 3 2 4 9 8
```

.
.
.

The shortest trip arises in generation 87, where a swap exchanges Silverton and Creede to find a route of only 559 kilometers:

```
Generation 87
Best: Alamosa  ->Salida    ->Gunnison ->Montrose ->Silverton->
      Lake City->Creede    ->Pagosa   ->Durango  ->Cortez
  559:  0 8 4 6 9 5 2 7 3 1
  605:  0 8 4 6 2 5 9 7 3 1
  605:  0 8 4 6 2 5 9 7 3 1
  605:  0 8 4 6 2 5 9 7 3 1
  643:  0 8 4 6 2 7 9 5 3 1
  706:  0 8 4 1 3 7 9 5 2 6
  733:  0 8 4 1 3 7 9 5 6 2
 1053:  1 7 4 2 5 0 9 8 3 6
 1060:  4 9 5 1 8 7 0 3 6 2
 1060:  4 9 5 1 8 7 0 3 6 2
```

In that run, inversion and mutation accounted for all improvements in the population. Various researchers—particularly David Goldberg of the University of Alabama—have analyzed the complex crossover operators, and they point out that such operators have greater value on long chromosomes than on short ones.

In most real-world applications, chromosomes will have hundreds, or perhaps thousands, of alleles. While it might appear that a simple random shuffle of alleles would be as efficacious as the complex heuristics of

PMX or CX, testing shows that the complex crossover operators preserve the symmetry of alleles, while a random shuffle destroys any extant order.

I've watched the PMX operator, for example, produce improvements in the population, such as in the following example, that reduces the shortest trip length by 60 kilometers:

```
Generation 22
Best: Salida   ->Gunnison ->Montrose ->Lake City->Pagosa   ->
      Alamosa ->Durango   ->Creede   ->Silverton->Cortez
 757:  8 4 6 5 7 0 3 2 9 1
 763:  1 3 6 5 7 0 9 2 8 4
 780:  0 4 8 3 9 6 5 2 7 1
 846:  3 1 0 2 5 9 7 6 8 4
 916:  1 0 8 3 9 6 4 7 2 5
 936:  9 6 4 3 5 8 2 7 0 1
 958:  1 8 6 5 7 0 4 9 2 3
 958:  1 8 6 5 7 0 4 9 2 3
 958:  1 8 6 5 7 0 4 9 2 3
 958:  1 8 6 5 7 0 4 9 2 3

Generation 23
Best: Cortez   ->Durango ->Pagosa   ->Alamosa   ->Lake City->
      Silverton->Montrose->Creede   ->Salida    ->Gunnison
 697:  1 3 7 0 5 9 6 2 8 4
 757:  8 4 6 5 7 0 3 2 9 1
 763:  1 3 6 5 7 0 9 2 8 4
 871:  1 0 2 3 9 6 5 7 8 4
 948:  1 4 6 5 7 0 9 3 8 2
 961:  7 2 9 5 1 0 3 6 8 4
 995:  9 1 6 5 7 0 4 3 8 2
1004:  3 2 6 5 7 0 8 1 4 9
1007:  1 4 7 0 5 9 6 3 8 2
1007:  1 4 7 0 5 9 6 3 8 2
```

Large blind TSPs, containing thousands of points, can be solved using deterministic algorithms; however, as I mentioned earlier in this chapter, such solutions require exhaustive searches and some knowledge of the distance between cities. For situations where internal values are unknown or where the search space cannot be reduced logically, a genetic algorithm may provide the only solution.

ONWARD

The last five chapters focused on genetic algorithms that manipulate strings of bits or symbols. These are traditional genetic algorithms of the type first introduced by Holland. Other computer scientists, however, have tried to apply the principle of evolution to finite state machines, and their work is the focus of the next two chapters.

CHAPTER 7

EVOLVING MACHINES

The threads of DNA that encode biological information provide a model for the genetic algorithms I've presented thus far. This chapter and the next explore the evolution of complete *programs,* as defined by finite state machines.

FINITE STATE MACHINES

An introduction to finite state machines (FSMs) is a part of most college courses in algorithm development. The concept of an FSM is quite simple: the machine contains a specific number of possible internal states, one of which represents the currently selected state. A finite set of input symbols is mapped to a finite set of output symbols by each state; an input symbol is given to the FSM, which returns an output symbol before making a possible transition to a new state. Figure 7.1 shows a three-state machine with an input alphabet of {0, 1} and an output set of {A , B, C}.

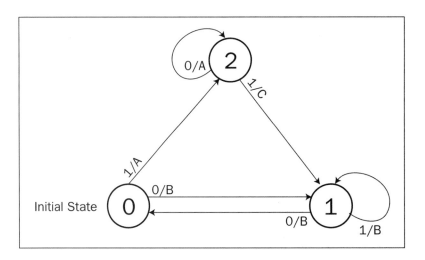

FIGURE 7.1   A FINITE STATE MACHINE.

Table 7.1 shows how a sequence of input values produces an output string and state changes within the machine.

The FSM in Figure 7.1 mapped the input string 11010001 to the output string AACBBBBA. While diagramming an FSM, as in Figure 7.1, shows graphically how it works, a program can implement an FSM as a simple two-dimensional look-up table with a number of rows equal to the number of states and a number of columns equal to the size of the input alphabet. Table 7.2 shows a sample finite state machine as a 3-by-2 table, with each element containing an output symbol and new state in the form O/S.

TABLE 7.1 EXAMPLE OF RUNNING MACHINE FROM FIGURE 7.1.

CURRENT STATE	INPUT SYMBOL	OUTPUT SYMBOL	NEXT STATE
0 (initial)	1	A	2
2	1	A	2
2	0	C	1
1	1	B	1
1	0	B	0
0	0	B	1
1	0	B	0
0	1	A	2

TABLE 7.2 TRANSITION TABLE FOR FIGURE 7.1.

STATE	INPUT 0	INPUT 1
State 0	B / 1	A / 2
State 1	B / 0	B / 1
State 2	A / 2	C / 1

Finite state machines are computationally complete—meaning that a finite state machine can be constructed to accomplish any programmatic task. You can think of an FSM as a program or algorithm, and you'll find them at use in database search routines, string comparison algorithms, and robotic control systems.

You needn't limit the symbol alphabets for FSMs to characters or numbers; in one application, my FSMs used function addresses for the output "symbols"; instead of defining a mapping between symbol sets, my

FSM mapped a series of values to a sequence of function calls. Used creatively, FSMs can be an incredibly powerful software tool, and their complexity and variety is a bit astonishing.

In 1990, a computer scientist named W. Atmar invented a formula for calculating the number of possible finite state machines (N) that can be constructed given a number of states (n) and sizes of input (a) and output alphabets (b): N = (naba)n. More than half a million FSMs can be created using the states and symbols shown in Figure 7.1. Expanding the number of states and its alphabets dramatically increases the variety of possible machines; for example, allowing five states with input and output alphabets of three symbols will allow the generation of nearly 438,000,000,000,000,000 FSMs!

Finite State Machine Class

My `FiniteStateMachine` template defines a class type:

```
//----------------
// FSM Error type
//----------------

class FSM_Ex : public ExceptionBase
    {
    public:
        virtual void Explain
            (
            DiagOutput & out
            );
    };

//----------------------
// state transition data
//----------------------

template
    <
    class Tout
    >
    struct FSM_TranData
        {
        size_t NextState;
```

```
        Tout   Osym;

        // default constructor
        FSM_TranData() : NextState(0), Osym() { }

        // constructor
        FSM_TranData
            (
            size_t ns,
            Tout   os
            )
            {
            NextState = ns;
            Osym = os;
            }
        };

//---------------------------------
// Core finite state machine class
//---------------------------------

template
    <
    class  Tin,
    size_t Nin,
    class  Tout
    >
    class FiniteStateMachine
        {
        public:
            // origination constructor
            FiniteStateMachine
                (
                size_t nState,
                FSM_TranData<Tout> * table,
                Tin  iset[Nin],
                size_t start
                );

            // destructor
            ~FiniteStateMachine();

            // copy constructor
            FiniteStateMachine
                (
                const FiniteStateMachine<Tin,Nin,Tout> & fsm
                );
```

```
        // assignment operator
        void operator =
            (
            const FiniteStateMachine<Tin,Nin,Tout> & fsm
            );

        // interrogators
        size_t GetNumStates() { return N;      }
        size_t GetCurState()  { return State; }

        // set to next state based on input
        Tout Transition
            (
            Tin in
            );

        // reset machine to initial state
        void Reset();

        // dump a description of this machine
        void DumpStructure
            (
            ostream & str
            );

    protected:
        FSM_TranData<Tout> (* TranTable)[Nin];
        Tin    InSymSet[Nin];
        size_t N;
        size_t State;
        size_t InitState;
    };
```

The template arguments define the types of input and output symbols and the size of the input alphabet. The constructor creates a new FiniteStateMachine from a table of state transitions and an array holding the input alphabet:

```
// origination constructor
template
    <
    class  Tin,
    size_t Nin,
    class  Tout
```

```
    >
    FiniteStateMachine<Tin,Nin,Tout>::FiniteStateMachine
        (
        size_t nState,
        FSM_TranData<Tout> * table,
        Tin  iset[Nin],
        size_t start
        )
        {
        if (start >= nState)
            throw FSM_Ex();

        N = nState;

        TranTable = new FSM_TranData<Tout>[N][Nin];

        if (TranTable == NULL) throw FSM_Ex();

        memcpy(TranTable,table,
                N * Nin * sizeof(FSM_TranData<Tout>));

        memcpy(InSymSet,iset,Nin * sizeof(Tin));

        State     = start;
        InitState = start;
        }
```

The destructor deletes the allocated transaction table, if necessary:

```
template
    <
    class  Tin,
    size_t Nin,
    class  Tout
    >
    FiniteStateMachine<Tin,Nin,Tout>::~FiniteStateMachine()
        {
        if (TranTable != NULL)
            delete [] TranTable;
        }
```

The copy constructor and assignment operator, respectively, duplicate and copy existing FiniteStateMachines:

```
template
```

```
        <
        class  Tin,
        size_t Nin,
        class  Tout
        >
        void FiniteStateMachine<Tin,Nin,Tout>::operator =
            (
            const FiniteStateMachine<Tin,Nin,Tout> & fsm
            )
            {
            if (N != fsm.N)
                {
                N = fsm.N;

                if (TranTable != NULL)
                    {
                    delete [] TranTable;
                    TranTable = NULL;
                    }
                }

            if (TranTable == NULL)
                {
                TranTable = new FSM_TranData<Tout>[N][Nin];

                if (TranTable == NULL)
                    throw FSM_Ex();
                }

            memcpy(TranTable,fsm.TranTable,
                N * Nin * sizeof(FSM_TranData<Tout>));

            memcpy(InSymSet,fsm.InSymSet,Nin * sizeof(Tin));

            State     = fsm.State;
            InitState = fsm.InitState;
            }

template
    <
    class  Tin,
    size_t Nin,
    class  Tout
    >
    FiniteStateMachine<Tin,Nin,Tout>::FiniteStateMachine
        (
        const FiniteStateMachine<Tin,Nin,Tout> & fsm
```

```
    )
    {
    TranTable = NULL;
    (*this) = fsm;
    }
```

The `Transition` member function returns an output symbol and performs a state transition based on an input symbol:

```
template
    <
    class  Tin,
    size_t Nin,
    class  Tout
    >
    Tout FiniteStateMachine<Tin,Nin,Tout>::Transition
        (
        Tin in
        )
        {
        if (TranTable == NULL)
            throw FSM_Ex();

        size_t i = 0;

        while ((i < Nin) && (InSymSet[i] != in)) ++i;

        if (i == Nin)
            throw FSM_Ex();

        Tout res = TranTable[State][i].Osym;

        State = TranTable[State][i].NextState;

        if (State >= N)
            throw FSM_Ex();

        return res;
        }
```

`Reset` sets the `FiniteStateMachine` to its initial state:

```
template
    <
    class  Tin,
```

```
    size_t Nin,
    class  Tout
    >
    inline void FiniteStateMachine<Tin,Nin,Tout>::Reset()
        {
        State = InitState;
        }
```

The `DumpStructure` function writes information about a `FiniteStateMachine` into a supplied buffer:

```
template
    <
    class  Tin,
    size_t Nin,
    class  Tout
    >
    void FiniteStateMachine<Tin,Nin,Tout>::DumpStructure
        (
        ostream & str
        )
        {
        str << "Initial state: " << InitState << "\r\n";
        str << "Current state: " << State    << "\r\n";
        str << " Total states: " << N         << "\r\n";

        for (size_t s = 0; s < N; ++s)
            {
            str << "s: " << s;

            for (size_t i = 0; i < Nin; ++i)
                {
                str << ", " << InSymSet[i]
                    << "=" << TranTable[s][i].Osym
                    << ">>" << TranTable[s][i].NextState;
                }

            str << "\r\n";
            }
        }
```

In my original design of `FiniteStateMachine`, a fourth template argument declared the number of states. I changed this to a parameter and dynamically allocated the transition table, because I needed to be able to change the number of states for evolutionary algorithms.

EVOLUTIONARY COMPUTATION

This is the level of complexity we're seeking in an evolutionary algorithm. DNA may encode a simple set of proteins, but the combinations of those proteins produce the near-infinite variety of life we see around us. Diversity is the key to success in the natural world; FSMs offer us that level of diversity in software, and evolutionary algorithms allow us to explore and manipulate the incredible assortment of possible FSMs.

Programmers construct most finite state machines to accomplish a specific task; in the case of evolutionary programming, however, we're interested in constructing FSMs based on natural selection. In the mid-1960s, Larry Fogel of the University of California suggested techniques for doing just that. Fogel defined intelligence as the ability to predict and react to one's environment; his goal was to find a mechanism for evolving machine intelligence.

Fogel's finite state machines evolve in much the same way as artificial chromosomes evolve in a genetic algorithm. A set of FSMs is tested against an environment that consists of a series of input symbols; the evolutionary algorithm calculates a fitness value for each FSM based on its performance. The fitness values define relative reproductive chances for the FSM population; offspring are generated by copying a parent FSM and possibly mutating it. Possible mutations include the change of an output symbol, alteration of a state transition, the assignment of a new initial state, the addition of a new state, or the deletion of an existing state. The new population then replaces its parents, and the cycle begins again.

In essence, an evolutionary algorithm is generating a program or algorithm by testing FSMs against a problem. This is an incredibly powerful concept in that it focuses on mechanism rather than data; where a genetic algorithm alters anonymous strings representing information, an *evolutionary algorithm* manipulates a *process*.

Mutable FSM Class

To implement evolutionary algorithms, I derived a mutable `EvolvingFSM` type from the `FiniteStateMachine` class. An

`EvolvingFSM` has four template arguments defining the types and sizes of the input and output alphabets:

```
typedef float EVFSM_MuteWts[5];

enum EVFSM_MuteType
    {
    EVFSM_OutSymbol = 0,
    EVFSM_Transition,
    EVFSM_AddState,
    EVFSM_DelState,
    EVFSM_InitState,
    EVFSM_None
    };

template
    <
    class  Tin,
    size_t Nin,
    class  Tout,
    size_t Nout
    >
    class EvolvingFSM : public FiniteStateMachine<Tin,Nin,Tout>
        {
        public:
            // default constructor
            EvolvingFSM();

            // origination constructor
            EvolvingFSM
                (
                size_t nState,
                FSM_TranData<Tout> * table,
                Tin  iset[Nin],
                Tout oset[Nout],
                size_t start,
                EVFSM_MuteWts wts
                );

            // copy constructor
            EvolvingFSM
                (
                const EvolvingFSM<Tin,Nin,Tout,Nout> & fsm
                );

            // assignment operator
```

```
        void operator =
            (
            const EvolvingFSM<Tin,Nin,Tout,Nout> & fsm
            );

        // mutation
        EVFSM_MuteType Mutate
            (
            size_t minstate,
            size_t maxstate
            );

    protected:
        Tout OutSymSet[Nout];
        RouletteWheel<float> MuteChooser;
        RandDev DevGen;

        size_t PickIsym();
        size_t PickOsym();
        size_t PickState();
    };
```

The EvolvingFSM constructor adds two parameters to those defined by
FiniteStateMachine: an output symbol alphabet and a set of weights
for selecting mutations:

```
template
    <
    class  Tin,
    size_t Nin,
    class  Tout,
    size_t Nout
    >
    EvolvingFSM<Tin,Nin,Tout,Nout>::EvolvingFSM
        (
        size_t nState,
        FSM_TranData<Tout> * table,
        Tin  iset[Nin],
        Tout oset[Nout],
        size_t start,
        EVFSM_MuteWts wts
        )
        : FiniteStateMachine<Tin,Nin,Tout>(nState,table,
                                           iset,start),
        MuteChooser(5,wts)
```

```
        {
        memcpy(OutSymSet,oset,Nout * sizeof(Tout));
        }
```

The copy constructor and assignment operator build on corresponding functions inherited from `FiniteStateMachine`:

```
// copy constructor
template
    <
    class Tin,
    size_t Nin,
    class Tout,
    size_t Nout
    >
    EvolvingFSM<Tin,Nin,Tout,Nout>::EvolvingFSM
        (
        const EvolvingFSM<Tin,Nin,Tout,Nout> & fsm
        )
        : FiniteStateMachine<Tin,Nin,Tout>(fsm),
          MuteChooser(fsm.MuteChooser)
        {
        memcpy(OutSymSet,fsm.OutSymSet,Nout * sizeof(Tout));
        }

// assignment operator
template
    <
    class Tin,
    size_t Nin,
    class Tout,
    size_t Nout
    >
    void EvolvingFSM<Tin,Nin,Tout,Nout>::operator =
        (
        const EvolvingFSM<Tin,Nin,Tout,Nout> & fsm
        )
        {
        FiniteStateMachine<Tin,Nin,Tout>::operator = (fsm);

        MuteChooser = fsm.MuteChooser;

        memcpy(OutSymSet,fsm.OutSymSet,Nin * sizeof(Tin));
        }
```

I defined a set of inline `Pick...` utility functions to simplify the random selection of states and symbols:

```
template
    <
    class  Tin,
    size_t Nin,
    class  Tout,
    size_t Nout
    >
    inline size_t EvolvingFSM<Tin,Nin,Tout,Nout>::PickIsym()
        {
        return size_t(DevGen() * float(Nin));
        }

template
    <
    class  Tin,
    size_t Nin,
    class  Tout,
    size_t Nout
    >
    inline size_t EvolvingFSM<Tin,Nin,Tout,Nout>::PickOsym()
        {
        return size_t(DevGen() * float(Nout));
        }

template
    <
    class  Tin,
    size_t Nin,
    class  Tout,
    size_t Nout
    >
    inline size_t EvolvingFSM<Tin,Nin,Tout,Nout>::PickState()
        {
        return size_t(DevGen() * float(N));
        }
```

`EvolvingFSM` exists to add a mutation function to `FiniteStateMachine`. The following function selects from the mutation types defined by Larry Fogel:

```
template
```

```
<
class  Tin,
size_t Nin,
class  Tout,
size_t Nout
>
EVFSM_MuteType EvolvingFSM<Tin,Nin,Tout,Nout>::Mutate
    (
    size_t minstate,
    size_t maxstate
    )
    {
    // correct and verify parameters
    if (minstate < 1)
        minstate = 1;

    if ((TranTable == NULL) || (minstate > maxstate))
        throw FSM_Ex();

    // define variables
    size_t n, i, j, s;
    EVFSM_MuteType c;
    FSM_TranData<Tout> (* newtable)[Nin];

    // select operation
    c = EVFSM_MuteType(MuteChooser.GetIndex());

    // skip invalid cases
    if ((c == EVFSM_AddState) && (N >= maxstate))
        return EVFSM_None;

    if ((c == EVFSM_DelState) && (N <= minstate))
        return EVFSM_None;

    if ((c == EVFSM_InitState) && (N <= 1))
        return EVFSM_None;

    // perform operation
    switch (c)
        {
        case EVFSM_OutSymbol:
            // pick state to modify
            n = PickState();

            // pick input symbol to modify
            i = PickIsym();
```

```
        // change output symbol
        TranTable[n][i].Osym = OutSymSet[PickOsym()];

        break;

case EVFSM_Transition:
        // pick state to modify
        n = PickState();

        // pick input state to modify
        i = PickIsym();

        // pick new output state
        s = PickState();

        // change state transition
        TranTable[n][i].NextState = s;
        break;

case EVFSM_AddState:
        newtable = new FSM_TranData<Tout>[N+1][Nin];

        if (newtable == NULL)
            throw FSM_Ex();

        // copy old states
        for (n = 0; n < N; ++n)
            memcpy(newtable[n],TranTable[n],
                    Nin * sizeof(FSM_TranData<Tin>));

        // fill new state with random transition data
        for (i = 0; i < Nin; ++i)
            {
            newtable[N][i].Osym = OutSymSet[PickOsym()];
            newtable[N][i].NextState = size_t(DevGen()
                                    * float(N + 1.0F));
            }

        // change some old states to point to new state
        i = size_t(DevGen() * N / 2) + 1;

        for (n = 0; n < i; ++n)
            newtable[PickState()][PickIsym()].NextState
                                    = N;

        // increment number of states
        ++N;
```

```
                // use new table, delete the old one
                delete [] TranTable;

                TranTable = newtable;

                break;

        case EVFSM_DelState:
                if (N == 1) break;

                // create new transition table
                newtable = new FSM_TranData<Tout>[N-1][Nin];

                if (newtable == NULL)
                    throw FSM_Ex();

                // choose state to be deleted
                n = PickState();

                // copy old states
                i = 0;

                for (s = 0; s < N; ++s)
                    {
                    if (s != n)
                        {
                        // copy state information
                        memcpy(newtable[i],TranTable[s],
                            Nin * sizeof(FSM_TranData<Tin>));

                        // change references to deleted state
                        for (j = 0; j < Nin; ++j)
                            {
                            if (newtable[i][j].NextState == n)
                                {
                                newtable[i][j].NextState =
                                    size_t(DevGen()
                                            * float(N - 1));
                                }
                            else
                                {
                                if (newtable[i][j].NextState > n)
                                    --newtable[i][j].NextState;
                                }
                            }
```

```
            ++i;
            }
        }

    // decrement number of states
    --N;

    // use new table, delete the old one
    delete [] TranTable;
    TranTable = newtable;

    // change initial state, if need be
    if (InitState == n)
        InitState = PickState();
    else
        if (InitState > n)
            --InitState;

    break;

case EVFSM_InitState:
    do  {
        i = PickState();
        }
    while (i == InitState);

    InitState = i;

    break;
    }

Reset();

return c;
}
```

These mutations have some restrictions, and Mutate returns the type of mutation performed.

THE PRISONER'S DILEMMA: A NEW DESIGN

In Chapter 5, my implementation of the Prisoner's Dilemma relied on bit strings to define a given strategy. In 1993, David Fogel (whose relationship to Larry is unknown to me) investigated dynamics of evolving the Prisoner's Dilemma strategies via finite state machines. His input alphabet consisted of the paired moves taken by a strategy and its opponent on the previous move; the output alphabet was {C, D}, indicating the FSM's next move.

David Fogel's simulation program conducted a round-robin tournament of 151 moves between 100 FSM strategies. FSMs began with between one and five states and were allowed to evolve as many as eight states. The initial population was generated randomly, and subsequent generations replaced the least-fit half of the original population with new offspring. Fogel tested with population sizes between 50 and 1000, for up to 25 generations.

Fogel noticed some interesting dynamics in the FSM population. The first successful strategies were those that relied on defection, but the most successful FSMs evolved to, as Fogel puts it, "recognize" cooperative opponents. The FSMs were able to adapt to their environment and the strategies presented by opponents.

One reason David Fogel is investigating FSMs is his interest in finding new techniques for evolving artificial intelligence. In his view, genetic algorithms limit themselves by focusing on the emulation of biological processes that may not have direct applicability to machine intelligence. For example, Fogel disputes the contention that crossover is essential to any evolutionary algorithm; his empirical studies in 1995 show that evolving finite state machines, which do not lend themselves to crossover, perform as well as genetic algorithms on function optimization problems.

Fogel's experiments with the Prisoner's Dilemma were limited by his computing hardware to only a few dozen generations; he could not verify the longevity of some trends or determine the long-term survival of various FSMs. In playing with evolving FSMs, I decided to try my hand at implementing a version that allowed for longer runs.

I decided that each FSM would react to the previous move of its opponent, whereas Fogel's implementation used the previous moves of both the FSM and its opponent. This has the effect of reducing the input alphabet from four to two symbols, limiting the complexity of the FSMs. Figure 7.2 shows a three-state Prisoner's Dilemma FSM.

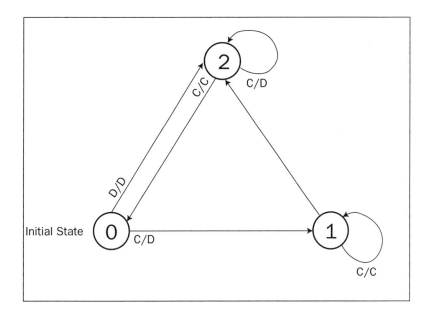

FIGURE 7.2 THREE-STATE PRISONER'S DILEMMA FSM.

Machines, of course, can be much simpler than the one in Figure 7.2. In Figure 7.3, I show a one-state version of the famous Tit-for-Tat strategy that simply repeats the last move of its opponent.

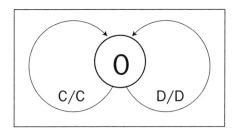

FIGURE 7.3 ONE-STATE FSM VERSION OF TIT-FOR-TAT.

I allow for the configuration of various parameters associated with a run, using the dialog box shown in Figure 7.4.

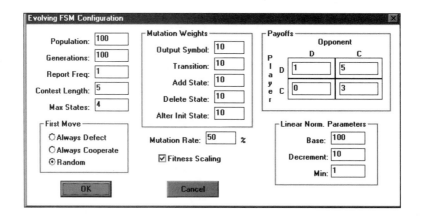

FIGURE 7.4   EVOLVING FSM CONFIGURATION DIALOG BOX.

I've defined the parameters as follows:

Population   The number of strategies to be tested. Several repro-
                     duction operators require two parents, and elitist
                     selection copies the best chromosome of the parent
                     generation into the offspring. Thus, the population
                     should be an odd number.

Generations   The number of generations to be run in this simula-
                     tion.

Report Frequency How often the simulation should report on the strate-
                     gies it has tested.

Contest Length   This is the number of contests (the size of the crime
                     spree, so to speak) that take place between opposing
                     FSMs.

Max States   The initial population comprises three-state machines;
                     this parameter sets the maximum number of states
                     allowed through mutation.

First Move   These radio buttons select the first move for every
                     machine in the population: **always cooperate**, **always
                     defect**, or a **random choice**.

Mutation Weights Five values defining the relative chances of various mutations being performed on offspring.

Mutation Rate The probability that a mutation will change any given offspring.

Payoffs Defines the payoff amounts for combinations of cooperation and defection.

Linear Normalization Parameters For the Traveling Artist Problem, I always use linear normalization to scale fitness values because the relative difference in fitness between chromosomes may not be high. In the group, you can define the base value, decrement, and minimum fitness allowed.

Following the pattern I've set in previous chapters, I've defined a class (`EVOptConfig`) to encapsulate the Configuration dialog box in Figure 7.4; I'll give the class definition here for information purposes:

```
enum EVMove
    {
    EVM_DEFECT,
    EVM_COOPER,
    EVM_RANDOM
    };

class EVOptConfig
    {
    public:
        EVOptConfig
            (
            HINSTANCE inst,
            HWND      parent
            );

        static void DlgInit
            (
            HWND  dlg
            );

        static BOOL DlgStore
            (
            HWND  dlg
            );
```

```
        // verify if this object is valid
        float   GetValidity()    { return Valid; }

        // interrogate dimensions of test
        size_t GetPopSize()     { return PopSize;     }
        size_t GetTestSize()    { return TestSize;    }
        size_t GetTestLen()     { return TestLen;     }
        size_t GetReptFreq()    { return ReptFreq;    }
        size_t GetMaxState()    { return MaxState;    }

        // interrogate operator parameters
        float   GetMuteRate()    { return MuteRate;   }
        float   GetWeight0()     { return Weight0;    }
        float   GetWeightT()     { return WeightT;    }
        float   GetWeightA()     { return WeightA;    }
        float   GetWeightD()     { return WeightD;    }
        float   GetWeightN()     { return WeightN;    }

        // interrogate payoff amounts
        double GetPayoffDD()    { return PayoffDD;    }
        double GetPayoffDC()    { return PayoffDC;    }
        double GetPayoffCD()    { return PayoffCD;    }
        double GetPayoffCC()    { return PayoffCC;    }

        // interrogate first move strategy
        EVMove GetFirstMove()  { return FirstMove;  }

        // interrogate fitness scaling parameters
        bool    GetFitScale()    { return FitScale;   }
        double GetFitLinBase() { return FitLinBase; }
        double GetFitLinDec()  { return FitLinDec;  }
        double GetFitLinMin()  { return FitLinMin;  }

    private:
        // validity flag
        float   Valid;

        // dimensions of test
        size_t  PopSize;
        size_t  TestSize;
        size_t  TestLen;
        size_t  ReptFreq;
        size_t  MaxState;

        // operator parameters
        float   MuteRate;
```

```
    float    Weight0;
    float    WeightT;
    float    WeightA;
    float    WeightD;
    float    WeightN;

    // payoff amounts
    double   PayoffDD;
    double   PayoffDC;
    double   PayoffCD;
    double   PayoffCC;

    // first move strategy
    EVMove   FirstMove;

    // fitness scaling parameters
    bool     FitScale;
    double   FitLinBase;
    double   FitLinDec;
    double   FitLinMin;

    // stored parameter values
    static size_t DefPopSize;
    static size_t DefTestSize;
    static size_t DefTestLen;
    static size_t DefReptFreq;
    static size_t DefMaxState;
    static float  DefMuteRate;
    static float  DefWeight0;
    static float  DefWeightT;
    static float  DefWeightA;
    static float  DefWeightD;
    static float  DefWeightN;
    static double DefPayoffDD;
    static double DefPayoffDC;
    static double DefPayoffCD;
    static double DefPayoffCC;
    static EVMove DefFirstMove;
    static bool   DefFitScale;
    static double DefFitLinBase;
    static double DefFitLinDec;
    static double DefFitLinMin;
};
```

The implementation code for `EVOptConfig` is very similar to that of other configuration classes in previous chapters.

IMPLEMENTATION

The FSM version of the Prisoner's Dilemma begins by creating a configuration object and displaying its contents:

```
// create configuration and verify it
EVOptConfig evoc(inst,wdw);

if (!evoc.GetValidity())
    {
    buffer << "Cancelled\r\n";
    return;
    }

// display parameters
buffer << "\r\n      Population: " << evoc.GetPopSize();
buffer << "\r\n       Test Size: " << evoc.GetTestSize();
buffer << "\r\n     Test Length: " << evoc.GetTestLen();
buffer << "\r\n       Max State: " << evoc.GetMaxState();
buffer << "\r\n   Mutation Rate: " << evoc.GetMuteRate();
buffer << "\r\n";
buffer << "\r\nOutput Symbol Wt: " << evoc.GetWeightO();
buffer << "\r\n   Transition Wt: " << evoc.GetWeightT();
buffer << "\r\n    Add State Wt: " << evoc.GetWeightA();
buffer << "\r\n Delete State Wt: " << evoc.GetWeightD();
buffer << "\r\nNew InitState Wt: " << evoc.GetWeightN();
buffer << "\r\n";
buffer << "\r\n       Payoff DD: " << evoc.GetPayoffDD();
buffer << "\r\n       Payoff DC: " << evoc.GetPayoffDC();
buffer << "\r\n       Payoff CD: " << evoc.GetPayoffCD();
buffer << "\r\n       Payoff CC: " << evoc.GetPayoffCC();
buffer << "\r\n";
buffer << "\r\n      First Move: ";

switch (evoc.GetFirstMove())
    {
    case EVM_DEFECT:
        buffer << "Always Defect";
        break;
    case EVM_COOPER:
        buffer << "Always Cooperate";
        break;
    case EVM_RANDOM:
        buffer << "Random";
    }
```

```
if (evoc.GetFitScale())
    {
    buffer << "\r\n";
    buffer << "\r\n    Fitness Base: "
            << evoc.GetFitLinBase();
    buffer << "\r\n    Fitness  Dec: "
            << evoc.GetFitLinDec();
    buffer << "\r\n    Fitness  Min: "
            << evoc.GetFitLinMin();
    }

buffer << "\r\n";
```

Then I define a set of variables and constants:

```
// data arrays
const size_t    SSZ = 2;
const size_t    NSZ = 3;
char   SSET[2] = { 'C', 'D' };
const size_t POP_SZ = evoc.GetPopSize();

// variables
size_t n, i, j, k, inc;
double vf;
char buf[64], mj, mk, tj;

EvolvingFSM<char,SSZ,char,SSZ> * vm;

RouletteWheel<double> * rw;

RandDev devgen;

FSM_TranData<char> td[NSZ][SSZ];

EVFSM_MuteWts wts =
    {
    evoc.GetWeight0(),
    evoc.GetWeightT(),
    evoc.GetWeightA(),
    evoc.GetWeightD(),
    evoc.GetWeightN()
    };
// allocate buffers
    EvolvingFSM<char,SSZ,char,SSZ> ** pop =
```

```
                    new EvolvingFSM<char,SSZ,char,SSZ> * [POP_SZ];

    if (pop == NULL)
        {
        buffer << "Memory allocation failed\r\n";
        return;
        }

    EvolvingFSM<char,SSZ,char,SSZ> ** newpop =
                    new EvolvingFSM<char,SSZ,char,SSZ> * [POP_SZ];

    if (newpop == NULL)
        {
        buffer << "Memory allocation failed\r\n";
        return;
        }

    double * fit = new double [POP_SZ];

    if (fit == NULL)
        {
        buffer << "Memory allocation failed\r\n";
        return;
        }

    // pointers for shell sort
    EvolvingFSM<char,SSZ,char,SSZ> * * ptrm = pop - 1;
    double * ptrf = fit    - 1;
```

The initial population is a random set of FSMs:

```
// create an initial population of FSMs
    for (j = 0; j < POP_SZ; ++j)
        {
        for (n = 0; n < NSZ; ++n)
            {
            for (i = 0; i < SSZ; ++i)
                {
                td[n][i].NextState =
                        size_t(devgen() * float(NSZ));

                if (devgen() < 0.5F)
                    td[n][i].Osym = SSET[0];
                else
                    td[n][i].Osym = SSET[1];
                }
```

```
        }

    pop[j] = new EvolvingFSM<char,SSZ,char,SSZ> (NSZ,
                                        &td[0][0],
                                        SSET,SSET,0,wts);

    if (pop[j] == NULL)
        {
        buffer << "Memory allocation failed\r\n";
        return;
        }
    }
```

The main loop begins by displaying status information in the application's title bar:

```
size_t g = 0;

    while (1)
        {
        // display progress in app header
        wsprintf(buf,"Forge (loop: %u of %u)",
                    g,evoc.GetTestSize());
        SetWindowText(wdw,buf);
        .
        .
        .
```

Fitness testing involves a set of three nested loops that perform a competition series between machines:

```
        // reset FSMs and clear fitness array
        for (j = 0; j < POP_SZ; ++j)
            {
            pop[j]->Reset();
            fit[j] = 0.0;
            }

        // fitness testing by competition
        for (j = 0; j < POP_SZ; ++j)
            {
            for (k = j; k < POP_SZ; ++k)
                {
                // reset machines to initial state
```

```
                pop[j]->Reset();
                pop[k]->Reset();

                // select first move
                switch (evoc.GetFirstMove())
                    {
                    case EVM_DEFECT:
                        mj = 'D';
                        mk = 'D';
                        break;
                    case EVM_COOPER:
                        mj = 'C';
                        mk = 'C';
                        break;
                    case EVM_RANDOM:
                        if (devgen() < 0.5F)
                            mj = 'C';
                        else
                            mj = 'D';

                        if (devgen() < 0.5F)
                            mk = 'C';
                        else
                            mk = 'D';
                    }

                n = 1;

                // calculate fitness based on moves
                while (1)
                    {
                    if (mj == SSET[0])
                        {
                        if (mk == SSET[0])
                            {
                            fit[j] += evoc.GetPayoffCC();
                            fit[k] += evoc.GetPayoffCC();
                            }
                        else
                            {
                            fit[j] += evoc.GetPayoffCD();
                            fit[k] += evoc.GetPayoffDC();
                            }
                        }
                    else
                        {
                        if (mk == SSET[0])
```

```
                    {
                    fit[j] += evoc.GetPayoffDC();
                    fit[k] += evoc.GetPayoffCD();
                    }
                else
                    {
                    fit[j] += evoc.GetPayoffDD();
                    fit[k] += evoc.GetPayoffDD();
                    }
                }

            // exit if done
            if (n == evoc.GetTestLen())
                break;


            // state transitions based on opponents move
            tj = pop[j]->Transition(mk);
            mk = pop[k]->Transition(mj);
            mj = tj;

            // next contest
            ++n;
            }
        }
    }
```

A shell sort reorganizes the array in order of fitness:

```
    // sort for selecting best
    for (inc = 1; inc <= POP_SZ / 9; inc = 3 * inc + 1) ;

    for ( ; inc > 0; inc /= 3)
        {
        for (i = inc + 1; i <= POP_SZ; i += inc)
            {
            vf = ptrf[i];
            vm = ptrm[i];

            j  = i;

            while ((j > inc) && (ptrf[j - inc] < vf))
                {
                ptrf[j] = ptrf[j - inc];
                ptrm[j] = ptrm[j - inc];
```

```
                            j  -= inc;
                            }

                    ptrf[j] = vf;
                    ptrm[j] = vm;
                    }
            }
```

I display the highest-fitness FSM from the population, which will be in
element 0 of the arrays:

```
// display best machine
if (((g % evoc.GetReptFreq()) == 0)
|| (g == evoc.GetTestSize()))
    {
    buffer << "\r\nGeneration " << g
           << "\r\n---------------\r\n";

    pop[0]->DumpStructure(buffer);

    buffer << "       Fitness: " << fit[0] << "\r\n";
    }
```

Fitness scaling, if enabled, sets new fitness values:

```
// exit, if it's time
if (g == evoc.GetTestSize())
    break;

// fitness scaling (linear normalization)
if (evoc.GetFitScale())
    {
    fit[0] = evoc.GetFitLinBase();
    i      = 1;

    while (fit[i-1] <= evoc.GetFitLinDec())
        {
        fit[i] = fit[i-1] - evoc.GetFitLinDec();
        ++i;
        }

    for (; i < POP_SZ; ++i)
        fit[i] = evoc.GetFitLinMin();
    }
```

A new population consists of copies of parent FSMs, which may be mutated:

```
// reproduce new members
rw = new RouletteWheel<double> (POP_SZ,fit);

if (rw == NULL)
    {
    buffer << "Memory allocation failed\r\n";
    return;
    }

for (j = 0; j < POP_SZ; ++j)
    {
    i = rw->GetIndex();

    newpop[j] = new EvolvingFSM<char,SSZ,char,SSZ>
                            (*(pop[i]));

    if (newpop[j] == NULL)
        {
        buffer << "Memory allocation failed\r\n";
        return;
        }

    if (devgen() < evoc.GetMuteRate())
        newpop[j]->Mutate(2,evoc.GetMaxState());
    }

delete rw;

// copy next generation and repeat!
for (j = 0; j < POP_SZ; ++j)
    delete pop[j];
```

Finally, the simulation generation loop ends by copying the new populations over the old ones:

```
memcpy(pop,newpop,POP_SZ * sizeof(EvolvingFSM<char,SSZ,
                                char,SSZ> *));

++g;
}
```

Once all generations have been run, the simulation deletes its buffers and restores the application title:

```
// delete buffers
for (j = 0; j < POP_SZ; ++j)
    delete pop[j];

delete [] pop;
delete [] newpop;
delete [] fit;

// restore window text
SetWindowText(wdw,"Forge");
}
```

ANALYSIS

A typical run of the FSM Prisoner's Dilemma can look like this:

```
Evolving Finite State Machines
- - - - - - - - - - - - - - - - - - - - - - - - - - -

       Population: 100
        Test Size: 1000
      Test Length: 100
        Max State: 5
    Mutation Rate: 0.5

Output Symbol Wt: 10
    Transition Wt: 10
     Add State Wt: 10
  Delete State Wt: 10
  New InitState Wt: 10

        Payoff DD: 1
        Payoff DC: 5
        Payoff CD: 0
        Payoff CC: 3

       First Move: Random

     Fitness Base: 100
     Fitness  Dec: 5
     Fitness  Min: 1
```

```
Generation 0
----------------
Initial state: 0
Current state: 1
 Total states: 3
s: 0, C=D>>1, D=D>>1
s: 1, C=D>>0, D=D>>1
s: 2, C=C>>2, D=C>>0
       Fitness: 3238

Generation 100
----------------
Initial state: 1
Current state: 2
 Total states: 4
s: 0, C=D>>1, D=D>>0
s: 1, C=D>>1, D=D>>2
s: 2, C=D>>2, D=D>>2
s: 3, C=D>>2, D=D>>1
       Fitness: 1180

Generation 200
----------------
Initial state: 3
Current state: 0
 Total states: 4
s: 0, C=C>>1, D=C>>3
s: 1, C=C>>3, D=D>>2
s: 2, C=C>>0, D=C>>0
s: 3, C=D>>2, D=C>>0
       Fitness: 2891

Generation 300
----------------
Initial state: 1
Current state: 1
 Total states: 2
s: 0, C=D>>0, D=D>>0
s: 1, C=C>>1, D=D>>1
       Fitness: 2415

Generation 400
----------------
Initial state: 4
Current state: 4
 Total states: 5
```

```
s: 0, C=C>>0, D=C>>4
s: 1, C=C>>1, D=D>>0
s: 2, C=D>>0, D=D>>2
s: 3, C=D>>1, D=D>>3
s: 4, C=D>>1, D=D>>4
        Fitness: 1997


Generation 500
----------------
Initial state: 0
Current state: 1
 Total states: 2
s: 0, C=D>>1, D=D>>1
s: 1, C=C>>0, D=C>>0
        Fitness: 2546


Generation 600
----------------
Initial state: 0
Current state: 1
 Total states: 2
s: 0, C=D>>0, D=D>>1
s: 1, C=D>>0, D=D>>1
        Fitness: 1176


Generation 700
----------------
Initial state: 3
Current state: 1
 Total states: 4
s: 0, C=C>>1, D=D>>3
s: 1, C=D>>2, D=C>>3
s: 2, C=C>>1, D=D>>2
s: 3, C=C>>3, D=D>>0
        Fitness: 2447


Generation 800
----------------
Initial state: 0
Current state: 0
 Total states: 2
s: 0, C=D>>0, D=C>>0
s: 1, C=D>>0, D=C>>0
        Fitness: 2670


Generation 900
----------------
```

```
Initial state: 0
Current state: 1
 Total states: 4
s: 0, C=C>>1, D=C>>3
s: 1, C=D>>2, D=C>>2
s: 2, C=C>>0, D=C>>1
s: 3, C=D>>3, D=C>>0
        Fitness: 3061

Generation 1000
----------------
Initial state: 3
Current state: 4
 Total states: 5
s: 0, C=D>>1, D=D>>2
s: 1, C=C>>2, D=C>>4
s: 2, C=D>>2, D=C>>1
s: 3, C=D>>1, D=D>>3
s: 4, C=D>>0, D=C>>4
        Fitness: 2803
```

In Figure 7.5, I show a graphic version of the best machine from the last generation.

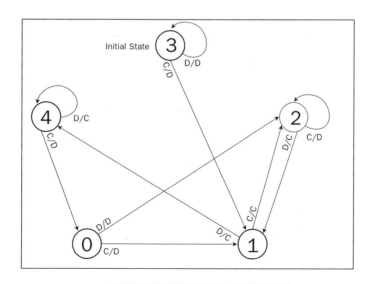

FIGURE 7.5   FIVE-STATE EVOLVED FSM.

Another machine, which has evolved on more than one run, is the four-state FSM shown in Figure 7.6.

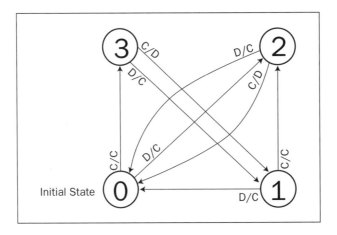

FIGURE 7.6   FOUR-STATE EVOLVED FSM.

Playing Figure 7.5 against Figure 7.6 for 10 rounds produces the following contest, for each of the four possible starting moves:

```
Figure 7.5: CDCDDDDDDD score: 46
Figure 7.6: CCCCCCCCCC score:  6
```

Playing Figure 7.5 against Tit-for-Tat for 10 rounds will result in this contest:

```
Figure 7.5: CCDCDCCCDC score: 27
Tit-for-Tat: CCCDCDCCCD score: 27
```

Playing Figure 7.6 against Tit-for-Tat for 10 rounds will result in this contest:

```
Figure 7.6: CCDCCCDCCC score: 28
Tit-for-Tat: CCCDCCCDCC score: 28
```

Tit-for-Tat scores 30 points against itself in an initially cooperative simulation. Mutual contests between Figures 7.5 and 7.6 look like this:

```
Figure 7.5: CDCDDCCDCC score: 22
Figure 7.5: CDCDDCCDCC score: 22


Figure 7.6: CCDCCDCCDC score: 24
Figure 7.6: CCDCCDCCDC score: 24
```

Nearly all contests evolve into a repeating pattern of strategies. One of the most common patterns alternates the two opponents so that their moves are always opposite, producing an average score of 2.5 per move. Patterns such as CCD, DCC, and DCCC also appear often, where cooperative behavior is occasionally interrupted by a defection. The invention of such competitive patterns occurs in almost all evolved state machines, representing the reproduction of successful strategies.

I have yet to see a dominant machine that only defects or only cooperates; such strategies are very vulnerable to exploitation by routines that recognize and adapt to their opponent's behavior, and machines that defect perform poorly against themselves.

Of the preceding machines, Figure 7.5 is clearly superior, explaining its dominance in the population after 1000 generations. When confronted with a cooperative strategy, Figure 7.5 takes advantage of the situation by defecting; when confronted with a Tit-for-Tat, the strategy in Figure 7.5 enters into a mutually beneficial pattern of cooperation and occasional defection.

How do I know my simulation isn't simply spitting out random state machines? To be honest, it is more difficult to analyze finite state machines than to count bit strings as I did in Chapter 5. However, distinct patterns in the actions of the FSMs indicate that they are, indeed, learning about their environment. For example, several simulations develop Tit-for-Tat, Pavlov, and other "classic" strategies, and the behavior of evolved machines, when analyzed, often shows the "intelligent" selection of responses to an opponent's moves.

My original assumption was that the average complexity of the FSMs would increase over long runs of the simulation. So far, that hasn't proven to be the case; no run has evolved an FSM with more than six active states, regardless of parameter settings.

Some machines will evolve unreachable states. My first thought was to develop an FSM "compression" routine to eliminate unused states, until I read Fogel's work in which he suggests that these apparently useless states correspond to the junk genes in DNA. "Superfluous" states may absorb otherwise damaging mutations. or the unused states may preserve once-useful algorithms that may be reintroduced through future mutations.

I've been running experiments that vary the relative probabilities of different FSM mutation operators, looking for an optimum mix. In general, a fair distribution of operator weights seems to produce the most effective set of mutations. In future experiments, I want to run the program for a very long time, hundreds of thousands of generations, to see what evolves. I urge you to experiment, looking for interesting patterns and strategies.

ONWARD

Like genetic algorithms, evolutionary programming has its supporters and detractors. In Chapter 8, I'll expand on arguments for and against evolutionary algorithms; I'll also demonstrate the development of search algorithms for robotic ants.

CHAPTER 8

ROBOT ANTS
AND OTHER APPLICATIONS

The Prisoner's Dilemma provides an interesting environment for evolving finite state machines, but lacking a definitive goal (other than survival), it doesn't show how natural selection can refine a process in light of a specific task. For such a demonstration, I've developed a simulation of robotic ants.

ROBOT ANTS

Assume, for a moment, that you are a robot ant, your movements defined by a finite state machine and your task to follow a trail of food. You can see the square directly in front of you, reacting to what is there by moving straight ahead or turning 90 degrees left or right before moving. The edges of your universe are barriers you cannot cross, and you can only spend so much time following the path. How best should your finite state machine be defined to maximize your search path?

I formulated the preceding problem as an evolutionary programming problem defining an ant's search strategy as a finite state machine with an input "view" alphabet of {F (food), E (empty), C (cliff)} and an output "move" alphabet of {A (ahead), L (turn left), R (turn right)}. Each ant begins its search at the top center of an 11-by-40 matrix, in which a zero square represents an empty space and a one element marks food. When an ant enters a "food" square, it eats the food, gaining a fitness point and converting the square to empty. The ant may face in one of four cardinal directions, and each move is determined by feeding the "view" an ant has into its finite machine to obtain a move symbol.

CONFIGURATION

To configure the robotic ant simulation, I defined the dialog box shown in Figure 8.1.

I've defined the robotic ant parameters as follows:

Population   The number of robotic ants in the population to be tested.

Generations   The number of generations to be run in this simulation.

Report Frequency How often the simulation should report on the strategies it has tested.

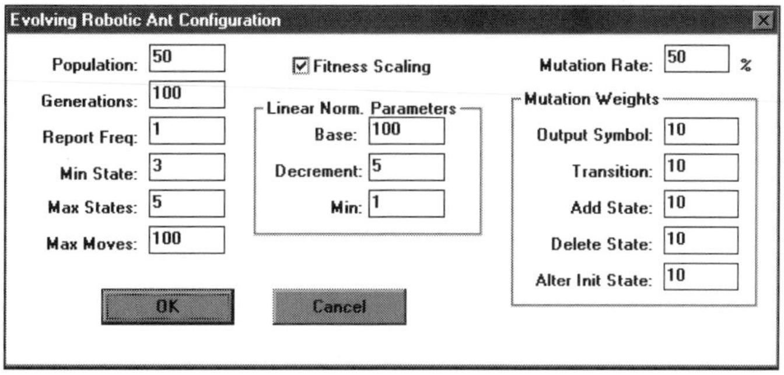

FIGURE 8.1   ROBOTIC ANT CONFIGURATION DIALOG BOX.

Min States	The minimal number of states for a robotic ant FSM. The initial population consists of ants with this many states.
Max States	The initial population comprises three-state machines; this parameter sets the maximum number of states allowed through mutation.
Max Moves	The maximum number of moves an ant may make if it does not encounter the end of the search grid.
Fitness Scaling	Toggles the application of fitness scaling via linear normalization.
Linear Normalization Parameters	In this group, you can define the base value, decrement, and minimum fitness allowed.
Mutation Rate	The probability that a mutation will change any given offspring.
Mutation Weights	These five values define the relative chances of various mutations being performed on offspring.

Following the pattern I've set in previous chapters, I've defined a class (RAOptConfig) to encapsulate the configuration dialog box in Figure 8.1; I'll give the class definition here for information purposes and leave you to explore the implementation provided on the enclosed source disk:

```
class RAOptConfig
    {
    public:
        RAOptConfig
            (
            HINSTANCE inst,
            HWND      parent
            );

        static void DlgInit
            (
            HWND  dlg
            );

        static BOOL DlgStore
            (
            HWND  dlg
            );

        // verify if this object is valid
        float  GetValidity()   { return Valid; }

        // interrogate dimensions of test
        size_t GetPopSize()    { return PopSize;    }
        size_t GetTestSize()   { return TestSize;   }
        size_t GetReptFreq()   { return ReptFreq;   }
        size_t GetMinState()   { return MinState;   }
        size_t GetMaxState()   { return MaxState;   }
        size_t GetMaxMoves()   { return MaxMoves;   }

        // interrogate operator parameters
        float  GetMuteRate()   { return MuteRate;   }
        float  GetWeight0()    { return Weight0;    }
        float  GetWeightT()    { return WeightT;    }
        float  GetWeightA()    { return WeightA;    }
        float  GetWeightD()    { return WeightD;    }
        float  GetWeightN()    { return WeightN;    }

        // interrogate fitness scaling parameters
        bool   GetFitScale()   { return FitScale;   }
        double GetFitLinBase() { return FitLinBase; }
        double GetFitLinDec()  { return FitLinDec;  }
        double GetFitLinMin()  { return FitLinMin;  }

    private:
        // validity flag
        float   Valid;
```

```
        // dimensions of test
        size_t  PopSize;
        size_t  TestSize;
        size_t  ReptFreq;
        size_t  MinState;
        size_t  MaxState;
        size_t  MaxMoves;

        // operator parameters
        float   MuteRate;
        float   Weight0;
        float   WeightT;
        float   WeightA;
        float   WeightD;
        float   WeightN;

        // fitness scaling parameters
        bool    FitScale;
        double  FitLinBase;
        double  FitLinDec;
        double  FitLinMin;

        // stored parameter values
        static size_t DefPopSize;
        static size_t DefTestSize;
        static size_t DefReptFreq;
        static size_t DefMinState;
        static size_t DefMaxState;
        static size_t DefMaxMoves;
        static float  DefMuteRate;
        static float  DefWeight0;
        static float  DefWeightT;
        static float  DefWeightA;
        static float  DefWeightD;
        static float  DefWeightN;
        static bool   DefFitScale;
        static double DefFitLinBase;
        static double DefFitLinDec;
        static double DefFitLinMin;
};
```

The implementation code for RAOptConfig is very similar to that of
other configuration classes in previous chapters.

IMPLEMENTATION

The robotic ant simulation begins by creating and validating a RAOptConfig object:

```
// create configuration and verify it
RAOptConfig raoc(inst,wdw);

if (!raoc.GetValidity())
    {
    buffer << "Cancelled\r\n";
    return;
    }

// display parameters
buffer << "\r\n       Population: " << raoc.GetPopSize();
buffer << "\r\n        Test Size: " << raoc.GetTestSize();
buffer << "\r\n        Min State: " << raoc.GetMinState();
buffer << "\r\n        Max State: " << raoc.GetMaxState();
buffer << "\r\n        Max Moves: " << raoc.GetMaxMoves();
buffer << "\r\n    Mutation Rate: " << raoc.GetMuteRate();
buffer << "\r\n";
buffer << "\r\nOutput Symbol Wt: " << raoc.GetWeightO();
buffer << "\r\n    Transition Wt: " << raoc.GetWeightT();
buffer << "\r\n     Add State Wt: " << raoc.GetWeightA();
buffer << "\r\n Delete State Wt: " << raoc.GetWeightD();
buffer << "\r\nNew InitState Wt: " << raoc.GetWeightN();

if (raoc.GetFitScale())
    {
    buffer << "\r\n";

    buffer << "\r\n     Fitness Base: "
           << raoc.GetFitLinBase();

    buffer << "\r\n     Fitness  Dec: "
           << raoc.GetFitLinDec();

    buffer << "\r\n     Fitness  Min: "
           << raoc.GetFitLinMin();
    }

buffer << "\r\n";
```

After obtaining the configuration, I create a set of data items to describe the ant's movements, views, and the search grid:

```
// data arrays
const size_t MoveSz = 3;
const size_t ViewSz = 3;
const size_t StatSz = raoc.GetMinState();
const size_t POP_SZ = raoc.GetPopSize();

char MoveSet[3] =
    {
    'A',    // ahead
    'L',    // left
    'R'     // right
    };

char ViewSet[3] =
    {
    'F',    // sees food
    'E',    // sees empty square
    'C'     // sees a cliff
    };

static const size_t GridLen = 40;
static const size_t GridWid = 11;

static const int MasterGrid[GridLen][GridWid] =
    {
    {0,0,0,0,0,1,0,0,0,0,0},
    {0,0,0,0,0,1,0,0,0,0,0},
    {0,0,0,0,0,1,0,0,0,0,0},
    {0,0,0,0,0,0,1,0,0,0,0},
    {0,0,0,0,0,0,1,0,0,0,0},
    {0,0,0,0,0,1,0,0,0,0,0},
    {0,0,0,0,0,1,0,0,0,0,0},
    {0,0,0,0,1,0,0,0,0,0,0},
    {0,0,0,0,1,0,0,0,0,0,0},
    {0,0,0,1,0,0,0,0,0,0,0},
    {0,0,1,0,0,0,0,0,0,0,0},
    {0,0,1,0,0,0,0,0,0,0,0},
    {0,0,1,0,0,0,0,0,0,0,0},
    {0,0,0,1,0,0,0,0,0,0,0},
    {0,0,0,0,1,0,0,0,0,0,0},
    {0,0,0,0,1,0,0,0,0,0,0},
    {0,0,0,0,1,0,0,0,0,0,0},
    {0,0,0,0,0,1,0,0,0,0,0},
    {0,0,0,0,0,0,1,0,0,0,0},
    {0,0,0,0,0,0,1,0,0,0,0},
    {0,0,0,0,0,0,0,1,0,0,0},
    {0,0,0,0,0,0,0,0,1,0,0},
```

```
        {0,0,0,0,0,0,1,0,0,0,0},
        {0,0,0,0,0,0,1,0,0,0,0},
        {0,0,0,0,0,0,0,1,0,0,0,0},
        {0,0,0,0,0,0,0,1,0,0,0,0},
        {0,0,0,0,0,0,0,1,0,0,0,0},
        {0,0,0,0,0,0,0,0,1,0,0,0},
        {0,0,0,0,0,0,0,1,0,0,0,0},
        {0,0,0,0,0,0,0,1,0,0,0,0},
        {0,0,0,0,0,0,1,0,0,0,0,0},
        {0,0,0,0,0,1,0,0,0,0,0,0},
        {0,0,0,0,0,1,0,0,0,0,0,0},
        {0,0,0,0,1,0,0,0,0,0,0,0},
        {0,0,0,0,1,0,0,0,0,0,0,0},
        {0,0,0,0,0,1,0,0,0,0,0,0},
        {0,0,0,0,0,0,1,0,0,0,0,0},
        {0,0,0,0,0,0,1,0,0,0,0,0},
        {0,0,0,0,0,0,0,1,0,0,0,0},
        {0,0,0,0,0,0,1,0,0,0,0,0}
        };

static const int Offset[4][2] =
        {
        {  0, -1 },
        {  1,  0 },
        {  0,  1 },
        {  -1, 0 }
        };

static const int Lturn[4] = { 3, 0, 1, 2 };
static const int Rturn[4] = { 1, 2, 3, 0 };
```

The grid is an 11-by-40 array containing ones and zeros, with a one representing a food particle and a zero an empty space. The top of the grid is considered "north" in these experiences; each ant begins its journey facing south in the middle of the first row. Figure 8.2 shows the grid, with gray squares representing the location of food.

MasterGrid is a constant that I copy into the Grid variable for each ant's test. Other variables define tools, directions, movements, and values needed for sorting ants by fitness:

```
// variables
int Grid[GridLen][GridWid];
size_t n, i, d, j, k, inc;
```

```
int viewx, viewy, x, y;
char move, view, buf[64];
double vf, minf;

EvolvingFSM<char,ViewSz,char,MoveSz> * vm;

RouletteWheel<double> * rw;

RandDev devgen;
```

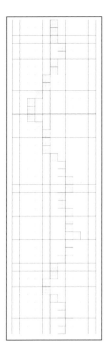

FIGURE 8.2   SEARCH GRID, WITH FOOD.

Creating the initial population requires the dynamic allocation of an
`FSM_TranData<char>` array based on the simulation's parameters.
This fits the size of the state transition data to the minimum number of
states specified by the user. I also create an `EVFSM_MuteWts` object to
define the relative chances of various mutations in offspring:

```
FSM_TranData<char> (* td)[MoveSz] =
                new FSM_TranData<char> [StatSz][MoveSz];

if (td == NULL)
    {
    buffer << "Memory allocation failed\r\n";
    return;
    }

EVFSM_MuteWts wts =
    {
    raoc.GetWeightO(),
    raoc.GetWeightT(),
    raoc.GetWeightA(),
    raoc.GetWeightD(),
    raoc.GetWeightN()
    };
```

Next, I allocate buffers to hold the population and its fitness values:

```
// allocate buffers
EvolvingFSM<char,ViewSz,char,MoveSz> ** pop
    = new EvolvingFSM<char,ViewSz,char,MoveSz> * [POP_SZ];

if (pop == NULL)
    {
    buffer << "Memory allocation failed\r\n";
    return;
    }

EvolvingFSM<char,ViewSz,char,MoveSz> ** newpop
    = new EvolvingFSM<char,ViewSz,char,MoveSz> * [POP_SZ];

if (newpop == NULL)
    {
    buffer << "Memory allocation failed\r\n";
    return;
    }

double * fit = new double [POP_SZ];

if (fit == NULL)
    {
    buffer << "Memory allocation failed\r\n";
    return;
    }
```

```
// pointers for shell sort
EvolvingFSM<char,ViewSz,char,MoveSz> * * ptrm = pop - 1;
double * ptrf = fit - 1;
```

I randomly generate the initial population. Nothing about these first ants
is planned or designed; they're simply a set of random machines from
which solutions will evolve:

```
// create an initial population of FSMs
for (j = 0; j < POP_SZ; ++j)
    {
    for (n = 0; n < StatSz; ++n)
        {
        for (i = 0; i < ViewSz; ++i)
            {
            td[n][i].NextState = size_t(devgen()
                                    * float(StatSz));

            if (i == 0)
                td[n][i].Osym = 'A';
            else
                td[n][i].Osym = MoveSet[size_t(devgen()
                                    * float(MoveSz))];
            }
        }

    pop[j] = new EvolvingFSM<char,ViewSz,char,MoveSz>
                (StatSz,&td[0][0],ViewSet,MoveSet,
                 size_t(devgen() * float(StatSz)),wts);

    if (pop[j] == NULL)
        {
        buffer << "Memory allocation failed\r\n";
        return;
        }
    }
```

The main simulation loop begins by displaying status information in the
application's program header:

```
size_t g = 0;

while (1)
```

```
{
// display progress in app header
wsprintf(buf,"Forge (loop: %u of %u)",
            g,raoc.GetTestSize());

SetWindowText(wdw,buf);
.
.
.
```

Fitness testing begins by resetting a robotic ant FSM and initializing its fitness and the Grid. For each move, the ant first scores a fitness point if it is sitting atop a piece of food; the food (if any) is then removed by replacing the one with a zero in Grid.

After the ant eats, I calculate the indexes that reference the grid cell directly in front of the ant. Note that an ant has a facing that determines its direction of travel and view. A position beyond the edge of the grid is considered to be an impassable "cliff"; otherwise, the view is either "empty" or "food." I feed this view to the ant's FSM, which returns the ant's next move of ahead, left turn, or right turn. I then change the ant's position (and possibly its heading) before handling the next move. If the ant reaches the southernmost row in the grid, it automatically stops:

```
.
.
.
minf = DBL_MAX;

// fitness testing by examining the trail
for (j = 0; j < POP_SZ; ++j)
    {
    // reset fsm
    pop[j]->Reset();
    fit[j] = 0.0;

    // initialize search grid
    memcpy(&(Grid[0][0]),
            &(MasterGrid[0][0]),
            sizeof(Grid));

    // start at beginning, in center, heading south
    y = 0;
```

```
x = 5;
d = 2;

// do the moves
for (k = 0; k < raoc.GetMaxMoves(); ++k)
    {
    // eat any food found in current location
    if (Grid[y][x])
        {
        fit[j] += 1.0;
        Grid[y][x] = 0;
        }

    // look ahead at next location
    viewx = x + Offset[d][0];
    viewy = y + Offset[d][1];

    // looking past end of grid -- done!
    if (viewy == GridLen)
        break;

    // what does the ant see?
    if ((viewx < 0)
    || (viewx >= GridWid)
    || (viewy < 0))
        {
        view = 'C'; // cliff
        }
    else
        {
        if (Grid[viewy][viewx])
            view = 'F'; // food
        else
            view = 'E'; // empty
        }

    // get move from state transition
    move = pop[j]->Transition(view);

    // apply move
    switch (move)
        {
        case 'L': // turn left
            d = Lturn[d];
            viewx = x + Offset[d][0];
            viewy = y + Offset[d][1];
            break;
```

```
            case 'R': // turn right
                d = Rturn[d];
                viewx = x + Offset[d][0];
                viewy = y + Offset[d][1];
            }

        if ((viewx >= 0)
        && (viewx < GridWid)
        && (viewy >= 0))
            {
            x = viewx;
            y = viewy;
            }
        }

    if (fit[j] < minf)
        minf = fit[j];
    }
.
.
.
```

After fitness testing, I sort the population by fitness to find and display the best ant:

```
.
.
.
// sort for selecting best
for (inc = 1; inc <= POP_SZ / 9; inc = 3 * inc + 1) ;

for ( ; inc > 0; inc /= 3)
    {
    for (i = inc + 1; i <= POP_SZ; i += inc)
        {
        vf = ptrf[i];
        vm = ptrm[i];

        j = i;

        while ((j > inc) && (ptrf[j - inc] < vf))
            {
            ptrf[j] = ptrf[j - inc];
            ptrm[j] = ptrm[j - inc];

            j -= inc;
```

```
            }
        ptrf[j] = vf;
        ptrm[j] = vm;
        }
    }

// display best machine
if (((g % raoc.GetReptFreq()) == 0)
  || (g == raoc.GetTestSize()))
    {
    buffer << "\r\nGeneration " << g
           << "\r\n---------------\r\n";

    pop[0]->DumpStructure(buffer);

    buffer << "        Fitness: " << fit[0] << "\r\n";
    }

// exit, if it's time
if (g == raoc.GetTestSize())
    break;
.
.
.
```

If fitness scaling is enabled, I perform linear normalization on the fitness values:

```
.
.
.
// fitness scaling (linear normalization)
if (raoc.GetFitScale())
    {
    fit[0] = raoc.GetFitLinBase();
    i      = 1;

    while ((i < POP_SZ)
           && (fit[i-1] <= raoc.GetFitLinDec()))
        {
        fit[i] = fit[i-1] - raoc.GetFitLinDec();
        ++i;
        }

    for (; i < POP_SZ; ++i)
```

```
                    fit[i] = raoc.GetFitLinMin();
        }
    .
    .
    .
```

Automatic elitist selection guarantees that the best ant will be represented in the new generation. Reproduction involves selecting a parent and applying mutations:

```
    .
    .
    .
// elitist selection
newpop[0] = pop[0];

// reproduce new members
rw = new RouletteWheel<double> (POP_SZ,fit);

if (rw == NULL)
    {
    buffer << "Memory allocation failed\r\n";
    return;
    }

for (j = 1; j < POP_SZ; ++j)
    {
    i = rw->GetIndex();

    newpop[j] = new EvolvingFSM<char,ViewSz,char,MoveSz>
                                    (*(pop[i]));

    if (newpop[j] == NULL)
        {
        buffer << "Memory allocation failed\r\n";
        return;
        }

    if (devgen() < raoc.GetMuteRate())
        newpop[j]->Mutate(2,raoc.GetMaxState());
    }

delete rw;
    .
    .
    .
```

The generation loop ends by copying the new generation over the old one:

```
        .
        .
        .
    // copy next generation and repeat!
    for (j = 1; j < POP_SZ; ++j)
        delete pop[j];

    memcpy(pop,newpop,
            POP_SZ *
              sizeof(EvolvingFSM<char,ViewSz,char,MoveSz> *));

    ++g;
    }
        .
        .
        .
```

At the end of the simulation, I delete buffers and restore the application's title bar:

```
        .
        .
        .
    // delete buffers
    for (j = 0; j < POP_SZ; ++j)
        delete pop[j];

    delete [] pop;
    delete [] newpop;
    delete [] fit;
    delete [] td;

    // restore window text
    SetWindowText(wdw,"Forge");
    }
```

ANALYSIS

The following output appeared after one of the most successful runs of the robotic ant simulation:

```
Evolving Robotic Ants
---------------------

        Population: 1000
        Test Size: 100
        Min State: 4
        Max State: 16
        Max Moves: 100
     Mutation Rate: 0.75

Output Symbol Wt: 10
    Transition Wt: 10
     Add State Wt: 10
  Delete State Wt: 10
New InitState Wt: 10

     Fitness Base: 100
     Fitness  Dec: 5
     Fitness  Min: 1

Generation 0
----------------
Initial state: 1
Current state: 1
 Total states: 4
s: 0, F=A>>1, E=R>>3, C=R>>2
s: 1, F=A>>3, E=L>>0, C=A>>0
s: 2, F=A>>1, E=R>>0, C=R>>2
s: 3, F=A>>3, E=L>>0, C=L>>1
        Fitness: 24


     .
     .
     .


Generation 12
----------------
Initial state: 3
Current state: 3
 Total states: 5
s: 0, F=A>>1, E=R>>3, C=R>>4
s: 1, F=A>>4, E=L>>0, C=A>>0
s: 2, F=A>>1, E=R>>0, C=R>>2
s: 3, F=A>>3, E=L>>0, C=L>>1
s: 4, F=L>>4, E=A>>2, C=R>>0
        Fitness: 35
```

The finite state machine that evolved in generation 12 is the best I've seen emerge from my tests, scoring 35 out of a possible 40 points. Figure 8.3 shows that 35-point robotic ant.

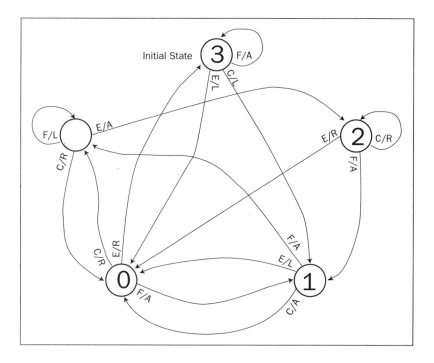

FIGURE 8.3   35-POINT ANT FSM.

The important question is: has the simulation evolved an "intelligent" ant with useful strategies, or is the finite state machine's success merely the result of luck? To find out, I manually mapped the movements of the 35-point ant, producing the grid shown in Figure 8.4.

In 94 moves, the ant finds 35 of 40 pieces of food. What struck me as most interesting was the "backtracking" algorithm evolved by this FSM ant. Upon losing contact with the food trail, the ant moves diagonally toward the edge of the grid until it encounters the edge. Once at the cliff, the ant turns around and backtracks northeast without walking over its previous path. The FSM's westward backtracking subroutine in the

FSM might have been a fortuitous accident, but remarkably, the ant also evolved a looping mechanism that travels to the east. In other simulation runs, I've seen similar behaviors appear in the most successful ants, indicating that certain patterns of movement are, indeed, being chosen through natural selection.

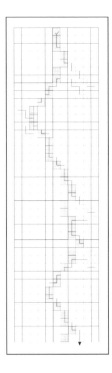

FIGURE 8.4   PATH OF THE 35-POINT ANT THROUGH THE GRID.

Certainly, this ant is not as intelligent as a real ant, and it is only evolved to follow the fixed, specific trail given in my program. Still, the ants do appear to get better at finding food in a smaller number of moves. Extending the simulation could involve penalties for reexamining squares and bonuses for reaching the end of the grid in the smallest number of moves. I've also experimented with evolving ants via a set of grids as opposed to the single grid implemented earlier. To evolve the most effective ants, it would be best to provide them with a varied environment. It might also be interesting to have ants compete, simultaneously, on a larger grid for a shared food supply.

FURTHER THOUGHTS

To accurately assess the value of evolutionary algorithms, you'll need to keep one important fact in mind: natural selection is not a deterministic process. There may be no "right" process for a given task, just as there is no "right" species to fill a specific niche. Different runs of the same program may produce substantially different results; the same process may be embodied by very different finite state machines. The 35-point ant is one of more than 438,000,000,000,000 possible five-state, three-symbol finite state machines. It's important to remember that the process invented through evolution will be an answer, *not* the answer.

You also need to keep in mind that a genetic algorithm does not proceed directly from chaos to order. It is quite possible for a population to become less fit during an optimization process. While better organisms will contribute to future generation, it may be necessary for an initial population to evolve away from a solution to rid itself of undesirable genes, before evolving an optimal solution. And a dynamic competitive environment does not have a final or absolute solution for an algorithm to find.

The primary proponent of evolutionary computation—the application of natural selection to finite state machines—is David L. Fogel of the Massachusetts Institute of Technology. Following the earlier work of Larry Fogel, David Fogel has experimented with the evolution of game-playing finite state machines and with advanced simulations of the Prisoner's Dilemma.

David Fogel argues about the lack of empirical data supporting many researchers' contentions about genetic algorithms—and, indeed, there is little comparative testing showing that, for example, various forms of crossover enhance the optimization process. On the other hand, David Fogel dismisses the application of crossover and sexual reproduction in evolutionary computing without testing if those techniques produce better performance. It should be possible, for example, to perform crossover between two finite state machines that contain the same number of states.

Critics of evolutionary computing point to its resemblance to past failed attempts at having computers program themselves. Indeed, it is not practical to produce a large-scale software program—a word processor or spreadsheet, for example— via evolutionary techniques. What evolutionary computing can do, however, is provide a mechanism for the refining and optimization of strategies within a larger program. While many researchers look for the Holy Grail of human-like intelligence, the efforts of practical programmers might be directed more toward providing intelligent behaviors on a more limited scale. People do not spring to full intelligence in a single bold leap; as children, we learn specific skills that combine to produce greater manifestations of intelligence. I think that is an appropriate metaphor for the implementation of intelligent software.

It is important to recognize that genetic algorithms and evolutionary computing solve different types of problems. Genetic algorithms manipulate and evolve information, looking for the information that best solves a specific problem. Evolutionary computing focuses on the emergence of processes. Each tool has its uses, advantages, and disadvantages, and you must recognize these if you're going to select the correct technique for your applications.

In seeking the answer to a problem, a genetic algorithm may become fixated on a specific near-optimal answer. Known as the *plateau* or *mesa* phenomenon, this problem occurs when the population has become very homogeneous without having found an optimal solution; for example, in optimizing a numerical function, a population may find itself trapped at a minor peak, unable to evolve toward another peak because the population lacks variety in its alleles.

To keep your genetic algorithms robust, you need to ensure that your populations are diverse. I've found a combination of elitist selection, fitness scaling, and strong mutation to be very effective in eliminating the plateau phenomenon. Strong mutation produces variety in new populations; elitist selection and fitness scaling prevent mutation from destroying useful alleles.

You will need to use crossover and mutation judiciously, as each has a different purpose. In a homogeneous population, crossover is meaningless because it can only exchange identical alleles. Crossover is thus most effective in the early running of a genetic algorithm, where it can select valuable alleles from a diverse population of chromosomes.

The effectiveness of mutation depends on the size of the chromosomes, the rate, and the algorithm used. Mutating a single bit in a 32-bit chromosome causes less change than does a bit mutation in an 8-bit chromosome. To counter the size/rate problem, many researchers use an algorithm whereby the mutation rate reflects the chance that any given bit will flip. Mutation by bit, however, is considerably slower than mutation by chromosomes.

Some researchers have suggested the implementation of a discredited biological concept known as *Lamarckian evolution.* Lamarck, the inventor of the modern binomial species naming system, believed that acquired characteristics could be inherited by offspring. In other words, if you cut the tails off dogs and let them breed, you'll have puppies born without tails. Simple observation shows that Lamarckian evolution does not occur in nature, but perhaps we can use it in our programs so that an evolving program structure passes along acquired capabilities to its offspring. Humanity performs its own form of Lamarckian evolution through documentation and teaching; we pass knowledge—a vital part of what makes us human—to subsequent generations via external mechanisms such as books and culture.

At the Cognitive Science Research Group in New Jersey, David Ackley and Michael Littman have experimented with Lamarckian evolution. In applying Lamarckian evolution to a difficult optimization problem, Ackley and Littman noted a dramatic increase in algorithm performance and accuracy compared to a purely Darwinian implementation. This shows that an artificial environment is amenable to the use of techniques that do not necessarily exist in nature. Elitist selection, for example, is a blatant circumvention of natural processes; after all, life offers only probabilities—not guarantees—about survival.

The performance of a genetic algorithm is directly tied to the efficacy of its fitness function. A good fitness function will clearly and significantly discern between "good" and "bad" chromosomes. If two different chromosomes have the same fitness value, the algorithm has no way of choosing which is better or worse for reproduction. Fitness scaling can solve some of this problem by adjusting fitness values to enhance differences between chromosomes, but remember that "bad" chromosomes may contain useful alleles that do not appear in "good" chromosomes. Again, your design depends on balancing an increase in the reproductive chances of "good" chromosomes with preventing the loss of important characteristics held in less-fit chromosomes.

Genetic algorithms are not a panacea, nor do they lack an inherent set of caveats and problems. Like any tool, they must be used judiciously, with their limitations kept in mind.

EVOLUTIONARY APPLICATIONS

Most of the commercial research in genetic algorithms is proprietary and copyrighted by corporate users. Reports in conference proceedings often lack sufficient detail to understand exactly how a genetic algorithm was used for a given problem. Research by defense contractors may be reported in the leading journals, but the information provided is often vague and incomplete. As with most science today, economic competition and corporate ownership of research are severely restricting the productive sharing of ideas.

Despite the legal and practical limitations, I've examined the available literature to give you a sampling of current applications involving genetic algorithms and evolutionary computing. The areas in which genetic algorithms have been found to be useful include: image interpretation and enhancement, expert systems, consumer analysis, game playing, pipeline control, and event prediction. What follows is an introduction to several other areas of current research.

GENETIC PROGRAMMING

John R. Koza of MIT introduced the concept of genetic programming, which involves the evolution of computer programs usually written in

LISP. A LISP program consists of a set of functions applied to lists of parameters, and a multibranch tree structure can represent any LISP program. In Koza's genetic programming, a population of LISP programs undergoes natural selection, with crossover (by exchanging tree branches) and mutation during reproduction.

Like evolutionary computing, genetic programming evolves algorithms fitted to a given problem environment. Some researchers have implemented genetic programming in languages other than LISP by building and evolving instruction trees. The data structures involved are similar to those used in parsing mathematical functions or programming language text.

An interesting concept from genetic programming may also be applicable to genetic algorithms and evolutionary computation. In some cases, researchers have prebred genetic programs in an artificial environment before exposing the results to real-world problems. This creates a partially optimized population, eliminating the slow early stages of natural selection on a random population.

Neural Network Synthesis

Perhaps the most intriguing use of artificial natural selection is in the generation and training of artificial neural networks. The construction of optimal neural networks is problematic, at best. Simply put, it is very difficult for a human programmer to comprehend a complex neural network. And what a programmer cannot understand, he or she cannot optimize; organizing the structure of a neural network is often accomplished by trial and error, using an intuitive understanding of the knowledge being represented.

Several computer scientists are now exploring the use of genetic algorithms in training and designing neural networks. I was most intrigued by a system named NeuroGENESYS, developed by Steven Harp and Tariq Samad of Honeywell Corporation. NeuroGENESYS optimizes chromosomes representing the structure of a neural network; fitness is determined by training each network architecture and testing its speed, complexity, and accuracy.

Evolution involved the combination of parent networks and random mutation. Harp and Samad admit surprise that NeuroGENESYS found unexpected solutions to various neural network problems. Evolving networks was shown to produce smaller and faster networks that were found using a purely random search, and such solutions were usually discovered in fewer than 50 generations.

Robotics and Computer Science

An appropriate application for genetic algorithms is in the generation of robotic processes. For the most part, robotic implementations of genetic algorithms involve evolution in an artificial environment, such as a simulated maze or arena. The focus has been on evolving algorithms for robot vision and movement, creating processes whereby artificial organisms can interact in useful ways with their environment. Fitness is generally determined by the ability of a robot to solve a given task, such as finding a given object or locating the exit from a maze.

Considerable research is now being focused on so-called *intelligent agents*, trainable software applications that respond to a user's needs based on past experience. The most interesting application of this concept is in information mining, wherein individual agents compete in locating information based on past experience with a user. The agents most effective in finding useful data will produce offspring better suited to the search history. The digital species can then adapt to changes in the user's needs, keeping important aspects of searching ("Scott doesn't like tabloid stories") while evolving to fit new tasks ("Scott now wants to see articles from foreign sources").

One of the greatest problems with today's software is its complexity. The reason so many large commercial applications have problems is the sheer enormity of the debugging task. When I first began programming in the mid-1970s, a "large" program was a few tens of thousands of lines of code; today, mainstream commercial applications have millions of lines of code. Genetic algorithms offer the opportunity to create smaller programs that generate larger applications based on experience.

ONWARD

With this book, I hope I provided you with a tool for experimenting with natural selection in software. My goal was to provide a catalyst for learning about genetic algorithms and evolutionary computing. Work with the code and experiment; look at your own applications to see where these techniques might prove useful. It's time to take evolving software out of the academic world and into practical applications, and I hope you'll be one of the people to facilitate that process.

Thanks for reading, and good luck.

APPENDIX

THE FORGE PROGRAM

This appendix contains the code for the main program used to demostrate the various algorithms and examples discussed in the book. The program is named FORGE for *program FOR Genetic algorithm Experimentation*. The program will run under Windows 3.1, Windows NT 3.5, or under Windows 95.

LISTING A.1   FORGE.CPP THE MAIN PROGRAM.

```
//----------------------------------------------------------------
//   program FOR Genetic algorithm Experimentation (FORGE)
//----------------------------------------------------------------
//
//       forge.cpp      v1.00
//
//       Main application module
//
//----------------------------------------------------------------
//   Copyright 1995 by Scott Robert Ladd. All rights reserved.
//----------------------------------------------------------------

#include "windows.h"   // Windows definitions
#include "limits.h"    // limits of types
#include "stdio.h"     // standard file I/O functions
#include "stdlib.h"    // misc. library functions
#include "string.h"    // C-style string functions
#include "strstrea.h"  // strstream definitions
#include "iomanip.h"   // stream manipulators
#include "diagwin.h"   // diagnostic display class for windows
#include "fontutil.h"  // font utilities and classes
#include "forgeres.h"  // resource constants
#include "bool.h"      // boolean type

//-----------------
// type definitions
//-----------------

enum ErrorType
    {
    ET_CRASH,
    ET_ERROR,
    ET_WARNING
    };

//----------------------
// global data
//----------------------

// constants
const char * ForgeClassName = "ForgeWindowClass";
```

```
const char * AppName          = "Forge";
const char * AppVersion       = "v1.01a";
const LPCSTR MenuForge         = MAKEINTRESOURCE(MENU_FORGE);
const LPCSTR IconForge         = MAKEINTRESOURCE(ICON_FORGE);
const LPCSTR NameDlgAbout      = MAKEINTRESOURCE(DLG_ABOUT);
const int    DisplayID         = 1;
const DWORD  DisplayStyle      = WS_CHILD |
                                 WS_VSCROLL |
                                 WS_HSCROLL |
                                 ES_MULTILINE |
                                 ES_READONLY |
                                 ES_LEFT |
                                 ES_AUTOHSCROLL |
                                 ES_AUTOVSCROLL;

// variables
HANDLE      ThisInstance = NULL;
HWND        Display  = NULL;
HWND        MainWdw   = NULL;
HACCEL      MainAccel = NULL;
DiagOutWin Diag(AppName);
Font        StdFont("Courier New",10,FALSE,FALSE);

//------------------------------
// external function prototypes
//------------------------------

int PASCAL WinMain
    (
    HANDLE instance,
    HANDLE prevInstance,
    LPSTR  commandLine,
    int    commandShow
    );

static BOOL InitApplication
    (
    HANDLE instance
    );

static BOOL InitInstance
    (
    HANDLE instance,
    int    commandShow
```

```
    );

LRESULT CALLBACK MainWindow
    (
    HWND  thisWindow,
    UINT  message,
    WPARAM wordParam,
    LPARAM longParam
    );

void RunTest
    (
    WPARAM testid
    );

void TestRoulette
    (
    strstream & buffer
    );

void TestBool
    (
    strstream & buffer
    );

void TestRandDev
    (
    strstream & buffer
    );

void TestMutableFloat
    (
    strstream & buffer
    );

void TestMutableDouble
    (
    strstream & buffer
    );

void TestMath
    (
    strstream & buffer
```

```
    );

void TestSorting
    (
    strstream & buffer
    );

void TestFSM
    (
    strstream & buffer
    );

void TestBlackbox
    (
    HINSTANCE inst,
    HWND      wdw,
    strstream & buffer
    );

void TestBBAnalysis
    (
    HINSTANCE inst,
    HWND      wdw,
    strstream & buffer
    );

void TestPeakSearch
    (
    HINSTANCE inst,
    HWND      wdw,
    strstream & buffer
    );

void TestDilemma
    (
    HINSTANCE inst,
    HWND      wdw,
    strstream & buffer
    );

void TestArtist
    (
    HINSTANCE inst,
    HWND      wdw,
```

```
    strstream & buffer
    );

void TestEvolvingMachines
    (
    HINSTANCE inst,
    HWND      wdw,
    strstream & buffer
    );

void TestRoboticAnts
    (
    HINSTANCE inst,
    HWND      wdw,
    strstream & buffer
    );

void CopyBuffer
    (
    bool allFlag
    );

void ErrorMessage
    (
    const char * msg,
    ErrorType etype = ET_WARNING
    );

BOOL CALLBACK DlgAbout
    (
    HWND  dlg,
    WORD  message,
    WORD  wParam,
    DWORD lParam
    );

//-------------------------------------------
// WinMain -- program start and message loop
//-------------------------------------------

#ifdef __BORLANDC__
    #pragma argsused
#endif
```

```
int PASCAL WinMain
    (
    HANDLE instance,
    HANDLE prevInstance,
    LPSTR  commandLine,
    int    commandShow
    )
    {
    MSG msg;

    if (prevInstance)
        {
        ErrorMessage("Forge is already running!", ET_WARNING);
        return 0;
        }

    if (!InitApplication(instance))
        return 0;

    if (!InitInstance(instance, commandShow))
        return 0;

    try {
        while (GetMessage(&msg, NULL, NULL, NULL))
            {
            if (TranslateAccelerator(MainWdw,MainAccel,&msg) ==
                0)
                {
                TranslateMessage(&msg);
                DispatchMessage(&msg);
                }
            }
        }
    catch (ExceptionBase & ex)
        {
        ex.Explain(Diag);
        }

    return msg.wParam;
    }

//-------------------------
// initialize an application
//-------------------------
```

```
static BOOL InitApplication
    (
    HANDLE instance
    )
    {
    WNDCLASS wc;

    wc.style          = 0;
    wc.lpfnWndProc    = MainWindow;
    wc.cbClsExtra     = 0;
    wc.cbWndExtra     = 0;
    wc.hInstance      = instance;
    wc.hIcon          = LoadIcon(instance,IconForge);
    wc.hCursor        = LoadCursor(NULL, IDC_ARROW);
    wc.hbrBackground  = GetStockObject(BLACK_BRUSH);
    wc.lpszMenuName   = MenuForge;
    wc.lpszClassName  = ForgeClassName;

    return RegisterClass(&wc);
    }

//-----------------------
// initialize an instance
//-----------------------

static BOOL InitInstance
    (
    HANDLE instance,
    int commandShow
    )
    {
    HWND hWnd;

    // save the instance handle
    ThisInstance = instance;

    // create a window
    hWnd = CreateWindow(ForgeClassName, AppName,
                        WS_OVERLAPPEDWINDOW,
                        CW_USEDEFAULT, CW_USEDEFAULT,
                        CW_USEDEFAULT, CW_USEDEFAULT,
                        NULL, NULL, instance, 0);

    if (!hWnd)
```

```
        {
        ErrorMessage("Cannot create main window", ET_WARNING);
        return FALSE;
        }

    ShowWindow(hWnd, commandShow);
    UpdateWindow(hWnd);

    MainWdw = hWnd;

    // get size of client area
    RECT area;

    GetClientRect(hWnd,&area);

    // create edit control
    Display = CreateWindow("EDIT","",DisplayStyle,
                            0, 0, area.right, area.bottom,
                            hWnd, (HMENU)DisplayID,instance,0);

    if (!Display)
        {
        ErrorMessage("Cannot create output window", ET_WARNING);
        return FALSE;
        }

    ShowWindow(Display, SW_SHOW);
    UpdateWindow(Display);

    // set edit window font
    SendMessage(Display,WM_SETFONT,(WPARAM)StdFont.GetFont(),OL);

    // load accelarator table
    MainAccel = LoadAccelerators(instance,MenuForge);

    if (MainAccel == NULL)
        return FALSE;

    return TRUE;
    }

//---------------------
// Main window function
//---------------------
```

```
LRESULT CALLBACK MainWindow
    (
    HWND  thisWindow,
    UINT  message,
    WPARAM wordParam,
    LPARAM longParam
    )
    {
#ifndef _WIN32
DLGPROC thunk;
#endif

    switch (message)
        {
        case WM_COMMAND:
            switch (wordParam)
                {
                case IDM_TEST_ROULETTE:
                case IDM_TEST_BOOL:
                case IDM_TEST_RANDDEV:
                case IDM_TEST_MFLOAT:
                case IDM_TEST_MDOUBLE:
                case IDM_TEST_MATH:
                case IDM_TEST_SORTS:
                case IDM_TEST_FSM:
                case IDM_OPT_BLACKBOX:
                case IDM_OPT_BBOX_ANALYSIS:
                case IDM_OPT_PEAK_SEARCH:
                case IDM_OPT_PDILEMMA:
                case IDM_OPT_TRAVART:
                case IDM_EVOL_MACHINES:
                case IDM_ROBOTIC_ANTS:
                    RunTest(wordParam);
                    break;

                case IDM_COPY:
                    // copy edit window selection to clipboard
                    CopyBuffer(false);
                    break;

                case IDM_COPYALL:
                    // copy edit window to clipboard
                    CopyBuffer(true);
                    break;
```

```
    case IDM_ABOUT:
        #ifdef _WIN32
        DialogBox(ThisInstance,NameDlgAbout,
                thisWindow,FARPROC(DlgAbout));
        #else
        thunk = MakeProcInstance(FARPROC(DlgAbout),
                                ThisInstance);

        DialogBox(ThisInstance,NameDlgAbout,
                thisWindow,thunk);

        FreeProcInstance(thunk);
        #endif
        break;

    case IDM_EXIT:
        // exit program
        DestroyWindow(thisWindow);
        break;

    default:
        return DefWindowProc(thisWindow, message,
                                wordParam, longParam);
    }

    break;

case WM_SETFOCUS:
    // set focus to edit control
    SetFocus(Display);
    break;

case WM_SIZE:
    // resize edit control
    MoveWindow(Display,0,0,
            LOWORD(longParam),
            HIWORD(longParam),
            TRUE);
    break;

case WM_DESTROY:
    PostQuitMessage(0);
    break;
```

```
        default:
            return DefWindowProc(thisWindow, message,
                                  wordParam, longParam);
        }

    return 0L;
    }

//-----------------------------------------
// framework for running test procedures
//-----------------------------------------

void RunTest
    (
    WPARAM testid
    )
    {
#if defined(__WIN32__) || defined(_WIN32)
    const size_t strbufsz = 100000;
#else
    const size_t strbufsz = 32000;
#endif

    char * strbuf = new char [strbufsz];

    if (strbuf == NULL)
        return;

    strstream buffer(strbuf,strbufsz,ios::out);

    HCURSOR cursor = SetCursor(LoadCursor(NULL,IDC_WAIT));

    try
        {
        switch (testid)
            {
            case IDM_TEST_ROULETTE:
                TestRoulette(buffer);
                break;

            case IDM_TEST_BOOL:
                TestBool(buffer);
                break;
```

```
case IDM_TEST_RANDDEV:
    TestRandDev(buffer);
    break;

case IDM_TEST_MFLOAT:
    TestMutableFloat(buffer);
    break;

case IDM_TEST_MDOUBLE:
    TestMutableDouble(buffer);
    break;

case IDM_TEST_MATH:
    TestMath(buffer);
    break;

case IDM_TEST_SORTS:
    TestSorting(buffer);
    break;

case IDM_TEST_FSM:
    TestFSM(buffer);
    break;

case IDM_OPT_BLACKBOX:
    TestBlackbox(ThisInstance,MainWdw,buffer);
    break;

case IDM_OPT_BBOX_ANALYSIS:
    TestBBAnalysis(ThisInstance,MainWdw,buffer);
    break;

case IDM_OPT_PEAK_SEARCH:
    TestPeakSearch(ThisInstance,MainWdw,buffer);
    break;

case IDM_OPT_PDILEMMA:
    TestDilemma(ThisInstance,MainWdw,buffer);
    break;

case IDM_OPT_TRAVART:
    TestArtist(ThisInstance,MainWdw,buffer);
    break;
```

```
                case IDM_EVOL_MACHINES:
                    TestEvolvingMachines(ThisInstance,MainWdw,buffer);
                    break;

                case IDM_ROBOTIC_ANTS:
                    TestRoboticAnts(ThisInstance,MainWdw,buffer);
                    break;

                default:
                    buffer << "unknown test selection!";
                }
            }
        catch (ExceptionBase & ex)
            {
            ex.Explain(Diag);
            buffer << "\r\nPROGRAM ERROR! BUFFER MAY BE INCOMPLETE!";
            }

        // terminate buffer
        buffer << ends;

        // display buffer in edit control
        #if defined(__WIN32__) || defined(_WIN32)

SendMessage(Display,WM_SETTEXT,0,(LPARAM)(LPSTR)buffer.str());
        #else
        SendMessage(Display,EM_SETSEL,0,MAKELONG(0,-1));

SendMessage(Display,EM_REPLACESEL,0,(LPARAM)(LPSTR)buffer.str());
        #endif
        SendMessage(Display,EM_SETSEL,0,0);

        // restore cursor and set focus to edit window
        SetCursor(cursor);
        SetFocus(Display);

        // delete stream buffer
        delete [] strbuf;
        }


//-----------------------------
// Copy buffer to the clipboard
//-----------------------------
```

```
void CopyBuffer
    (
    bool allFlag
    )
    {
#ifdef __WIN32__
    if (allFlag)
        SendMessage(Display,EM_SETSEL,0,-1L);
#else
    if (allFlag)
        SendMessage(Display,EM_SETSEL,0,MAKELONG(0,-1));
#endif

    SendMessage(Display,WM_COPY,0,0L);
    SendMessage(Display,EM_SETSEL,0,0L);
    }

//---------------------------------------------
// Display an error message of given severity
//---------------------------------------------

void ErrorMessage
    (
    const char * msg,
    ErrorType etype
    )
    {
    UINT style;
    UINT sound;
    int response;
    char text[128];

    // copy message to output buffer
    strcpy(text,msg);

    // set values specific to error severity
    switch (etype)
        {
        case ET_CRASH:
            sound = MB_ICONSTOP;
            style = MB_OK;
            strcat(text," PROGRAM WILL TERMINATE!");
            break;
        case ET_ERROR:
```

```
            sound = MB_ICONEXCLAMATION;
            style = MB_YESNO;
            strcat(text,"Click 'Yes' to terminate program, "
                        "or 'No' to continue");
            break;
        case ET_WARNING:
            sound = MB_ICONASTERISK;
            style = MB_OK;
        }

    // match icon to sound
    style |= sound;

    // sound off and display message
    MessageBeep(sound);
    response = MessageBox(NULL,text,AppName,style);

    // check for termination
    switch (etype)
        {
        case ET_ERROR:
            if (response == IDNO)
                break;
        case ET_CRASH:
            PostQuitMessage(1); // boom-boom
            // program should never reach this point!
        }
    }

//-------------------
// About... dialog box
//-------------------

#ifdef __BORLANDC__
#pragma argsused
#endif

BOOL CALLBACK DlgAbout
    (
    HWND  dlg,
    WORD  message,
    WORD  wParam,
    DWORD lParam
    )
```

```
    {
    switch (message)
        {
        case WM_INITDIALOG:
            SetDlgItemText(dlg,IDD_ABOUT_VERSION,AppVersion);
            break;

        case WM_COMMAND:
            EndDialog(dlg, TRUE);
            return TRUE;
        }

    return FALSE;
    }
```

LISTING A.2   FORGE.RC RESOURCE SCRIPT FOR THE FORGE APPLICATION.

```
#ifdef _MSC_VER
#include "winres.h"
#endif

#include "forgeres.h"

/////////////////////////////////////////////////////////////////
// Icon

ICON_FORGE                  ICON    DISCARDABLE    "forge.ico"

/////////////////////////////////////////////////////////////////
// Menu

MENU_FORGE MENU DISCARDABLE
BEGIN
    POPUP "&Program"
    BEGIN
        POPUP "&Tool Tests"
        BEGIN
            MENUITEM "&Roulette Wheel",              IDM_TEST_
                                                     ROULETTE
            MENUITEM "Type ""&bool""",               IDM_TEST_BOOL
            MENUITEM "&Uniform Deviates (Random #'s)",
                        IDM_TEST_RANDDEV
            MENUITEM "Mutable &Float",               IDM_TEST_MFLOAT
```

```
        MENUITEM "Mutable &Double",          IDM_TEST_MDOUBLE
        MENUITEM "&C++ Math Functions",      IDM_TEST_MATH
        MENUITEM "&Sorting",                 IDM_TEST_SORTS
        MENUITEM "Finite State &Machines",   IDM_TEST_FSM
    END
    POPUP "&Genetic Algorithms"
    BEGIN
        MENUITEM "&Black Box",               IDM_OPT_BLACKBOX
        MENUITEM "Black Box (&Analysis)",    IDM_OPT_BBOX_
                                             ANALYSIS

        MENUITEM "&Peak Search",             IDM_OPT_PEAK_
                                             SEARCH

        MENUITEM "Prisoner's &Dilemma",      IDM_OPT_PDILEMMA
        MENUITEM "&Travelling Artist",       IDM_OPT_TRAVART
    END
    POPUP "&Evolutionary Programming"
    BEGIN
        MENUITEM "Finite State &Machines",   IDM_EVOL_
                                             MACHINES

        MENUITEM "&Robotic Ants",            IDM_ROBOTIC_ANTS
    END
    MENUITEM SEPARATOR
    MENUITEM "Cop&y",                        IDM_COPY
    MENUITEM "Copy &All",                    IDM_COPYALL
    MENUITEM SEPARATOR
    MENUITEM "About",                        IDM_ABOUT
    MENUITEM SEPARATOR
    MENUITEM "E&xit",                        IDM_EXIT
  END
END


/////////////////////////////////////////////////////////////////
// Accelerator

MENU_FORGE ACCELERATORS MOVEABLE PURE
BEGIN
    VK_INSERT,      IDM_COPY,                VIRTKEY, CONTROL
END


/////////////////////////////////////////////////////////////////
// Dialog
```

```
DLG_GAOPTCFG DIALOG DISCARDABLE  15, 20, 420, 224
STYLE DS_MODALFRAME | S_POPUP | WS_VISIBLE | WS_CAPTION |
                    WS_SYSMENU
CAPTION "GA Peak Search Configuration"
FONT 8, "MS Sans Serif"
BEGIN
    RTEXT           "Population:",-1,4,12,44,8
    EDITTEXT        IDD_GAOPTCFG_POP,52,8,40,12,ES_AUTOHSCROLL
    RTEXT           "Generations:",-1,0,28,48,8
    EDITTEXT        IDD_GAOPTCFG_GEN,52,24,40,12,ES_AUTOHSCROLL
    RTEXT           "Report Freq:",-1,96,12,60,8
    EDITTEXT        IDD_GAOPTCFG_FREQ,160,8,40,12,ES_AUTOHSCROLL
    RTEXT           "Significant Digits:",-1,96,28,60,8
    EDITTEXT        IDD_GAOPTCFG_SIGDIG,160,24,40,12,ES_
                    AUTOHSCROLL
    GROUPBOX        "Value Ranges",-1,8,44,192,48
    RTEXT           "X Min:",-1,12,60,28,8
    EDITTEXT        IDD_GAOPTCFG_XMIN,44,56,56,12,ES_AUTOHSCROLL
    RTEXT           "X Max:",-1,104,60,28,8
    EDITTEXT        IDD_GAOPTCFG_XMAX,136,56,56,12,ES_AUTOHSCROLL
    RTEXT           "Y Min:",-1,12,77,28,8
    EDITTEXT        IDD_GAOPTCFG_YMIN,44,72,56,12,ES_AUTOHSCROLL
    RTEXT           "Y Max:",-1,104,76,28,8
    EDITTEXT        IDD_GAOPTCFG_YMAX,136,72,56,12,ES_AUTOHSCROLL
    RTEXT           "Mutation Rate:",-1,56,104,52,8
    EDITTEXT        IDD_GAOPTCFG_MPROB,112,100,28,12,ES_
                    AUTOHSCROLL
    LTEXT           "%",-1,144,104,12,8
    GROUPBOX        "Mutation Weights",112,8,116,192,36
    RTEXT           "Sign:",-1,12,136,24,8
    EDITTEXT        IDD_GAOPTCFG_MUTES,40,132,28,12,ES_
                    AUTOHSCROLL
    RTEXT           "Expon:",-1,72,136,28,8
    EDITTEXT        IDD_GAOPTCFG_MUTEE,104,132,28,12,ES_
                    AUTOHSCROLL
    RTEXT           "Mant:",-1,136,136,24,8
    EDITTEXT        IDD_GAOPTCFG_MUTEM,164,132,28,12,ES_
                    AUTOHSCROLL
    GROUPBOX        "Mutation Flags",109,8,156,192,28
    CONTROL         "Mutate X",IDD_GAOPTCFG_MUTEX,"Button",
                    BS_AUTOCHECKBOX |
                    WS_TABSTOP,16,168,52,12
    CONTROL         "Mutate Y",IDD_GAOPTCFG_MUTEY,"Button",
                    BS_AUTOCHECKBOX |
```

```
                        WS_TABSTOP,72,168,48,12
    CONTROL             "Looped Mutation",IDD_GAOPTCFG_MLOOP,
                        "Button",
                        BS_AUTOCHECKBOX | WS_TABSTOP,124,168,72,12
    RTEXT               "Crossover Chance:",-1,236,12,68,8
    EDITTEXT            IDD_GAOPTCFG_CPROB,308,8,28,12,ES_AUTOHSCROLL
    LTEXT               "%",-1,340,12,12,8
    GROUPBOX            "Crossover Techniques",108,216,24,156,28
    CONTROL             "X Value",IDD_GAOPTCFG_CROSSX,"Button",
                        BS_AUTOCHECKBOX |
                        WS_TABSTOP,224,36,44,12
    CONTROL             "Y Value",IDD_GAOPTCFG_CROSSY,"Button",
                        BS_AUTOCHECKBOX |
                        WS_TABSTOP,272,36,44,12
    CONTROL             "Between",IDD_GAOPTCFG_CROSSB,"Button",
                        BS_AUTOCHECKBOX |
                        WS_TABSTOP,320,36,48,12
    CONTROL             "Fitness Scaling",IDD_GAOPTCFG_FSCALE,
                        "Button",
                        BS_AUTOCHECKBOX | WS_TABSTOP,216,64,68,12
    CONTROL             "Elitist Selection",IDD_GAOPTCFG_ELITE,
                        "Button",
                        BS_AUTOCHECKBOX | WS_TABSTOP,304,64,68,12
    GROUPBOX            "Fitness Scaling Technique",-1,216,80,196,28
    CONTROL             "Windowing",IDD_GAOPTCFG_FTWDW,"Button",
                        BS_AUTORADIOBUTTON | WS_GROUP | WS_TAB-
                                         STOP,224,92,52,12
    CONTROL             "Exponential",IDD_GAOPTCFG_FTEXP,"Button",
                        BS_AUTORADIOBUTTON | WS_TABSTOP,280,92,52,12
    CONTROL             "Linear Normalize",IDD_GAOPTCFG_FTLIN,
                        "Button",
                        BS_AUTORADIOBUTTON | WS_TABSTOP,336,92,72,12
    GROUPBOX            "Linear Normalization Parameters",
                        111,216,112,196,32
    RTEXT               "Base:",-1,220,128,20,8
    EDITTEXT            IDD_GAOPTCFG_LNBASE,244,124,32,12,ES_
                        AUTOHSCROLL
    RTEXT               "Decrement:",-1,280,128,40,8
    EDITTEXT            IDD_GAOPTCFG_LNDEC,324,124,28,12,ES_
                        AUTOHSCROLL
    RTEXT               "Min:",-1,356,128,16,8
    EDITTEXT            IDD_GAOPTCFG_LNMIN,376,124,28,12,ES_
                        AUTOHSCROLL
    GROUPBOX            "Equation",-1,216,152,196,64
```

```
    CTEXT               "p = pi (3.14...)",-1,356,180,52,12,WS_BORDER
    CONTROL             "x\262+2y\262-0.3cos(3px)-0.4cos(4py)+0.7",
                        IDD_GAOPTCFG_EQF6,"Button",BS_AUTORADIOBUTTON
                        | WS_GROUP |
                        WS_TABSTOP,224,164,132,12
    CONTROL             "x\262+2y\262-0.3[cos(3px)cos(4py)]+0.3",
                        IDD_GAOPTCFG_EQF7,"Button",BS_AUTORADIOBUTTON
                        |
                        WS_TABSTOP,224,176,128,12
    CONTROL             "x\262+2y\262-0.3[cos(3px)+cos(4py)]+0.3",
                        IDD_GAOPTCFG_EQF8,"Button",BS_AUTORADIOBUTTON |
                        WS_TABSTOP,224,188,128,12
    CONTROL             "1/((x+0.5)\262+2(y-0.5)\262-0.3cos(3px)-
                        0.4cos(4py)+0.8)",
                        IDD_GAOPTCFG_EQCUST,"Button",BS_AUTORADIO-
                        BUTTON |
                        WS_TABSTOP,224,200,180,12
    DEFPUSHBUTTON       "OK",IDOK,24,196,52,20
    PUSHBUTTON          "Cancel",IDCANCEL,128,196,52,20
END

DLG_BLACKBOX DIALOG DISCARDABLE  17, 30, 216, 88
STYLE DS_MODALFRAME | WS_POPUP | WS_VISIBLE | WS_CAPTION |
                    WS_SYSMENU
CAPTION "Blackbox Configuration"
FONT 8, "MS Sans Serif"
BEGIN
    RTEXT               "Population:",-1,4,12,48,8
    EDITTEXT            IDD_BBOX_POP,56,8,44,12
    RTEXT               "Generations:",-1,4,28,48,8
    EDITTEXT            IDD_BBOX_GEN,56,24,44,12
    CONTROL             "Crossover",IDD_BBOX_CROSS,"Button",
                        BS_AUTOCHECKBOX |
                        WS_TABSTOP,116,8,48,12
    EDITTEXT            IDD_BBOX_CPROB,164,8,32,12
    LTEXT               "%",-1,200,12,8,8
    CONTROL             "Mutation",IDD_BBOX_MUTE,"Button",
                        BS_AUTOCHECKBOX |
                        WS_TABSTOP,116,24,48,12
    EDITTEXT            IDD_BBOX_MPROB,164,24,32,12
    LTEXT               "%",-1,200,28,8,8
    CONTROL             "Elitist
                         Selection",IDD_BBOX_ELITISM,"Button",
                        BS_AUTOCHECKBOX | WS_TABSTOP,124,48,68,12
```

```
    CONTROL         "Fitness Scaling",IDD_BBOX_FSCALE,"Button",
                    BS_AUTOCHECKBOX | WS_TABSTOP,124,64,68,12
    DEFPUSHBUTTON   "OK",IDOK,28,44,56,16
    PUSHBUTTON      "Cancel",IDCANCEL,28,64,56,16
END

DLG_PDOPTCFG DIALOG DISCARDABLE  16, 28, 344, 145
STYLE DS_MODALFRAME | WS_POPUP | WS_VISIBLE | WS_CAPTION |
                    WS_SYSMENU
CAPTION "Prisoner's Dilemma Configuration"
FONT 8, "MS Sans Serif"
BEGIN
    RTEXT           "Population:",-1,4,12,60,8
    EDITTEXT        IDD_PDOPTCFG_POP,68,8,32,12,ES_AUTOHSCROLL
    RTEXT           "Generations:",-1,4,28,60,8
    EDITTEXT        IDD_PDOPTCFG_GEN,68,24,32,12,ES_AUTOHSCROLL
    RTEXT           "Report Freq:",-1,4,44,60,8
    EDITTEXT        IDD_PDOPTCFG_FREQ,68,40,32,12,ES_AUTOHSCROLL
    RTEXT           "Start Level (1-3):",-1,4,60,60,8
    EDITTEXT        IDD_PDOPTCFG_START,68,56,32,12,ES_AUTOHSCROLL
    RTEXT           "Max Level (2-4):",-1,4,76,60,8
    EDITTEXT        IDD_PDOPTCFG_MAXLVL,68,72,32,12,
                    ES_AUTOHSCROLL
    CONTROL         "Crossover",IDD_PDOPTCFG_CROSS,"Button",
                    BS_AUTOCHECKBOX |
                    WS_TABSTOP,112,8,48,12
    EDITTEXT        IDD_PDOPTCFG_CRATE,164,8,32,12,ES_AUTOHSCROLL
    LTEXT           "%",-1,200,12,12,8
    CONTROL         "Mutation",IDD_PDOPTCFG_MUTE,"Button",
                    BS_AUTOCHECKBOX |
                    WS_TABSTOP,112,24,48,12
    EDITTEXT        IDD_PDOPTCFG_MRATE,164,24,32,12,
                    ES_AUTOHSCROLL
    LTEXT           "%",-1,200,28,12,8
    CONTROL         "Doubling",IDD_PDOPTCFG_DBLING,"Button",
                    BS_AUTOCHECKBOX |
                    WS_TABSTOP,112,40,48,12
    EDITTEXT        IDD_PDOPTCFG_DRATE,164,40,32,12,
                    ES_AUTOHSCROLL
    LTEXT           "%",-1,200,44,12,8
    CONTROL         "Averaging",IDD_PDOPTCFG_AVG,"Button",
                    BS_AUTOCHECKBOX |
                    WS_TABSTOP,112,56,48,12
    CONTROL         "Fair Start",IDD_PDOPTCFG_FAIR,
```

```
"Button",BS_AUTOCHECKBOX |
                        WS_TABSTOP,164,56,48,12
        CONTROL         "Random 1st
                         Move",IDD_PDOPTCFG_RAND1,"Button",
                        BS_AUTOCHECKBOX | WS_TABSTOP,112,72,76,12
        GROUPBOX        "Payoffs",-1,216,4,120,80
        CTEXT           "P\nl\na\ny\ne\nr",-1,220,28,8,52
        LTEXT           "D",-1,232,40,8,8
        LTEXT           "C",-1,232,60,8,8
        CTEXT           "Opponent",-1,268,12,32,8
        LTEXT           "D",-1,260,24,8,8
        LTEXT           "C",-1,304,24,8,8
        CONTROL         "",-1,"Static",SS_BLACKFRAME,240,32,44,20
        CONTROL         "",-1,"Static",SS_BLACKFRAME,240,52,44,20
        CONTROL         "",-1,"Static",SS_BLACKFRAME,284,32,44,20
        CONTROL         "",-1,"Static",SS_BLACKFRAME,284,52,44,20
        EDITTEXT        IDD_PDOPTCFG_PAYDD,244,36,36,12,ES_AUTOHSCROLL
        EDITTEXT        IDD_PDOPTCFG_PAYDC,288,36,36,12,ES_AUTOHSCROLL
        EDITTEXT        IDD_PDOPTCFG_PAYCD,244,56,36,12,ES_AUTOHSCROLL
        EDITTEXT        IDD_PDOPTCFG_PAYCC,288,56,36,12,ES_AUTOHSCROLL
        CONTROL         "File Output To:",IDD_PDOPTCFG_FILE,"Button",
                        BS_AUTOCHECKBOX | WS_TABSTOP,4,96,64,12
        LTEXT           "",IDD_PDOPTCFG_FNAME,72,96,264,12
        PUSHBUTTON      "Set File Name...",IDD_PDOPTCFG_SETFILE,
                        8,120,64,16
        DEFPUSHBUTTON   "OK",IDOK,220,120,48,16
        PUSHBUTTON      "Cancel",IDCANCEL,280,120,48,16
END

DLG_TAOPTCFG DIALOG DISCARDABLE  13, 32, 249, 154
STYLE DS_MODALFRAME | WS_POPUP | WS_VISIBLE | WS_CAPTION |
                        WS_SYSMENU
CAPTION "Travelling Artist Configuration"
FONT 8, "MS Sans Serif"
BEGIN
        RTEXT           "Population:",-1,12,20,48,8
        EDITTEXT        IDD_TAOPTCFG_POP,64,16,34,12,ES_AUTOHSCROLL
        RTEXT           "Generations:",-1,14,34,48,8
        EDITTEXT        IDD_TAOPTCFG_GEN,64,30,34,12,ES_AUTOHSCROLL
        RTEXT           "Report Freq:",-1,14,48,48,8
        EDITTEXT        IDD_TAOPTCFG_FREQ,64,44,34,12,ES_AUTOHSCROLL
        RTEXT           "Show Best:",-1,14,62,48,8
        EDITTEXT        IDD_TAOPTCFG_SHOW,64,58,34,12,ES_AUTOHSCROLL
        RTEXT           "Oper Probability:",-1,2,76,60,8
```

```
        EDITTEXT        IDD_TAOPTCFG_PROB,64,72,34,12,ES_AUTOHSCROLL
        LTEXT           "%",-1,100,76,10,8
        GROUPBOX        "Reproduction Operators",-1,116,10,126,78
        CTEXT           "W\ne\ni\ng\nh\nt\ns",-1,228,24,10,60
        CONTROL         "Mutation...
                        ",IDD_TAOPTCFG_MUTE,"Button",
                        BS_AUTOCHECKBOX | WS_TABSTOP,124,22,68,12
        EDITTEXT        IDD_TAOPTCFG_WTM,194,22,32,12,ES_AUTOHSCROLL
        CONTROL         "Inversion...........
                        ",IDD_TAOPTCFG_INV,"Button",
                        BS_AUTOCHECKBOX | WS_TABSTOP,124,34,68,12
        EDITTEXT        IDD_TAOPTCFG_WTI,194,34,32,12,ES_AUTOHSCROLL
        CONTROL         "PM Crossover......",
                        IDD_TAOPTCFG_PMX,"Button",
                        BS_AUTOCHECKBOX | WS_TABSTOP,124,46,68,12
        EDITTEXT        IDD_TAOPTCFG_WTP,194,46,32,12,ES_AUTOHSCROLL
        CONTROL         "Cyclic Crossover..",
                        IDD_TAOPTCFG_CX,"Button",
                        BS_AUTOCHECKBOX | WS_TABSTOP,124,58,68,12
        EDITTEXT        IDD_TAOPTCFG_WTC,194,58,32,12,ES_AUTOHSCROLL
        CONTROL         "Order Crossover...",
                        IDD_TAOPTCFG_OX,"Button",
                        BS_AUTOCHECKBOX | WS_TABSTOP,124,70,68,12
        EDITTEXT        IDD_TAOPTCFG_WTO,194,70,32,12
        GROUPBOX        "Linear Normalization
                        Parameters",111,12,96,228,28
        RTEXT           "Base:",-1,18,112,24,8
        EDITTEXT        IDD_TAOPTCFG_LNBASE,44,108,40,12,
                        ES_AUTOHSCROLL
        RTEXT            "Decrement:",-1,90,112,42,8
        EDITTEXT        IDD_TAOPTCFG_LNDEC,134,108,36,12,
                        ES_AUTOHSCROLL
        RTEXT           "Min:",-1,176,112,18,8
        EDITTEXT        IDD_TAOPTCFG_LNMIN,196,108,36,12,
                        ES_AUTOHSCROLL
        DEFPUSHBUTTON   "OK",IDOK,46,132,48,16
        PUSHBUTTON      "Cancel",IDCANCEL,152,132,48,16
END

DLG_EVOPTCFG DIALOG DISCARDABLE  18, 31, 348, 176
STYLE DS_MODALFRAME | WS_POPUP | WS_VISIBLE | WS_CAPTION |
                      WS_SYSMENU
CAPTION "Evolving FSM Configuration"
FONT 8, "MS Sans Serif"
```

```
BEGIN
    RTEXT           "Population:",-1,4,12,56,8
    EDITTEXT        IDD_EVOPTCFG_POP,64,8,32,12,ES_AUTOHSCROLL
    RTEXT           "Generations:",-1,4,28,56,8
    EDITTEXT        IDD_EVOPTCFG_GEN,64,24,32,12,ES_AUTOHSCROLL
    RTEXT           "Report Freq:",-1,4,44,56,8
    EDITTEXT        IDD_EVOPTCFG_FREQ,64,40,32,12,ES_AUTOHSCROLL
    RTEXT           "Contest Length:",-1,4,60,56,8
    EDITTEXT        IDD_EVOPTCFG_LEN,64,56,32,12,ES_AUTOHSCROLL
    RTEXT           "Max States:",-1,4,76,56,8
    EDITTEXT        IDD_EVOPTCFG_MAX,64,72,32,12,ES_AUTOHSCROLL
    GROUPBOX        "First Move",-1,12,92,84,52
    CONTROL         "Always Defect",IDD_EVOPTCFG_M1D,"Button",
                    BS_AUTORADIOBUTTON | WS_GROUP | WS_TAB-
                                        STOP,20,104,72,12
    CONTROL         "Always Cooperate",IDD_EVOPTCFG_M1C,"Button",
                    BS_AUTORADIOBUTTON | WS_TABSTOP,20,116,72,12
    CONTROL         "Random",IDD_EVOPTCFG_M1R,"Button",
                    BS_AUTO-RADIOBUTTON |
                    WS_TABSTOP,20,128,72,12
    GROUPBOX        "Mutation Weights",-1,108,4,104,96
    RTEXT           "Output Symbol:",-1,112,20,60,8
    EDITTEXT        IDD_EVOPTCFG_WTO,176,16,28,12,ES_AUTOHSCROLL
    RTEXT           "Transition:",-1,112,36,60,8
    EDITTEXT        IDD_EVOPTCFG_WTT,176,32,28,12,ES_AUTOHSCROLL
    RTEXT           "Add State:",-1,112,52,60,8
    EDITTEXT        IDD_EVOPTCFG_WTA,176,48,28,12,ES_AUTOHSCROLL
    RTEXT           "Delete State:",-1,112,68,60,8
    EDITTEXT        IDD_EVOPTCFG_WTD,176,64,28,12,ES_AUTOHSCROLL
    RTEXT           "Alter Init State:",-1,112,84,60,8
    EDITTEXT        IDD_EVOPTCFG_WTN,176,80,28,12,ES_AUTOHSCROLL
    RTEXT           "Mutation Rate:",-1,112,108,52,8
    EDITTEXT        IDD_EVOPTCFG_MRATE,168,104,28,12,
                    ES_AUTOHSCROLL
    LTEXT           "%",-1,200,108,8,8
    CONTROL         "Fitness Scaling",IDD_EVOPTCFG_FSCALE,
                    "Button",
                    BS_AUTOCHECKBOX | WS_TABSTOP,124,124,68,12
    GROUPBOX        "Payoffs",-1,220,4,120,80
    CTEXT           "P\nl\na\ny\ne\nr",-1,224,28,8,52
    LTEXT           "D",-1,236,40,8,8
    LTEXT           "C",-1,236,60,8,8
    CTEXT           "Opponent",-1,272,12,32,8
    LTEXT           "D",-1,264,24,8,8
```

```
    LTEXT              "C",-1,308,24,8,8
    CONTROL            "",-1,"Static",SS_BLACKFRAME,244,32,44,20
    CONTROL            "",-1,"Static",SS_BLACKFRAME,244,52,44,20
    CONTROL            "",-1,"Static",SS_BLACKFRAME,288,32,44,20
    CONTROL            "",-1,"Static",SS_BLACKFRAME,288,52,44,20
    EDITTEXT           IDD_EVOPTCFG_PAYDD,248,36,36,12,
                       ES_AUTOHSCROLL
    EDITTEXT           IDD_EVOPTCFG_PAYDC,292,36,36,12,
                       ES_AUTOHSCROLL
    EDITTEXT           IDD_EVOPTCFG_PAYCD,248,56,36,12,
                       ES_AUTOHSCROLL
    EDITTEXT           IDD_EVOPTCFG_PAYCC,292,56,36,12,
                       ES_AUTOHSCROLL
    GROUPBOX           "Linear Norm. Parameters",111,232,92,96,64
    RTEXT              "Base:",-1,256,108,24,8
    EDITTEXT           IDD_EVOPTCFG_LNBASE,284,104,32,12,
                       ES_AUTOHSCROLL
    RTEXT              "Decrement:",-1,240,124,42,8
    EDITTEXT           IDD_EVOPTCFG_LNDEC,284,120,32,12,
                       ES_AUTOHSCROLL
    RTEXT              "Min:",-1,264,140,18,8
    EDITTEXT           IDD_EVOPTCFG_LNMIN,284,136,32,12,
                       ES_AUTOHSCROLL
    DEFPUSHBUTTON      "OK",IDOK,32,152,48,16
    PUSHBUTTON         "Cancel",IDCANCEL,132,152,48,16
END

DLG_RAOPTCFG DIALOG DISCARDABLE  0, 0, 324, 145
STYLE DS_MODALFRAME | WS_POPUP | WS_VISIBLE | WS_CAPTION |
                   WS_SYSMENU
CAPTION "Evolving Robotic Ant Configuration"
FONT 8, "MS Sans Serif"
BEGIN
    RTEXT              "Population:",-1,8,9,48,8
    EDITTEXT           IDD_RAOPTCFG_POP,60,4,32,12,ES_AUTOHSCROLL
    RTEXT              "Generations:",-1,8,25,48,8
    EDITTEXT           IDD_RAOPTCFG_GEN,60,20,32,12,ES_AUTOHSCROLL
    RTEXT              "Report Freq:",-1,8,41,48,8
    EDITTEXT           IDD_RAOPTCFG_FREQ,60,36,32,12,ES_AUTOHSCROLL
    RTEXT              "Min State:",-1,8,57,48,8
    EDITTEXT           IDD_RAOPTCFG_MINSTATE,60,52,32,12,
                       ES_AUTOHSCROLL
    RTEXT              "Max States:",-1,8,72,48,8
    EDITTEXT           IDD_RAOPTCFG_MAXSTATE,60,68,32,12,
```

```
        ES_AUTOHSCROLL
    RTEXT            "Max Moves:",-1,8,88,48,8
    EDITTEXT         IDD_RAOPTCFG_MAXMOVES,60,84,32,12,
                     ES_AUTOHSCROLL
    CONTROL          "Fitness Scaling",IDD_RAOPTCFG_FSCALE,
                     "Button",
                     BS_AUTOCHECKBOX | WS_TABSTOP,120,8,68,12
    GROUPBOX         "Linear Norm. Parameters",111,104,28,96,60
    RTEXT            "Base:",-1,124,40,24,8
    EDITTEXT         IDD_RAOPTCFG_LNBASE,152,36,32,12,
                     ES_AUTOHSCROLL
    RTEXT            "Decrement:",-1,108,56,42,8
    EDITTEXT         IDD_RAOPTCFG_LNDEC,152,52,32,12,
                     ES_AUTOHSCROLL
    RTEXT            "Min:",-1,132,72,18,8
    EDITTEXT         IDD_RAOPTCFG_LNMIN,152,68,32,12,
                     ES_AUTOHSCROLL
    RTEXT            "Mutation Rate:",-1,220,9,52,8
    EDITTEXT         IDD_RAOPTCFG_MRATE,276,4,28,12,ES_AUTOHSCROLL
    LTEXT            "%",-1,308,9,8,8
    GROUPBOX         "Mutation Weights",-1,212,24,104,96
    RTEXT            "Output Symbol:",-1,216,40,56,8
    EDITTEXT         IDD_RAOPTCFG_WTO,276,36,32,12,ES_AUTOHSCROLL
    RTEXT            "Transition:",-1,216,56,56,8
    EDITTEXT         IDD_RAOPTCFG_WTT,276,52,32,12,ES_AUTOHSCROLL
    RTEXT            "Add State:",-1,216,72,56,8
    EDITTEXT         IDD_RAOPTCFG_WTA,276,68,32,12,ES_AUTOHSCROLL
    RTEXT            "Delete State:",-1,216,88,56,8
    EDITTEXT         IDD_RAOPTCFG_WTD,276,84,32,12,ES_AUTOHSCROLL
    RTEXT            "Alter Init State:",-1,220,104,52,8
    EDITTEXT         IDD_RAOPTCFG_WTN,276,100,32,12,ES_AUTOHSCROLL
    DEFPUSHBUTTON    "OK",IDOK,40,112,56,16
    PUSHBUTTON       "Cancel",IDCANCEL,112,112,56,16
END

DLG_ABOUT DIALOG 11, 23, 128, 265
STYLE DS_MODALFRAME | WS_POPUP | WS_VISIBLE | WS_CAPTION |
                     WS_SYSMENU
CAPTION "About Forge..."
FONT 8, "MS Sans Serif"
{
 DEFPUSHBUTTON "OK", IDOK, 36,244,56,14
 ICON ICON_FORGE, -1, 8, 4, 18, 20
 CTEXT "Forge", -1, 52, 8, 24, 8
```

```
CTEXT "Exploring Genetic Algorithms", -1, 8,28,112,8
CTEXT "Version #", IDD_ABOUT_VERSION, 36,36,56,8
CONTROL "", -1, "Static", SS_BLACKFRAME | WS_CHILD | WS_VISIBLE,
            12,52,104,52
CTEXT "from the book:", -1, 20,56,88,8
CTEXT "C++ Genetic Algorithms", -1, 20, 68, 88, 8
CTEXT "written by Scott Robert Ladd", -1, 16,80,96,8
CTEXT "published by M&&T Books", -1, 20,92,88,8
CTEXT "Copyright 1995 Scott Robert Ladd", -1, 8,108,112,8
CTEXT "All rights reserved", -1, 8,116,112,8
CONTROL "", -1, "Static", SS_BLACKFRAME | WS_CHILD | WS_VISIBLE,
            8,128,113,5
CTEXT "The executable version of this program may be freely
distributed without royalties or obligation to the original
author.", -1, 8,136,112,32
CTEXT "Unauthorized distribution of this program's SOURCE CODE
is a violation of copyright law. If you want the source code
(with an explanation of the science behind this program), please
purchase the book. Thank you.", -1, 8,172,112,64
CONTROL "", -1, "Static", SS_BLACKFRAME | WS_CHILD | WS_VISIBLE,
            48, 4, 33, 17
}
```

LISTING A.3   FORGERES.H CONSTANT DEFINITIONS FOR THE FORGE APPLICATION.

```
#define ICON_FORGE              10

#define MENU_FORGE              100
#define IDM_TEST_ROULETTE       101
#define IDM_TEST_BOOL           102
#define IDM_TEST_RANDDEV        103
#define IDM_TEST_MFLOAT         104
#define IDM_TEST_MDOUBLE        105
#define IDM_TEST_MATH           106
#define IDM_TEST_SORTS          107
#define IDM_TEST_FSM            108
#define IDM_OPT_BLACKBOX        111
#define IDM_OPT_BBOX_ANALYSIS   112
#define IDM_OPT_PEAK_SEARCH     113
#define IDM_OPT_PDILEMMA        114
#define IDM_OPT_TRAVART         115
#define IDM_EVOL_MACHINES       121
#define IDM_ROBOTIC_ANTS        122
```

```
#define IDM_COPY            191
#define IDM_COPYALL         192
#define IDM_ABOUT           193
#define IDM_EXIT            199

#define DLG_BLACKBOX        1000
#define IDD_BBOX_POP        1001
#define IDD_BBOX_GEN        1002
#define IDD_BBOX_CROSS      1003
#define IDD_BBOX_MUTE       1004
#define IDD_BBOX_FSCALE     1005
#define IDD_BBOX_ELITISM    1006
#define IDD_BBOX_CPROB      1007
#define IDD_BBOX_MPROB      1008

#define DLG_GAOPTCFG        2000
#define IDD_GAOPTCFG_POP    2001
#define IDD_GAOPTCFG_GEN    2002
#define IDD_GAOPTCFG_FREQ   2003
#define IDD_GAOPTCFG_SIGDIG 2104
#define IDD_GAOPTCFG_XMIN   2004
#define IDD_GAOPTCFG_XMAX   2005
#define IDD_GAOPTCFG_YMIN   2006
#define IDD_GAOPTCFG_YMAX   2007
#define IDD_GAOPTCFG_CROSSX 2008
#define IDD_GAOPTCFG_CROSSY 2009
#define IDD_GAOPTCFG_CROSSB 2010
#define IDD_GAOPTCFG_MUTES  2011
#define IDD_GAOPTCFG_MUTEE  2012
#define IDD_GAOPTCFG_MUTEM  2013
#define IDD_GAOPTCFG_MUTEX  2014
#define IDD_GAOPTCFG_MUTEY  2015
#define IDD_GAOPTCFG_MPROB  2016
#define IDD_GAOPTCFG_MLOOP  2017
#define IDD_GAOPTCFG_CPROB  2018
#define IDD_GAOPTCFG_ELITE  2019
#define IDD_GAOPTCFG_FSCALE 2020
#define IDD_GAOPTCFG_FTEXP  2021
#define IDD_GAOPTCFG_FTWDW  2022
#define IDD_GAOPTCFG_FTLIN  2023
#define IDD_GAOPTCFG_LNBASE 2024
#define IDD_GAOPTCFG_LNDEC  2025
#define IDD_GAOPTCFG_LNMIN  2026
#define IDD_GAOPTCFG_EQF6   2027
```

```
#define IDD_GAOPTCFG_EQF7     2028
#define IDD_GAOPTCFG_EQF8     2029
#define IDD_GAOPTCFG_EQCUST   2030

#define DLG_PDOPTCFG          3000
#define IDD_PDOPTCFG_POP      3001
#define IDD_PDOPTCFG_GEN      3002
#define IDD_PDOPTCFG_FREQ     3003
#define IDD_PDOPTCFG_MAXLVL   3004
#define IDD_PDOPTCFG_CROSS    3005
#define IDD_PDOPTCFG_CRATE    3006
#define IDD_PDOPTCFG_MUTE     3007
#define IDD_PDOPTCFG_MRATE    3008
#define IDD_PDOPTCFG_DBLING   3009
#define IDD_PDOPTCFG_DRATE    3010
#define IDD_PDOPTCFG_FILE     3011
#define IDD_PDOPTCFG_SETFILE  3012
#define IDD_PDOPTCFG_FNAME    3013
#define IDD_PDOPTCFG_AVG      3014
#define IDD_PDOPTCFG_FAIR     3015
#define IDD_PDOPTCFG_PAYDD    3016
#define IDD_PDOPTCFG_PAYDC    3017
#define IDD_PDOPTCFG_PAYCD    3018
#define IDD_PDOPTCFG_PAYCC    3019
#define IDD_PDOPTCFG_START    3020
#define IDD_PDOPTCFG_RAND1    3021

#define DLG_TAOPTCFG          4000
#define IDD_TAOPTCFG_POP      4001
#define IDD_TAOPTCFG_GEN      4002
#define IDD_TAOPTCFG_FREQ     4003
#define IDD_TAOPTCFG_SHOW     4004
#define IDD_TAOPTCFG_PROB     4005
#define IDD_TAOPTCFG_MUTE     4006
#define IDD_TAOPTCFG_WTM      4007
#define IDD_TAOPTCFG_INV      4008
#define IDD_TAOPTCFG_WTI      4009
#define IDD_TAOPTCFG_PMX      4010
#define IDD_TAOPTCFG_WTP      4011
#define IDD_TAOPTCFG_CX       4012
#define IDD_TAOPTCFG_WTC      4013
#define IDD_TAOPTCFG_OX       4014
#define IDD_TAOPTCFG_WTO      4015
#define IDD_TAOPTCFG_LNBASE   4016
```

```
#define IDD_TAOPTCFG_LNDEC     4017
#define IDD_TAOPTCFG_LNMIN     4018

#define DLG_EVOPTCFG           5000
#define IDD_EVOPTCFG_POP       5001
#define IDD_EVOPTCFG_GEN       5002
#define IDD_EVOPTCFG_LEN       5003
#define IDD_EVOPTCFG_MAX       5004
#define IDD_EVOPTCFG_MRATE     5005
#define IDD_EVOPTCFG_FSCALE    5006
#define IDD_EVOPTCFG_LNBASE    5007
#define IDD_EVOPTCFG_LNDEC     5008
#define IDD_EVOPTCFG_LNMIN     5009
#define IDD_EVOPTCFG_WTO       5010
#define IDD_EVOPTCFG_WTT       5011
#define IDD_EVOPTCFG_WTA       5012
#define IDD_EVOPTCFG_WTD       5013
#define IDD_EVOPTCFG_WTN       5014
#define IDD_EVOPTCFG_PAYCC     5015
#define IDD_EVOPTCFG_PAYDC     5016
#define IDD_EVOPTCFG_PAYCD     5017
#define IDD_EVOPTCFG_PAYDD     5018
#define IDD_EVOPTCFG_M1D       5019
#define IDD_EVOPTCFG_M1C       5020
#define IDD_EVOPTCFG_M1R       5021
#define IDD_EVOPTCFG_FREQ      5022

#define DLG_RAOPTCFG           6000
#define IDD_RAOPTCFG_GEN       6001
#define IDD_RAOPTCFG_POP       6002
#define IDD_RAOPTCFG_FREQ      6003
#define IDD_RAOPTCFG_MINSTATE  6004
#define IDD_RAOPTCFG_MAXSTATE  6005
#define IDD_RAOPTCFG_MAXMOVES  6006
#define IDD_RAOPTCFG_MRATE     6007
#define IDD_RAOPTCFG_FSCALE    6008
#define IDD_RAOPTCFG_LNBASE    6009
#define IDD_RAOPTCFG_LNDEC     6010
#define IDD_RAOPTCFG_LNMIN     6011
#define IDD_RAOPTCFG_WTO       6012
#define IDD_RAOPTCFG_WTT       6013
#define IDD_RAOPTCFG_WTA       6014
#define IDD_RAOPTCFG_WTD       6015
#define IDD_RAOPTCFG_WTN       6016
```

```
#define DLG_ABOUT              7000
#define IDD_ABOUT_VERSION      7001
```

LISTING A.4   FORGEBB.CPP FORGE BLACK BOX IMPLEMENTATION.

```cpp
//------------------------------------------------------------
// program FOR Genetic algorithm Experimentation (FORGE)
//------------------------------------------------------------
//
//      forgebb.cpp     v1.00
//
//      Blackbox optimization
//
//------------------------------------------------------------
// Copyright 1995 by Scott Robert Ladd. All rights reserved.
//------------------------------------------------------------

#include "windows.h"   // Windows definitions
#include "forgeres.h"  // resource constants
#include "strstrea.h"  // strstream definitions
#include "iomanip.h"   // stream manipulators
#include "math.h"      // math functions
#include "bool.h"      // ANSI-like 'bool' class
#include "limits.h"    // limits of types
#include "stdio.h"     // standard file I/O functions
#include "stdlib.h"    // misc. library functions
#include "time.h"      // time functions and types


//------------------
// class definitions
//------------------

class BBOptConfig
    {
    public:
        BBOptConfig
            (
            HINSTANCE inst,
            HWND      parent
            );

        static void DlgInit
            (
```

```
        HWND    dlg
        );

    static BOOL DlgStore
        (
        HWND    dlg
        );

    // interrogation
    bool    GetValidity()   { return Valid;     }
    size_t  GetPopSize()    { return PopSize;   }
    size_t  GetTestSize()   { return TestSize;  }
    bool    GetCrossover()  { return Crossover; }
    float   GetCrossProb()  { return CrossProb; }
    bool    GetMutate()     { return Mutate;    }
    float   GetMuteProb()   { return MuteProb;  }
    bool    GetScaling()    { return Scaling;   }
    bool    GetElitist()    { return Elitist;   }

private:
    // parameters
    bool    Valid;
    size_t  PopSize;
    size_t  TestSize;
    bool    Crossover;
    float   CrossProb;
    bool    Mutate;
    float   MuteProb;
    bool    Scaling;
    bool    Elitist;

    // stored parameter values
    static size_t DefPopSize;
    static size_t DefTestSize;
    static bool   DefCrossover;
    static float  DefCrossProb;
    static bool   DefMutate;
    static float  DefMuteProb;
    static bool   DefScaling;
    static bool   DefElitist;
    };

size_t BBOptConfig::DefPopSize   =   25;
size_t BBOptConfig::DefTestSize  =  100;
```

```
bool    BBOptConfig::DefCrossover = true;
float   BBOptConfig::DefCrossProb =    1.00F;
bool    BBOptConfig::DefMutate    = true;
float   BBOptConfig::DefMuteProb  =    0.85F;
bool    BBOptConfig::DefScaling   = true;
bool    BBOptConfig::DefElitist   = true;

static LPCSTR BBOptConfigDlgName = MAKEINTRESOURCE(DLG_BLACKBOX);

static const char * BBOptConfigDlgErr =
    "Your input is in error!\n\n"
    "Population  must be >= 10.\n"
    "Generations must be > 0.";

BOOL CALLBACK BBOptConfigDlgProc
    (
    HWND  dlg,
    WORD  message,
    WORD  wParam,
    DWORD lParam
    );

BBOptConfig::BBOptConfig
    (
    HINSTANCE inst,
    HWND      parent
    )
    {
    DLGPROC thunk =
MakeProcInstance(FARPROC(BBOptConfigDlgProc),inst);
    int res = DialogBox(inst,BBOptConfigDlgName,parent,thunk);
    FreeProcInstance(thunk);

    if (res)
        Valid = true;
    else
        Valid = false;

    PopSize   = DefPopSize;
    TestSize  = DefTestSize;
    Crossover = DefCrossover;
    CrossProb = DefCrossProb;
    Mutate    = DefMutate;
    MuteProb  = DefMuteProb;
```

```
    Scaling   = DefScaling;
    Elitist   = DefElitist;
    }

#ifdef __BORLANDC__
#pragma argsused
#endif

BOOL CALLBACK BBOptConfigDlgProc
    (
    HWND  dlg,
    WORD  message,
    WORD  wParam,
    DWORD lParam
    )
    {
    switch (message)
        {
        case WM_INITDIALOG:
            BBOptConfig::DlgInit(dlg);
            return TRUE;

        case WM_COMMAND:
            switch (wParam)
                {
                case IDOK:
                    if (TRUE == BBOptConfig::DlgStore(dlg))
                        EndDialog(dlg, 1);

                    break;

                case IDCANCEL:
                    EndDialog(dlg, 0);
                }

            return TRUE;
        }

    return FALSE;
    }

void BBOptConfig::DlgInit
    (
    HWND  dlg
```

```
    )
    {
    char temp[64];

    sprintf(temp,"%u",DefPopSize);
    SetDlgItemText(dlg,IDD_BBOX_POP,temp);

    sprintf(temp,"%u",DefTestSize);
    SetDlgItemText(dlg,IDD_BBOX_GEN,temp);

    sprintf(temp,"%.6g",DefCrossProb * 100.0F);
    SetDlgItemText(dlg,IDD_BBOX_CPROB,temp);

    sprintf(temp,"%.6g",DefMuteProb * 100.0F);
    SetDlgItemText(dlg,IDD_BBOX_MPROB,temp);

    if (DefCrossover)
        SendDlgItemMessage(dlg,IDD_BBOX_CROSS,BM_SETCHECK,1,0L);
    else
        SendDlgItemMessage(dlg,IDD_BBOX_CROSS,BM_SETCHECK,0,0L);

    if (DefMutate)
        SendDlgItemMessage(dlg,IDD_BBOX_MUTE,BM_SETCHECK,1,0L);
    else
        SendDlgItemMessage(dlg,IDD_BBOX_MUTE,BM_SETCHECK,0,0L);

    if (DefScaling)
        SendDlgItemMessage(dlg,IDD_BBOX_FSCALE,BM_SETCHECK,1,0L);
    else
        SendDlgItemMessage(dlg,IDD_BBOX_FSCALE,BM_SETCHECK,0,0L);

    if (DefElitist)

SendDlgItemMessage(dlg,IDD_BBOX_ELITISM,BM_SETCHECK,1,0L);
    else

SendDlgItemMessage(dlg,IDD_BBOX_ELITISM,BM_SETCHECK,0,0L);
    }

BOOL BBOptConfig::DlgStore
    (
    HWND  dlg
    )
    {
```

```
char temp[64];

GetDlgItemText(dlg,IDD_BBOX_POP,temp,64);
size_t psz = abs(atoi(temp));

GetDlgItemText(dlg,IDD_BBOX_GEN,temp,64);
size_t gen = abs(atoi(temp));

if ((psz < 10) || (gen == 0))
    {
    MessageBeep(MB_ICONHAND);
    MessageBox(NULL,BBOptConfigDlgErr,"Configuration
            Error",MB_OK | MB_ICONHAND);
    return FALSE;
    }

DefPopSize  = psz;
DefTestSize = gen;

GetDlgItemText(dlg,IDD_BBOX_CPROB,temp,64);
DefCrossProb = float(fabs(atof(temp))) / 100.0F;

GetDlgItemText(dlg,IDD_BBOX_MPROB,temp,64);
DefMuteProb = float(fabs(atof(temp))) / 100.0F;

if (SendDlgItemMessage(dlg,IDD_BBOX_CROSS,BM_GETCHECK,0,0L))
    DefCrossover = true;
else
    DefCrossover = false;

if (SendDlgItemMessage(dlg,IDD_BBOX_MUTE,BM_GETCHECK,0,0L))
    DefMutate = true;
else
    DefMutate = false;

if (SendDlgItemMessage(dlg,IDD_BBOX_FSCALE,BM_GETCHECK,0,0L))
    DefScaling = true;
else
    DefScaling = false;

if
(SendDlgItemMessage(dlg,IDD_BBOX_ELITISM,BM_GETCHECK,0,0L))
    DefElitist = true;
else
```

```
        DefElitist = false;

    return TRUE;
    }

//----------------------
// Blackbox optimization
//----------------------

long Blackbox
    (
    long x
    )
    {
    // test value -- the speed of light in meters per second
    static const long n =  0x11DE784AL; // 299,792,458;

    long fit  = 0L;
    long mask = 1L;

    // count matching bits
    for (int i = 0; i < 32; ++i)
        {
        if ((x & mask) == (n & mask))
            ++fit;

        mask <<= 1;
        }

    // return fitness between 0 and 32
    return fit;
    }

void TestBlackbox
    (
    HINSTANCE inst,
    HWND      wdw,
    strstream & buffer
    )
    {
    // display header
    buffer << "Blackbox Optimization\r\n"
              "---------------------\r\n\r\n"
            << setprecision(7);
```

```
// get configuration and verify it
BBOptConfig cfg(inst,wdw);

if (!cfg.GetValidity())
    {
    buffer << "Cancelled\r\n";
    return;
    }

// display parameters for this run
buffer << "Pop. Size: " << cfg.GetPopSize()   << "\r\n";
buffer << "Test Size: " << cfg.GetTestSize()  << "\r\n";
buffer << "Crossover: " << cfg.GetCrossover() << " (" <<
        cfg.GetCrossProb() * 100.0F << "%)\r\n";
buffer << " Mutation: " << cfg.GetMutate()    << " (" <<
        cfg.GetMuteProb()  * 100.0F << "%)\r\n";
buffer << "  Scaling: " << cfg.GetScaling()   << "\r\n";
buffer << "  Elitism: " << cfg.GetElitist()   << "\r\n\r\n";

// get dimensions
const size_t POP_SZ = cfg.GetPopSize();
const size_t GEN_SZ = cfg.GetTestSize();
const bool   cross  = cfg.GetCrossover();
const float  crate  = cfg.GetCrossProb();
const bool   mutate = cfg.GetMutate();
const float  mrate  = cfg.GetMuteProb();
const bool   elite  = cfg.GetElitist();
const bool   scale  = cfg.GetScaling();

// initialize psuedo-random number generator
srand((unsigned)time(NULL));

// allocate population and fitness buffers
long * pop = new long[POP_SZ];

if (pop == NULL)
    {
    buffer << "Memory allocation failed\r\n";
    return;
    }

long * newpop = new long[POP_SZ];

if (newpop == NULL)
```

```
    {
    buffer << "Memory allocation failed\r\n";
    return;
    }

long * fit = new long[POP_SZ];

if (fit == NULL)
    {
    buffer << "Memory allocation failed\r\n";
    return;
    }

// various variables
long bestl, bestf, minf, mask, sel, totf, avgf;
size_t i, g, p1, p2;
char buf[64];

// create initial population
for (i = 0; i < POP_SZ; ++i)
    pop[i] = long(rand());

// start with generation zero
g = 0;

while (1) // loop breaks in middle
    {
    // display progress
    wsprintf(buf,"Forge (loop: %5u of %5u)",g,GEN_SZ);
    SetWindowText(wdw,buf);

    // initialize for fitness testing
    bestf = -1L;
    totf  = 0L;
    minf  = LONG_MAX;

    // fitness testing
    for (i = 0; i < POP_SZ; ++i)
        {
        // call fitness function and store result
        fit[i] = Blackbox(pop[i]);

        // keep track of best fitness
        if (fit[i] > bestf)
```

```
        {
        bestf = fit[i];
        bestl = pop[i];
        }

    // keep track of least fit
    if (fit[i] < minf)
        minf = fit[i];

    // total fitness
    totf += fit[i];
    }

// make sure we have at least some fit values
if (totf == 0L)
    {
    buffer << "Population has total fitness of ZERO\r\n";
    return;
    }

// compute average fitness
avgf = totf / POP_SZ;

// sum (and maybe scale) fitness values
if (scale)
    {
    // ensures that the least fitness is one
    ++minf;

    // recalculate total fitness to reflect scaled values
    totf = 0L;

    for (i = 0; i < POP_SZ; ++i)
        {
        fit[i] -= minf;   // reduce by smallest fitness
        fit[i] *= fit[i]; // square result of above
        totf   += fit[i]; // add into total fitness
        }
    }

// display stats for this generation
buffer << setw(4) << g
       << " best: " << setw(8) << hex << bestl
       << " (" << setw(2) << dec << bestf
```

```
                    << ") avg. fit = " << setw(2) << avgf
                    << " min. fit = "  << setw(2) << minf << "\r\n";

            // exit if this is final generation
            if (g == GEN_SZ)
                break;

            // create new population
            for (i = 0; i < POP_SZ; ++i)
                {
                // roulette-select parent
                sel = (long)((float(rand()) / float(RAND_MAX)) *
                                            float(totf));

                p1  = 0;

                while (sel > fit[p1])
                    {
                    sel -= fit[p1];
                    ++p1;
                    }

                // crossover reproduction
                if (cross && ((float(rand()) / float(RAND_MAX)) <
                crate))
                    {
                    // roulette-select second parent
                    sel = (long)((float(rand()) / float(RAND_MAX)) *
                    float(totf));
                    p2 = 0;

                    while (sel > fit[p2])
                        {
                        sel -= fit[p2];
                        ++p2;
                        }

                    // mask of bits to be copied from first parent
                    mask = 0xFFFFFFFFL << (int)((float(rand()) /
                    float(RAND_MAX)) * 32.0F);

                    // new string from two parents
                    newpop[i] = (pop[p1] & mask) | (pop[p2] &
                    (~mask));
                    }
```

```
            else
                // one parent, no crossover reproduction
                newpop[i] = pop[p1];

            // mutation
            if (mutate && ((float(rand()) / float(RAND_MAX)) <
            mrate))
                {
                // select bit to be changed
                mask = 1L << (int)((float(rand()) /
                float(RAND_MAX)) * 32.0F);

                // flip the bit
                if (newpop[i] & mask)
                    newpop[i] &= ~mask;
                else
                    newpop[i] |= mask;
                }
            }

        // if elitist selection, replace first item with best
        if (elite)
            newpop[0] = best1;

        // replace old population with new one
        memcpy(pop,newpop,POP_SZ * sizeof(long));

        // increment generation
        ++g;
        }

    // set window header to application name
    SetWindowText(wdw,"Forge");

    // delete population and fitness arrays
    delete [] pop;
    delete [] newpop;
    delete [] fit;
    }

//---------------------------------
// Blackbox Optimization (Analysis)
//---------------------------------
```

```
void TestBBAnalysis
    (
    HINSTANCE inst,
    HWND      wdw,
    strstream & buffer
    )
    {
    buffer << "Blackbox Optimization (Analysis)\r\n"
              "-------------------------------\r\n\r\n"
           << setprecision(7);

    // get configuration and verify it
    BBOptConfig cfg(inst,wdw);

    if (!cfg.GetValidity())
        {
        buffer << "Cancelled\r\n";
        return;
        }

    // display parameters for this run
    buffer << "Pop. Size: " << cfg.GetPopSize()   << "\r\n";
    buffer << "Test Size: " << cfg.GetTestSize()  << "\r\n";
    buffer << "Crossover: " << cfg.GetCrossover() << " (" <<
    cfg.GetCrossProb() * 100.0F << "%)\r\n";
    buffer << " Mutation: " << cfg.GetMutate()    << " (" <<
    cfg.GetMuteProb()  * 100.0F << "%)\r\n";
    buffer << "  Scaling: " << cfg.GetScaling()   << "\r\n";
    buffer << "  Elitism: " << cfg.GetElitist()   << "\r\n\r\n";

    // get dimensions
    const size_t POP_SZ = cfg.GetPopSize();
    const size_t GEN_SZ = cfg.GetTestSize();
    const size_t ANL_SZ = 100U;
    const bool   cross  = cfg.GetCrossover();
    const float  crate  = cfg.GetCrossProb();
    const bool   mutate = cfg.GetMutate();
    const float  mrate  = cfg.GetMuteProb();
    const bool   elite  = cfg.GetElitist();
    const bool   scale  = cfg.GetScaling();

    // initialize psuedo-random number generator
    srand((unsigned)time(NULL));
```

```
// allocate population and fitness buffers
long * pop = new long[POP_SZ];

if (pop == NULL)
    {
    buffer << "Memory allocation failed\r\n";
    return;
    }

long * newpop = new long[POP_SZ];

if (newpop == NULL)
    {
    buffer << "Memory allocation failed\r\n";
    return;
    }

long * fit = new long[POP_SZ];

if (fit == NULL)
    {
    buffer << "Memory allocation failed\r\n";
    return;
    }

// various variables
long bestl, bestf, minf, mask, sel, totf;
long sumg = 0L, sumt = 0L;
size_t a, i, g, p1, p2, ming = UINT_MAX, maxg = 0;
clock_t start, elapsed, mint = UINT_MAX, maxt = 0;
char buf[64];

for (a = 0; a < ANL_SZ; ++a)
    {
    // get starting time
    start = clock();

    // create initial population
    for (i = 0; i < POP_SZ; ++i)
        pop[i] = long(rand());

    // start with generation zero
    g = 0;
```

```
while (1) // loop breaks in middle
    {
    // display progress
    wsprintf(buf,"Forge (analysis %5u of %u, loop %5u of
%u)",
            a,ANL_SZ,g,GEN_SZ);
    SetWindowText(wdw,buf);

    // initialize for fitness testing
    bestf = -1L;
    totf  = 0L;
    minf  = LONG_MAX;

    // fitness testing
    for (i = 0; i < POP_SZ; ++i)
        {
        // call fitness function and store result
        fit[i] = Blackbox(pop[i]);

        // keep track of best fitness
        if (fit[i] > bestf)
            {
            bestf = fit[i];
            bestl = pop[i];
            }

        // keep track of least fit
        if (fit[i] < minf)
            minf = fit[i];

        // total fitness
        totf += fit[i];
        }

    // exit if this is final generation
    if ((totf == 0L) || (bestf == 32L) || (g == GEN_SZ))
        break;

    // sum (and maybe scale) fitness values
    if (scale)
        {
        // ensures that the least fitness is one
        ++minf;
```

```
    // recalculate total fitness to reflect scaled
       values
    totf = 0L;

    for (i = 0; i < POP_SZ; ++i)
        {
        fit[i] -= minf;   // reduce by smallest fitness
        fit[i] *= fit[i]; // square result of above
        totf   += fit[i]; // add into total fitness
        }
    }

// create new population
for (i = 0; i < POP_SZ; ++i)
    {
    // roulette-select parent
    sel = (long)((float(rand()) / float(RAND_MAX)) *
    float(totf));
    p1  = 0;

    while (sel > fit[p1])
        {
        sel -= fit[p1];
        ++p1;
        }

    // crossover reproduction
    if (cross && ((float(rand()) / float(RAND_MAX)) <
    crate))
        {
        // roulette-select second parent
        sel = (long)((float(rand()) /
                float(RAND_MAX)) * float(totf));
        p2 = 0;

        while (sel > fit[p2])
            {
            sel -= fit[p2];
            ++p2;
            }

        // mask of bits to be copied from first
           parent
        mask = 0xFFFFFFFFL << (int)((float(rand()) /
```

```
float(RAND_MAX)) * 32.0F);

                    // new string from two parents
                    newpop[i] = (pop[p1] & mask) | (pop[p2] &
                    (~mask));
                    }
            else
                    // one parent, no crossover reproduction
                    newpop[i] = pop[p1];

            // mutation
            if (mutate && ((float(rand()) / float(RAND_MAX))
            < mrate))
                    {
                    // select bit to be changed
                    mask = 1L << (int)((float(rand()) /
                    float(RAND_MAX)) * 32.0F);

                    // flip the bit
                    if (newpop[i] & mask)
                        newpop[i] &= ~mask;
                    else
                        newpop[i] |= mask;
                    }
            }

        // if elitist selection, replace first item with best
        if (elite)
            newpop[0] = best1;

        // replace old population with new one
        memcpy(pop,newpop,POP_SZ * sizeof(long));

        // increment generation
        ++g;
        }

    // calculate elapsed time
    elapsed = clock() - start;
    sumt += elapsed;

    if (elapsed < mint) mint = elapsed;
    if (elapsed > maxt) maxt = elapsed;
```

```
        if (g < ming) ming = g;
        if (g > maxg) maxg = g;

        sumg += g;
        }

    // report statistics
    buffer << "gen  average = "
           << (float(sumg) / float(ANL_SZ)) << "\r\n";
    buffer << "gen  minimum = " << ming << "\r\n";
    buffer << "gen  maximum = " << maxg << "\r\n\r\n";

    buffer << "tick average = "
           << (float(sumt) / float(ANL_SZ)) << "\r\n";
    buffer << "tick minimum = " << mint << "\r\n";
    buffer << "tick maximum = " << maxt << "\r\n";

    // set window header to application name
    SetWindowText(wdw,"Forge");

    // delete population and fitness arrays
    delete [] pop;
    delete [] newpop;
    delete [] fit;
    }
```

LISTING A.5   FORGEEV.CPP PRISONER'S DILEMMA WITH EVOLVING FINITE STATE MACHINES.

```
//-------------------------------------------------------------
// program FOR Genetic algorithm Experimentation (FORGE)
//-------------------------------------------------------------
//
//      forgeev.cpp     v1.00
//
//      Prisoner's Dilemma by evolving finite state machines
//
//-------------------------------------------------------------
// Copyright 1995 by Scott Robert Ladd. All rights reserved.
//-------------------------------------------------------------

#include "windows.h"  // Windows definitions
#include "forgeres.h" // resource constants
```

```
#include "strstrea.h" // strstream definitions
#include "iomanip.h"  // stream manipulators
#include "string.h"   // memory management functions
#include "randdev.h"  // uniform random deviate generator
#include "roulette.h" // RouletteWheel class
#include "bool.h"     // ANSI-like 'bool' class
#include "fsm.h"      // finite state machines
#include "evoptcfg.h" // configuration dialog box

//------------------------------------
// Test evolving finite state machines
//------------------------------------

void TestEvolvingMachines
    (
    HINSTANCE inst,
    HWND      wdw,
    strstream & buffer
    )
    {
    buffer << "Evolving Finite State Machines\r\n"
              "------------------------------\r\n";

    // create configuration and verify it
    EVOptConfig evoc(inst,wdw);

    if (!evoc.GetValidity())
        {
        buffer << "Cancelled\r\n";
        return;
        }

    // data arrays
    const size_t    SSZ = 2;
    const size_t    NSZ = 3;
    char  SSET[2] = { 'C', 'D' };
    const size_t POP_SZ = evoc.GetPopSize();

    // variables
    size_t n, i, j, k, inc;
    double vf;
    char buf[64], mj, mk, tj;

    EvolvingFSM<char,SSZ,char,SSZ> * vm;
```

```
RouletteWheel<double> * rw;

RandDev devgen;

FSM_TranData<char> td[NSZ][SSZ];

EVFSM_MuteWts wts =
    {
    evoc.GetWeight0(),
    evoc.GetWeightT(),
    evoc.GetWeightA(),
    evoc.GetWeightD(),
    evoc.GetWeightN()
    };

// display parameters
buffer << "\r\n        Population: " << evoc.GetPopSize();
buffer << "\r\n         Test Size: " << evoc.GetTestSize();
buffer << "\r\n       Test Length: " << evoc.GetTestLen();
buffer << "\r\n         Max State: " << evoc.GetMaxState();
buffer << "\r\n     Mutation Rate: " << evoc.GetMuteRate();
buffer << "\r\n";
buffer << "\r\nOutput Symbol Wt: " << evoc.GetWeight0();
buffer << "\r\n    Transition Wt: " << evoc.GetWeightT();
buffer << "\r\n     Add State Wt: " << evoc.GetWeightA();
buffer << "\r\n  Delete State Wt: " << evoc.GetWeightD();
buffer << "\r\nNew InitState Wt: " << evoc.GetWeightN();
buffer << "\r\n";
buffer << "\r\n         Payoff DD: " << evoc.GetPayoffDD();
buffer << "\r\n         Payoff DC: " << evoc.GetPayoffDC();
buffer << "\r\n         Payoff CD: " << evoc.GetPayoffCD();
buffer << "\r\n         Payoff CC: " << evoc.GetPayoffCC();
buffer << "\r\n";
buffer << "\r\n        First Move: ";

switch (evoc.GetFirstMove())
    {
    case EVM_DEFECT:
        buffer << "Always Defect";
        break;
    case EVM_COOPER:
        buffer << "Always Cooperate";
        break;
    case EVM_RANDOM:
```

```
            buffer << "Random";
        }

if (evoc.GetFitScale())
    {
    buffer << "\r\n";
    buffer << "\r\n  Fitness Base: " << evoc.GetFitLinBase();
    buffer << "\r\n  Fitness  Dec: " << evoc.GetFitLinDec();
    buffer << "\r\n  Fitness  Min: " << evoc.GetFitLinMin();
    }

buffer << "\r\n";

// allocate buffers
EvolvingFSM<char,SSZ,char,SSZ> ** pop = new
EvolvingFSM<char,SSZ,char,SSZ> * [POP_SZ];

if (pop == NULL)
    {
    buffer << "Memory allocation failed\r\n";
    return;
    }

EvolvingFSM<char,SSZ,char,SSZ> ** newpop = new
EvolvingFSM<char,SSZ,char,SSZ> * [POP_SZ];

if (newpop == NULL)
    {
    buffer << "Memory allocation failed\r\n";
    return;
    }

double * fit = new double [POP_SZ];

if (fit == NULL)
    {
    buffer << "Memory allocation failed\r\n";
    return;
    }

// pointers for shell sort
EvolvingFSM<char,SSZ,char,SSZ> * * ptrm = pop - 1;
double * ptrf = fit   - 1;
```

```
// create an initial population of FSMs
for (j = 0; j < POP_SZ; ++j)
    {
    for (n = 0; n < NSZ; ++n)
        {
        for (i = 0; i < SSZ; ++i)
            {
            td[n][i].NextState = size_t(devgen() *
            float(NSZ));

            if (devgen() < 0.5F)
                td[n][i].Osym = SSET[0];
            else
                td[n][i].Osym = SSET[1];
            }
        }

    pop[j] = new EvolvingFSM<char,SSZ,char,SSZ>
    (NSZ,&td[0][0],SSET,SSET,0,wts);

    if (pop[j] == NULL)
        {
        buffer << "Memory allocation failed\r\n";
        return;
        }
    }

size_t g = 0;

while (1)
    {
    // display progress in app header
    wsprintf(buf,"Forge (loop: %u of %u)",g,evoc.GetTestSize());
    SetWindowText(wdw,buf);

    // reset FSMs and clear fitness array
    for (j = 0; j < POP_SZ; ++j)
        {
        pop[j]->Reset();
        fit[j] = 0.0;
        }

    // fitness testing by competition
    for (j = 0; j < POP_SZ; ++j)
```

```
{
for (k = j; k < POP_SZ; ++k)
    {
    // reset machines to initial state
    pop[j]->Reset();
    pop[k]->Reset();

    // select first move
    switch (evoc.GetFirstMove())
        {
        case EVM_DEFECT:
            mj = 'D';
            mk = 'D';
            break;
        case EVM_COOPER:
            mj = 'C';
            mk = 'C';
            break;
        case EVM_RANDOM:
            if (devgen() < 0.5F)
                mj = 'C';
            else
                mj = 'D';

            if (devgen() < 0.5F)
                mk = 'C';
            else
                mk = 'D';
        }

    n = 1;

    // calculate fitness based on moves
    while (1)
        {
        if (mj == SSET[0])
            {
            if (mk == SSET[0])
                {
                fit[j] += evoc.GetPayoffCC();
                fit[k] += evoc.GetPayoffCC();
                }
            else
                {
```

```
                         fit[j] += evoc.GetPayoffCD();
                         fit[k] += evoc.GetPayoffDC();
                         }
                    }
                else
                    {
                    if (mk == SSET[0])
                        {
                        fit[j] += evoc.GetPayoffDC();
                        fit[k] += evoc.GetPayoffCD();
                        }
                    else
                        {
                        fit[j] += evoc.GetPayoffDD();
                        fit[k] += evoc.GetPayoffDD();
                        }
                    }

                // exit if done
                if (n == evoc.GetTestLen())
                    break;


                // state transitions based on opponents move
                tj = pop[j]->Transition(mk);
                mk = pop[k]->Transition(mj);
                mj = tj;

                // next contest
                ++n;
                }
            }
        }

// sort for selecting best
for (inc = 1; inc <= POP_SZ / 9; inc = 3 * inc + 1) ;

for ( ; inc > 0; inc /= 3)
    {
    for (i = inc + 1; i <= POP_SZ; i += inc)
        {
        vf = ptrf[i];
        vm = ptrm[i];
```

```
            j  = i;

            while ((j > inc) && (ptrf[j - inc] < vf))
                {
                ptrf[j] = ptrf[j - inc];
                ptrm[j] = ptrm[j - inc];

                j -= inc;
                }

            ptrf[j] = vf;
            ptrm[j] = vm;
            }
        }

// display best machine
if (((g % evoc.GetReptFreq()) == 0)
||  (g == evoc.GetTestSize())))
    {
    buffer << "\r\nGeneration " << g
           << "\r\n----------------\r\n";

    pop[0]->DumpStructure(buffer);

    buffer << "        Fitness: " << fit[0] << "\r\n";
    }

// exit, if it's time
if (g == evoc.GetTestSize())
    break;

// fitness scaling (linear normalization)
if (evoc.GetFitScale())
    {
    fit[0] = evoc.GetFitLinBase();
    i      = 1;

    while (fit[i-1] <= evoc.GetFitLinDec())
        {
        fit[i] = fit[i-1] - evoc.GetFitLinDec();
        ++i;
        }

    for (; i < POP_SZ; ++i)
```

```
                        fit[i] = evoc.GetFitLinMin();
            }

        // reproduce new members
        rw = new RouletteWheel<double> (POP_SZ,fit);

        if (rw == NULL)
            {
            buffer << "Memory allocation failed\r\n";
            return;
            }

        for (j = 0; j < POP_SZ; ++j)
            {
            i = rw->GetIndex();

            newpop[j] = new
            EvolvingFSM<char,SSZ,char,SSZ>(*(pop[i]));

             if (newpop[j] == NULL)
                 {
                 buffer << "Memory allocation failed\r\n";
                 return;
                 }

             if (devgen() < evoc.GetMuteRate())
                 newpop[j]->Mutate(2,evoc.GetMaxState());
             }

        delete rw;

        // copy next generation and repeat!
        for (j = 0; j < POP_SZ; ++j)
            delete pop[j];

        memcpy(pop,newpop,POP_SZ *
            sizeof(EvolvingFSM<char,SSZ,char,SSZ> *));

        ++g;
        }

// delete buffers
for (j = 0; j < POP_SZ; ++j)
    delete pop[j];
```

```
    delete [] pop;
    delete [] newpop;
    delete [] fit;

    // restore window text
    SetWindowText(wdw,"Forge");
    }
```

LISTING A.6   FORGEGA.CPP FUNCTION OPTIMIZATION WITH A GENETIC ALGORITHM.

```
//------------------------------------------------------------
//  program FOR Genetic algorithm Experimentation (FORGE)
//------------------------------------------------------------
//
//       forgega.cpp      v1.00
//
//       Function optimization via genetic algorithm
//
//------------------------------------------------------------
//  Copyright 1995 by Scott Robert Ladd. All rights reserved.
//------------------------------------------------------------

#include "windows.h"  // Windows definitions
#include "forgeres.h" // resource constants
#include "strstrea.h" // strstream definitions
#include "iomanip.h"  // stream manipulators
#include "randdev.h"  // uniform random deviate generator
#include "roulette.h" // RouletteWheel class
#include "bool.h"     // ANSI-like 'bool' class
#include "gaoptcfg.h" // optimization configuration dialog box
#include "math.h"     // math functions
#include "float.h"    // floating point parameters
#include "fpconst.h"  // floating point constants
#include "fputil.h"   // floating-point utility functions
#include "gafloat.h"  // mutation and crossover for IEEE floats

//------------------------------------
// Function Optimization (Peak Search)
//------------------------------------

template <class T>
    inline T sqr(const T & n) { return n * n; }
```

```
inline double FitnessF6
    (
    double x,
    double y
    )
    {
    return  0.7 + sqr(x)
              + 2.0 * sqr(y)
              - 0.3 * cos(3.0 * N_DPI * x)
              - 0.4 * cos(4.0 * N_DPI * y);
    }

inline double FitnessF7
    (
    double x,
    double y
    )
    {
    return  0.3 + sqr(x)
              + 2.0 * sqr(y)
              - 0.3 * (cos(3.0 * N_DPI * x)
                  * cos(4.0 * N_DPI * y));
    }

inline double FitnessF8
    (
    double x,
    double y
    )
    {
    return  0.3 + sqr(x)
              + 2.0 * sqr(y)
              - 0.3 * (cos(3.0 * N_DPI * x)
                  + cos(4.0 * N_DPI * y));
    }

inline double FitnessCust
    (
    double x,
    double y
    )
    {
    return 1.0 / (0.8 + sqr(x + 0.5)
                  + 2.0 * sqr(y - 0.5)
```

```
                            - 0.3 * cos(3.0 * N_DPI * x)
                            - 0.4 * cos(4.0 * N_DPI * y));
    }

void TestPeakSearch
    (
    HINSTANCE inst,
    HWND      wdw,
    strstream & buffer
    )
    {
    buffer << "Function Optimization (Peak Search)\r\n"
              "-----------------------------------\r\n";

    // create configuration and verify it
    GAOptConfig gaoc(inst,wdw);

    if (!gaoc.GetValidity())
        {
        buffer << "Cancelled\r\n";
        return;
        }

    // display parameters for this run
    buffer << "\r\n   Equation: ";

    switch (gaoc.GetEquation())
        {
        case 0:
            buffer << "f6(x,y) = x2+2y2-0.3cos(3px)-
            0.4cos(4py)+0.7";
            break;
        case 1:
            buffer << "f7(x,y) = x2+2y2-
            0.3[cos(3px)cos(4py)]+0.3";
            break;
        case 2:
            buffer << "f8(x,y) = x2+2y2-
            0.3[cos(3px)+cos(4py)]+0.3";
            break;
        case 3:
            buffer << "f(x,y) = 1/((x+0.5)2+2(y-0.5)2-
            0.3cos(3px)-0.4cos(4py)+0.8)";
        }
```

```
buffer << "\r\n  Pop. Size: " << gaoc.GetPopSize();
buffer << "\r\n  Test Size: " << gaoc.GetTestSize();
buffer << "\r\n  Rep. Freq: " << gaoc.GetReptFreq();
buffer << "\r\nSig. Digits: " << gaoc.GetSigDigits();
buffer << "\r\n       X Min: " << gaoc.GetXMin();
buffer << "\r\n       X Max: " << gaoc.GetXMax();
buffer << "\r\n       Y Min: " << gaoc.GetYMin();
buffer << "\r\n       Y Max: " << gaoc.GetYMax();
buffer << "\r\nCrossover %: " << gaoc.GetCrossRate() *
         100.0F;
buffer << "\r\n     Cross X: " << gaoc.GetCrossX();
buffer << "\r\n     Cross Y: " << gaoc.GetCrossY();
buffer << "\r\n     Cross B: " << gaoc.GetCrossB();
buffer << "\r\n Mutation %: " << gaoc.GetMuteRate() * 100.0F;
buffer << "\r\n    Wt. Sign: " << gaoc.GetWtSign();
buffer << "\r\n    Wt. Expt: " << gaoc.GetWtExp();
buffer << "\r\n    Wt. Mant: " << gaoc.GetWtMant();
buffer << "\r\n    Mutate X: " << gaoc.GetMutateX();
buffer << "\r\n    Mutate Y: " << gaoc.GetMutateY();
buffer << "\r\nMutate Loop: " << gaoc.GetMuteLoop();
buffer << "\r\n     Elitism: " << gaoc.GetElitist();
buffer << "\r\nFit Scaling: " << gaoc.GetFitScale();
buffer << "\r\n  Fit Algor: ";

switch(gaoc.GetFitAlgor())
    {
    case FSA_EXPON:
        buffer << "Exponential";
        break;
    case FSA_WINDOW:
        buffer << "Windowing";
        break;
    case FSA_LINEAR:
        buffer << "Linear Normalization";
        buffer << "\r\nFS Lin Base: " <<
        gaoc.GetFitLinBase();
        buffer << "\r\nFS Lin  Dec: " << gaoc.GetFitLinDec();
        buffer << "\r\nFS Lin  Min: " << gaoc.GetFitLinMin();
    }

buffer << "\r\n\r\n";

// store dimensions of test
const size_t POP_SZ  = gaoc.GetPopSize();
```

```
const size_t GEN_SZ  = gaoc.GetTestSize();
const size_t EQ_ID   = gaoc.GetEquation();
const size_t SIG_DIG = gaoc.GetSigDigits();

buffer << setprecision(SIG_DIG) << dec;

// create random deviate and mutation objects
RandDev devgen;
FloatMutagen
fmute(gaoc.GetWtSign(),gaoc.GetWtExp(),gaoc.GetWtMant());

// allocate population and fitness arrays
double * x = new double [POP_SZ];

if (x == NULL)
    {
    buffer << "Memory allocation failed\r\n";
    return;
    }

double * xnew = new double [POP_SZ];

if (xnew == NULL)
    {
    buffer << "Memory allocation failed\r\n";
    return;
    }

double * y = new double [POP_SZ];

if (y == NULL)
    {
    buffer << "Memory allocation failed\r\n";
    return;
    }

double * ynew = new double [POP_SZ];

if (ynew == NULL)
    {
    buffer << "Memory allocation failed\r\n";
    return;
    }
```

```
double * fit = new double [POP_SZ];

if (fit == NULL)
    {
    buffer << "Memory allocation failed\r\n";
    return;
    }

double * ptrf = fit - 1;
double * ptrx =  x  - 1;
double * ptry =  y  - 1;

// various variables
double best, lowf, fitn, vf, vx, vy;
size_t i, j, inc, g, ibest, p1, p2;
char buf[64];

// calculate ranges
const double rangex = gaoc.GetXMax() - gaoc.GetXMin();
const double rangey = gaoc.GetYMax() - gaoc.GetYMin();

// generate initial X values
for (i = 0; i < POP_SZ; ++i)
    {
    x[i] = SigDig(rangex * devgen() +
    gaoc.GetXMin(),SIG_DIG);
    y[i] = SigDig(rangey * devgen() +
    gaoc.GetYMin(),SIG_DIG);
    }

// do the generations
for (g = 0; g < GEN_SZ; ++g)
    {
    // display progress in app header
    wsprintf(buf,"Forge (loop: %u of %u)",g,GEN_SZ);
    SetWindowText(wdw,buf);

    // calculate fitness for x values
    best  = DBL_MIN;
    lowf  = DBL_MAX;
    ibest = 0;

    for (i = 0; i < POP_SZ; ++i)
        {
```

```
switch (EQ_ID)
    {
    case 0:
        fit[i] = 1.0 - FitnessF6(x[i],y[i]);
        break;
    case 1:
        fit[i] = 1.0 - FitnessF7(x[i],y[i]);
        break;
    case 2:
        fit[i] = 1.0 - FitnessF8(x[i],y[i]);
        break;
    case 3:
        fit[i] = FitnessCust(x[i],y[i]);
    }

fit[i] = SigDig(fit[i],SIG_DIG);

// track best fitness
if (fit[i] > best)
    {
    best  = fit[i];
    ibest = i;
    }

// track lowest fitness
if (fit[i] < lowf)
    lowf = fit[i];
}

// display best solution so far
if ((g % gaoc.GetReptFreq()) == 0)
    {
    buffer << setw(4) << g << ": (" << x[ibest]
           << "," << y[ibest] << ") fit = "
           << best << "\r\n";
    }

// sort by fitness if linear normalization
if (FSA_LINEAR == gaoc.GetFitAlgor())
    {
    // shell sort three arrays in order of fitness
    fitn = gaoc.GetFitLinBase();

    for (inc = 1; inc <= POP_SZ / 9; inc = 3 * inc + 1) ;
```

```
for ( ; inc > 0; inc /= 3)
    {
    for (i = inc + 1; i <= POP_SZ; i += inc)
        {
        vf = ptrf[i];
        vx = ptrx[i];
        vy = ptry[i];

        j  = i;

        while ((j > inc) && (ptrf[j - inc] < vf))
            {
            ptrf[j] = ptrf[j - inc];
            ptrx[j] = ptrx[j - inc];
            ptry[j] = ptry[j - inc];

            j -= inc;
            }

        ptrf[j] = vf;
        ptrx[j] = vx;
        ptry[j] = vy;
        }
    }
}

for (i = 0; i < POP_SZ; ++i)
    {
    // fitness scaling
    if (gaoc.GetFitScale())
        {
        switch (gaoc.GetFitAlgor())
            {
            case FSA_EXPON:
                fit[i] = sqr(fit[i] + 1.0);
                break;
            case FSA_WINDOW:
                fit[i] -= lowf;
                break;
            case FSA_LINEAR:
                {
                fit[i] = fitn;

                if (fitn > gaoc.GetFitLinMin())
```

```
                              {
                              fitn -= gaoc.GetFitLinDec();

                              if (fitn < gaoc.GetFitLinMin())
                                  fitn = gaoc.GetFitLinMin();
                              }
                          }
                      }
                  }
          }

    // create roulette wheel for reproduction selection
    RouletteWheel<double> * sel;
    sel = new RouletteWheel<double> (POP_SZ,fit);

    if (sel == NULL)
        {
        buffer << "Failed to allocate roulette wheel\r\n";
        return;
        }

    // if elitist, include best from orig. population
    if (gaoc.GetElitist())
        {
        if (FSA_LINEAR == gaoc.GetFitAlgor())
            {
            xnew[0] = x[0];
            ynew[0] = y[0];
            }
        else
            {
            xnew[0] = x[ibest];
            ynew[0] = y[ibest];
            }

        i = 1;
        }
    else
        i = 0;

    // create new population of x's
    for ( ; i < POP_SZ; ++i)
        {
        // create a new x
```

```
p1 = sel->GetIndex();

if (gaoc.GetCrossX()
&&  (devgen() <= gaoc.GetCrossRate()))
    {
    p2 = sel->GetIndex();
    xnew[i] = Crossover(x[p1],x[p2]);
    }
else
    xnew[i] = x[p1];

// create a new y
if (gaoc.GetCrossB())
    p1 = sel->GetIndex();

if (gaoc.GetCrossY()
&&  (devgen() <= gaoc.GetCrossRate()))
    {
    p2 = sel->GetIndex();
    ynew[i] = Crossover(y[p1],y[p2]);
    }
else
    ynew[i] = y[p1];

// mutate X
if (gaoc.GetMutateX())
    {
    if (gaoc.GetMuteLoop())
        {
        while (devgen() <= gaoc.GetMuteRate())
            xnew[i] = fmute.Mutate(xnew[i]);
        }
    else
        {
        if (devgen() <= gaoc.GetMuteRate())
            xnew[i] = fmute.Mutate(xnew[i]);
        }
    }

// mutate Y
if (gaoc.GetMutateY())
    {
    if (gaoc.GetMuteLoop())
        {
```

```
                    while (devgen() <= gaoc.GetMuteRate())
                        ynew[i] = fmute.Mutate(ynew[i]);
                }
            else
                {
                if (devgen() <= gaoc.GetMuteRate())
                    ynew[i] = fmute.Mutate(ynew[i]);
                }
            }

        // make sure x & y fit ranges
        if (xnew[i] > gaoc.GetXMax())
            xnew[i] = gaoc.GetXMax();

        if (xnew[i] < gaoc.GetXMin())
            xnew[i] = gaoc.GetXMin();

        if (ynew[i] > gaoc.GetYMax())
            ynew[i] = gaoc.GetYMax();

        if (ynew[i] < gaoc.GetYMin())
            ynew[i] = gaoc.GetYMin();

        // truncate digits
        xnew[i] = SigDig(xnew[i],SIG_DIG);
        ynew[i] = SigDig(ynew[i],SIG_DIG);
        }

    // remove roulette wheel
    delete sel;

    // copy new population
    memcpy(x,xnew,POP_SZ * sizeof(double));
    memcpy(y,ynew,POP_SZ * sizeof(double));
    }

// delete buffers
delete [] fit;
delete [] ynew;
delete [] y;
delete [] xnew;
delete [] x;

// restore app window name
```

```
SetWindowText(wdw,"Forge");
}
```

LISTING A.7   FORGEPD PRISONER'S DILEMMA WITH BIT STRINGS.

```cpp
//------------------------------------------------------------
// program FOR Genetic algorithm Experimentation (FORGE)
//------------------------------------------------------------
//
//       forgepd.cpp      v1.00
//
//       Prisoner's Dilemma by bit strings
//
//------------------------------------------------------------
// Copyright 1995 by Scott Robert Ladd. All rights reserved.
//------------------------------------------------------------

#include "windows.h"   // Windows definitions
#include "forgeres.h"  // resource constants
#include "strstrea.h"  // strstream definitions
#include "iomanip.h"   // stream manipulators
#include "string.h"    // memory management functions
#include "randdev.h"   // uniform random deviate generator
#include "roulette.h"  // RouletteWheel class
#include "bool.h"      // ANSI-like 'bool' class
#include "pdoptcfg.h"  // configuration dialog box
#include "fstream.h"   // external file stream classes
#include "bintreek.h"  // keyed binary tree container

//-------------------
// Prisoner's Dilemma
//-------------------

typedef unsigned long Chromosome;

struct CData
    {
    size_t     Level;
    Chromosome Chrom;

    CData()
        {
        Level = 0;
```

```
            Chrom = OUL;
            }

    CData
        (
        size_t      l,
        Chromosome c
        )
        {
        Level = l;
        Chrom = c;
        }

    bool operator ==
        (
        CData c
        ) const
        {
        if ((Chrom == c.Chrom) && (Level == c.Level))
            return true;
        else
            return false;
        }

    bool operator !=
        (
        CData c
        ) const
        {
        if ((Chrom != c.Chrom) || (Level != c.Level))
            return true;
        else
            return false;
        }

    bool operator <
        (
        CData c
        ) const
        {
        if (Level < c.Level)
            return true;

        if ((Level == c.Level) && (Chrom < c.Chrom))
```

```
                return true;

            return false;
            }
        };

void TestDilemma
    (
    HINSTANCE inst,
    HWND      wdw,
    strstream & buffer
    )
    {
    buffer << "Prisoner's Dilemma\r\n"
              "------------------\r\n";

    // create configuration and verify it
    PDOptConfig pdoc(inst,wdw);

    if (!pdoc.GetValidity())
        {
        buffer << "Cancelled\r\n";
        return;
        }

    // open output file (if required)
    ofstream * fout = NULL;

    if  (pdoc.GetFileOut())
        {
        fout = new ofstream (pdoc.GetFileName());

        if (fout == NULL)
            {
            buffer << "Memory allocation failed\r\n";
            return;
            }
        }

// display parameters
    size_t POP_SZ  = pdoc.GetPopSize();
    size_t GEN_SZ  = pdoc.GetTestSize();
    size_t s;
```

```
switch (pdoc.GetStartLvl())
    {
    case  1: s =      8U; break;
    case  2: s =    128U; break;
    case  3: s = 32768U; break;
    default: s =      2U;
    }

if (pdoc.GetFairStart() && (POP_SZ % s))
    POP_SZ = (POP_SZ / s + 1) * s;

buffer << "\r\n Population: " << POP_SZ;
buffer << "\r\n  Test Size: " << GEN_SZ;
buffer << "\r\nReport Freq: " << pdoc.GetReptFreq();
buffer << "\r\nStart Level: " << pdoc.GetStartLvl();

buffer << "\r\n  Crossover: " << pdoc.GetCrossover();
if (pdoc.GetCrossover())
    buffer << " (" << pdoc.GetCrossRate() * 100.0F << "%)";

buffer << "\r\n   Mutation: "<< pdoc.GetMutation();
if (pdoc.GetMutation())
    buffer << " (" << pdoc.GetMuteRate() * 100.0F << "%)";

buffer << "\r\n   Doubling: " << pdoc.GetDoubling();
if (pdoc.GetDoubling())
    {
    buffer << " (" << pdoc.GetDblRate() * 100.0F << "%)";
    buffer << "\r\n Max. Level: " << pdoc.GetMaxLevel();
    }

buffer << "\r\n  Averaging: " << pdoc.GetAveraging();
buffer << "\r\n Fair Start: " << pdoc.GetFairStart();
buffer << "\r\n Random 1st: " << pdoc.GetRandom1st();
buffer << "\r\n  Payoff DD: " << pdoc.GetPayoffDD();
buffer << "\r\n  Payoff DC: " << pdoc.GetPayoffDC();
buffer << "\r\n  Payoff CD: " << pdoc.GetPayoffCD();
buffer << "\r\n  Payoff CC: " << pdoc.GetPayoffCC();
buffer << "\r\nFile Output: " << pdoc.GetFileOut();

if (pdoc.GetFileOut())
    buffer << " (" << pdoc.GetFileName() << ")";

buffer << "\r\n\r\n" << dec;
```

```
if (fout != NULL)
    {
    (*fout) << "\n Population: " << pdoc.GetPopSize();
    (*fout) << "\n  Test Size: " << pdoc.GetTestSize();
    (*fout) << "\nReport Freq: " << pdoc.GetReptFreq();
    (*fout) << "\nStart Level: " << pdoc.GetStartLvl();

    (*fout) << "\n  Crossover: " << pdoc.GetCrossover();
    if (pdoc.GetCrossover())
       (*fout) << " (" << pdoc.GetCrossRate() * 100.0F << "%)";

    (*fout) << "\n   Mutation: "<< pdoc.GetMutation();
    if (pdoc.GetMutation())
       (*fout) << " (" << pdoc.GetMuteRate() * 100.0F << "%)";

    (*fout) << "\n   Doubling: " << pdoc.GetDoubling();
    if (pdoc.GetDoubling())
        {
        (*fout) << " (" << pdoc.GetDblRate() * 100.0F << "%)";
        (*fout) << "\n Max. Level: " << pdoc.GetMaxLevel();
        }

    (*fout) << "\n  Averaging: " << pdoc.GetAveraging();
    (*fout) << "\n Fair Start: " << pdoc.GetFairStart();
    (*fout) << "\n Random 1st: " << pdoc.GetRandom1st();
    (*fout) << "\n  Payoff DD: " << pdoc.GetPayoffDD();
    (*fout) << "\n  Payoff DC: " << pdoc.GetPayoffDC();
    (*fout) << "\n  Payoff CD: " << pdoc.GetPayoffCD();
    (*fout) << "\n  Payoff CC: " << pdoc.GetPayoffCC();
    (*fout) << "\nFile Output: " << pdoc.GetFileOut();

    if (pdoc.GetFileOut())
        (*fout) << " (" << pdoc.GetFileName() << ")";

    (*fout) << dec << "\n\n";
    }

// create random deviate and mutation objects
RandDev devgen;

// allocate population and fitness arrays
Chromosome * pop = new Chromosome [POP_SZ];

if (pop == NULL)
```

```
        {
    buffer << "Memory allocation failed\r\n";
    return;
        }

Chromosome * newpop = new Chromosome [POP_SZ];

if (newpop == NULL)
        {
    buffer << "Memory allocation failed\r\n";
    return;
        }

size_t * lvl = new size_t [POP_SZ];

if (lvl == NULL)
            {
        buffer << "Memory allocation failed\r\n";
        return;
            }

size_t * newlvl = new size_t [POP_SZ];

if (newlvl == NULL)
        {
    buffer << "Memory allocation failed\r\n";
    return;
        }

double * fit = new double [POP_SZ];

if (fit == NULL)
        {
    buffer << "Memory allocation failed\r\n";
    return;
        }

// shifts for move selection
static const int shift[4] = { 1, 3, 7, 15 };

// level masks
static const Chromosome lmask[5] =
        {
    0x00000001UL,
```

```
    0x00000007UL,
    0x0000007FUL,
    0x00007FFFUL,
    0x7FFFFFFFUL
    };

static const float   lbits[5]  = { 1.0F, 3.0F, 7.0F, 15.0F,
31.0F };
static const size_t lbitsn[5] = { 1, 3, 7, 15, 31 };

// strategy masks
static const Chromosome smask[5] =
    {
    0x00000001UL,
    0x00000006UL,
    0x00000078UL,
    0x00007F80UL,
    0x7FFF8000UL
    };

static const int sbits[5] = { 1, 2, 4, 8, 16 };

// various variables
size_t g, i, j, k, l, p1, p2, pl, ps;
Chromosome strati, stratj, tempi, tempj, bit, m, vb;
char buf[64];
RouletteWheel<double> * rw;

// mask off low bit if start is random
if (pdoc.GetRandom1st())
    vb = 0xFFFFFFFEUL;
else
    vb = 0xFFFFFFFFUL;

// generate initial 3-bit population
k = 0;

if (pdoc.GetFairStart())
    {
    for (i = 0; i < POP_SZ / s; ++i)
        {
        for (m = 0; m < s; ++m)
            {
            pop[k] = m;
```

```
                    lvl[k] = pdoc.GetStartLvl();
                    ++k;
                    }
                }
            }
        else
            {
            for (i = 0; i < POP_SZ; ++i)
                {
                pop[i] = Chromosome(devgen() * float(s));
                lvl[i] = pdoc.GetStartLvl();
                }
            }

    // do the generations
    for (g = 0; g < GEN_SZ; ++g)
        {
        // display progress in app header
        wsprintf(buf,"Forge (loop: %u of %u)",g,GEN_SZ);
        SetWindowText(wdw,buf);

        // calculate fitness for x values
        for (i = 0; i < POP_SZ; ++i)
            fit[i] = 0.0;

        for (i = 0; i < POP_SZ; ++i)
            {
            for (j = i + 1; j < POP_SZ; ++j)
                {
                // compete
                l = (lvl[i] < lvl[j]) ? lvl[i] : lvl[j];

                // level l
                if (pdoc.GetRandom1st())
                    {
                    strati = (devgen() > 0.5F) ? 1 : 0;
                    stratj = (devgen() > 0.5F) ? 1 : 0;
                    }
                else
                    {
                    strati = pop[i] & 1UL;
                    stratj = pop[j] & 1UL;
                    }
```

```
// levels 2 through 5
for (k = 0; k < l; ++k)
    {
    // select my move
    bit   = pop[i] & (1UL << int(shift[k] +
    stratj));
    tempi = (strati << 1) | (bit >> int(shift[k]
    + stratj));

    // select his move
    bit   = pop[j] & (1UL << int(shift[k] +
    strati));
    tempj = (stratj << 1) | (bit >> int(shift[k]
    + strati));

    strati = tempi;
    stratj = tempj;
    }

// compete
if (pdoc.GetRandom1st())
    {
    k = 1;
    m = 2;
    }
else
    {
    k = 0;
    m = 1;
    }

for (; k <= 1; ++k)
    {
    if (strati & m)
        {
        if (stratj & m)
            {
            fit[i] += pdoc.GetPayoffCC();
            fit[j] += pdoc.GetPayoffCC();
            }
        else
            {
            fit[i] += pdoc.GetPayoffCD();
            fit[j] += pdoc.GetPayoffDC();
```

```
                        }
                    }
                else
                    {
                    if (stratj & m)
                        {
                        fit[i] += pdoc.GetPayoffDC();
                        fit[j] += pdoc.GetPayoffCD();
                        }
                    else
                        {
                        fit[i] += pdoc.GetPayoffDD();
                        fit[j] += pdoc.GetPayoffDD();
                        }
                    }

                m <<= 1;
                }
            }

        // scale fitness to number of bits tested
        if (pdoc.GetAveraging())
            fit[i] /= float(1+(pdoc.GetRandom1st() ? 0 : 1));
        }

    // display results
    if ((fout != NULL) || ((g % pdoc.GetReptFreq()) == 0))
        {
        if ((g % pdoc.GetReptFreq()) == 0)
            buffer << "\r\nGeneration " << g << "\r\n";

        if (fout != NULL)
            (*fout) << "\nGeneration " << g << "\n";

        BinaryTreeKeyed < CData, size_t > tree;

        for (i = 0; i < POP_SZ; ++i)
            {
            CData d(lvl[i],(pop[i] & vb));

            try {
                j = tree.LookUp(d);
                ++j;
                tree.Insert(d,j);
```

```
            }
        catch (TreeEx & ex)
            {
            if (ex.WhatsWrong() == BTX_NOTFOUND)
                tree.Insert(d,1);
            else
                throw;
            }
        }

BinaryTreeKeyedIterator < CData, size_t > iter(tree);

while (1)
    {
    try {
        CData d(iter.GetKey());

        if ((g % pdoc.GetReptFreq()) == 0)
            buffer << setw(5) << (*iter) << ": ";

        if (fout != NULL)
            (*fout) << setw(5) << (*iter) << ": ";

        m = 1UL;

        for (j = 0; j < lbitsn[d.Level]; ++j)
            {
            if ((j == 0) && pdoc.GetRandom1st())
                {
                m <<= 1;
                continue;
                }

            if ((g % pdoc.GetReptFreq()) == 0)
                buffer << ((d.Chrom & m) ? 'C' : 'D');

            if (fout != NULL)
                (*fout) << ((d.Chrom & m) ? 'C' : 'D');

            if ((j == 0) || (j == 2)
            || (j == 6) || (j == 14))
                {
                if ((g % pdoc.GetReptFreq()) == 0)
                    buffer << ' ';
```

```
                            if (fout != NULL)
                                (*fout) << ' ';
                            }

                    m <<= 1;
                    }

                if ((g % pdoc.GetReptFreq()) == 0)
                    buffer << "\r\n";

                if (fout != NULL)
                    (*fout) << "\n";

                ++iter;
                }
            catch (TreeEx & ex)
                {
                if (ex.WhatsWrong() == BTX_NOTFOUND)
                    break;
                else
                    throw;
                }
            }
        }

    // create new generation
    rw = new RouletteWheel<double> (POP_SZ,fit);

    if (rw == NULL)
        {
        buffer << "Failed to allocate roulette wheel\r\n";
        return;
        }

    for (i = 0; i < POP_SZ; ++i)
        {
        // select a parent
        p1 = rw->GetIndex();

        // crossover
        if (pdoc.GetCrossover()
        &&  (devgen() < pdoc.GetCrossRate()))
            {
            // get second parent
```

```
    p2 = rw->GetIndex();

    // find longer of two strings
    if (lvl[p1] >= lvl[p2])
        {
        l  = lvl[p2];
        pl = p1;
        ps = p2;
        }
    else
        {
        l  = lvl[p1];
        pl = p2;
        ps = p1;
        }

    // create crossover bitmask
    m = lmask[l] >> int(devgen() * lbits[l]);

    // combine for new child
    newpop[i] = (pl & (~m)) | (ps & m);
    newlvl[i] = lvl[pl];
    }
else
    {
    newpop[i] = pop[p1];
    newlvl[i] = lvl[p1];
    }

// doubling
if (pdoc.GetDoubling()
&& (newlvl[i] < pdoc.GetMaxLevel())
&& (devgen()  < pdoc.GetDblRate()))
    {
    bit       = newpop[i] & smask[newlvl[i]];
    newpop[i] |= (bit <<  sbits[newlvl[i]]);
    newpop[i] |= (bit << (sbits[newlvl[i]] * 2));
    ++newlvl[i];
    }

// mutation
if (pdoc.GetMutation()
&& (devgen() < pdoc.GetMuteRate()))
    {
```

```
                    m = 1UL << int(devgen() * lbits[newlvl[i]]);

                    if (newpop[i] & m)
                        newpop[i] &= (~m);
                    else
                        newpop[i] |= m;
                    }

                newpop[i] &= lmask[newlvl[i]];
                }

        delete rw;

        // copy new generation
        memcpy(pop,newpop,POP_SZ * sizeof(Chromosome));
        memcpy(lvl,newlvl,POP_SZ * sizeof(size_t));
        }

    // remove arrays
    delete [] fit;
    delete [] newlvl;
    delete [] lvl;
    delete [] newpop;
    delete [] pop;
    delete    fout;

    // restore window text
    SetWindowText(wdw,"Forge");
    }
```

LISTING A.8   FORGERA.CPP ROBOTIC ANTS

```
//------------------------------------------------------------------
//  program FOR Genetic algorithm Experimentation (FORGE)
//------------------------------------------------------------------
//
//      forgera.cpp     v1.00
//
//      Evolving robotic ants
//
//------------------------------------------------------------------
//  Copyright 1995 by Scott Robert Ladd. All rights reserved.
//------------------------------------------------------------------
```

```
#include "windows.h"   // Windows definitions
#include "forgeres.h"  // resource constants
#include "strstrea.h"  // strstream definitions
#include "iomanip.h"   // stream manipulators
#include "string.h"    // memory management functions
#include "randdev.h"   // uniform random deviate generator
#include "roulette.h"  // RouletteWheel class
#include "bool.h"      // ANSI-like 'bool' class
#include "float.h"     // floating-point dimensions
#include "fsm.h"       // finite state machines
#include "raoptcfg.h"  // configuration dialog box


//---------------------------
// Test evolving robotic ants
//---------------------------

void TestRoboticAnts
    (
    HINSTANCE inst,
    HWND      wdw,
    strstream & buffer
    )
    {
    buffer << "Evolving Robotic Ants\r\n"
              "---------------------\r\n";

    // create configuration and verify it
    RAOptConfig raoc(inst,wdw);

    if (!raoc.GetValidity())
        {
        buffer << "Cancelled\r\n";
        return;
        }

    // display parameters
    buffer << "\r\n      Population: " << raoc.GetPopSize();
    buffer << "\r\n       Test Size: " << raoc.GetTestSize();
    buffer << "\r\n       Min State: " << raoc.GetMinState();
    buffer << "\r\n       Max State: " << raoc.GetMaxState();
    buffer << "\r\n       Max Moves: " << raoc.GetMaxMoves();
    buffer << "\r\n   Mutation Rate: " << raoc.GetMuteRate();
    buffer << "\r\n";
    buffer << "\r\nOutput Symbol Wt: " << raoc.GetWeight0();
```

```
buffer << "\r\n   Transition Wt: " << raoc.GetWeightT();
buffer << "\r\n    Add State Wt: " << raoc.GetWeightA();
buffer << "\r\n Delete State Wt: " << raoc.GetWeightD();
buffer << "\r\nNew InitState Wt: " << raoc.GetWeightN();

if (raoc.GetFitScale())
    {
    buffer << "\r\n";
    buffer << "\r\n     Fitness Base: " <<
    raoc.GetFitLinBase();
    buffer << "\r\n      Fitness  Dec: " <<
    raoc.GetFitLinDec();
    buffer << "\r\n      Fitness  Min: " <<
    raoc.GetFitLinMin();
    }

buffer << "\r\n";

// data arrays
const size_t MoveSz = 3;
const size_t ViewSz = 3;
const size_t StatSz = raoc.GetMinState();
const size_t POP_SZ = raoc.GetPopSize();

char MoveSet[3] =
    {
    'A',    // ahead
    'L',    // left
    'R'     // right
    };

char ViewSet[3] =
    {
    'F',    // sees food
    'E',    // sees empty square
    'C'     // sees a cliff
    };

static const size_t GridLen = 40;
static const size_t GridWid = 11;

static const int MasterGrid[GridLen][GridWid] =
    {
    {0,0,0,0,0,1,0,0,0,0,0},
```

```
    {0,0,0,0,0,1,0,0,0,0,0},
    {0,0,0,0,0,1,0,0,0,0,0},
    {0,0,0,0,0,0,1,0,0,0,0},
    {0,0,0,0,0,0,1,0,0,0,0},
    {0,0,0,0,0,1,0,0,0,0,0},
    {0,0,0,0,0,1,0,0,0,0,0},
    {0,0,0,0,1,0,0,0,0,0,0},
    {0,0,0,0,1,0,0,0,0,0,0},
    {0,0,0,1,0,0,0,0,0,0,0},
    {0,0,1,0,0,0,0,0,0,0,0},
    {0,0,1,0,0,0,0,0,0,0,0},
    {0,0,1,0,0,0,0,0,0,0,0},
    {0,0,0,1,0,0,0,0,0,0,0},
    {0,0,0,0,1,0,0,0,0,0,0},
    {0,0,0,0,1,0,0,0,0,0,0},
    {0,0,0,0,1,0,0,0,0,0,0},
    {0,0,0,0,0,1,0,0,0,0,0},
    {0,0,0,0,0,0,1,0,0,0,0},
    {0,0,0,0,0,0,1,0,0,0,0},
    {0,0,0,0,0,0,0,1,0,0,0},
    {0,0,0,0,0,0,0,1,0,0,0},
    {0,0,0,0,0,0,1,0,0,0,0},
    {0,0,0,0,0,0,1,0,0,0,0},
    {0,0,0,0,0,0,0,1,0,0,0},
    {0,0,0,0,0,0,0,1,0,0,0},
    {0,0,0,0,0,0,0,1,0,0,0},
    {0,0,0,0,0,0,0,0,1,0,0},
    {0,0,0,0,0,0,0,1,0,0,0},
    {0,0,0,0,0,0,0,1,0,0,0},
    {0,0,0,0,0,0,1,0,0,0,0},
    {0,0,0,0,0,1,0,0,0,0,0},
    {0,0,0,0,0,1,0,0,0,0,0},
    {0,0,0,0,1,0,0,0,0,0,0},
    {0,0,0,0,1,0,0,0,0,0,0},
    {0,0,0,0,0,1,0,0,0,0,0},
    {0,0,0,0,0,0,1,0,0,0,0},
    {0,0,0,0,0,0,1,0,0,0,0},
    {0,0,0,0,0,0,0,1,0,0,0},
    {0,0,0,0,0,0,1,0,0,0,0}
    };

static const int Offset[4][2] =
    {
    {  0, -1 },
```

```
        { 1,  0 },
        { 0,  1 },
        { -1, 0 }
        };

static const int Lturn[4] = { 3, 0, 1, 2 };
static const int Rturn[4] = { 1, 2, 3, 0 };

// variables
int Grid[GridLen][GridWid];
size_t n, i, d, j, k, inc;
int viewx, viewy, x, y;
char move, view, buf[64];
double vf, minf;

EvolvingFSM<char,ViewSz,char,MoveSz> * vm;

RouletteWheel<double> * rw;

RandDev devgen;

// FSM_TranData<char> td[3][3];
FSM_TranData<char> (* td)[MoveSz] = new FSM_TranData<char>
[StatSz][MoveSz];

if (td == NULL)
    {
    buffer << "Memory allocation failed\r\n";
    return;
    }

EVFSM_MuteWts wts =
    {
    raoc.GetWeight0(),
    raoc.GetWeightT(),
    raoc.GetWeightA(),
    raoc.GetWeightD(),
    raoc.GetWeightN()
    };

// allocate buffers
EvolvingFSM<char,ViewSz,char,MoveSz> ** pop
    = new EvolvingFSM<char,ViewSz,char,MoveSz> * [POP_SZ];
```

```
if (pop == NULL)
    {
    buffer << "Memory allocation failed\r\n";
    return;
    }

EvolvingFSM<char,ViewSz,char,MoveSz> ** newpop
    = new EvolvingFSM<char,ViewSz,char,MoveSz> * [POP_SZ];

if (newpop == NULL)
    {
    buffer << "Memory allocation failed\r\n";
    return;
    }

double * fit = new double [POP_SZ];

if (fit == NULL)
    {
    buffer << "Memory allocation failed\r\n";
    return;
    }

// pointers for shell sort
EvolvingFSM<char,ViewSz,char,MoveSz> * * ptrm = pop - 1;
double * ptrf = fit - 1;

// create an initial population of FSMs
for (j = 0; j < POP_SZ; ++j)
    {
    for (n = 0; n < StatSz; ++n)
        {
        for (i = 0; i < ViewSz; ++i)
            {
            td[n][i].NextState = size_t(devgen()
                                    * float(StatSz));

            if (i == 0)
                td[n][i].Osym = 'A';
            else
                td[n][i].Osym = MoveSet[size_t(devgen()
                                    * float(MoveSz))];
            }
        }
```

```
        pop[j] = new EvolvingFSM<char,ViewSz,char,MoveSz>
                    (StatSz,&td[0][0],ViewSet,MoveSet,
                     size_t(devgen() * float(StatSz)),wts);

        if (pop[j] == NULL)
            {
            buffer << "Memory allocation failed\r\n";
            return;
            }
        }

size_t g = 0;

while (1)
    {
    // display progress in app header
    wsprintf(buf,"Forge (loop: %u of %u)",
                g,raoc.GetTestSize());

    SetWindowText(wdw,buf);

    minf = DBL_MAX;

    // fitness testing by examining the trail
    for (j = 0; j < POP_SZ; ++j)
        {
        // reset fsm
        pop[j]->Reset();
        fit[j] = 0.0;

        // initialize search grid
        memcpy(&(Grid[0][0]),
               &(MasterGrid[0][0]),
               sizeof(Grid));

        // start at beginning, in center, heading south
        y = 0;
        x = 5;
        d = 2;

        // do the moves
        for (k = 0; k < raoc.GetMaxMoves(); ++k)
            {
```

```
// eat any food found in current location
if (Grid[y][x])
    {
    fit[j] += 1.0;
    Grid[y][x] = 0;
    }

// look ahead at next location
viewx = x + Offset[d][0];
viewy = y + Offset[d][1];

// looking past end of grid -- done!
if (viewy == GridLen)
    break;

// what does the ant see?
if ((viewx < 0)
|| (viewx >= GridWid)
|| (viewy < 0))
    {
    view = 'C'; // cliff
    }
else
    {
    if (Grid[viewy][viewx])
        view = 'F'; // food
    else
        view = 'E'; // empty
    }

// get move from state transition
move = pop[j]->Transition(view);

// apply move
switch (move)
    {
    case 'L': // turn left
        d = Lturn[d];
        viewx = x + Offset[d][0];
        viewy = y + Offset[d][1];
        break;
    case 'R': // turn right
        d = Rturn[d];
```

```
                      viewx = x + Offset[d][0];
                      viewy = y + Offset[d][1];
                }

           if ((viewx >= 0)
           && (viewx < GridWid)
           && (viewy >= 0))
                {
                x = viewx;
                y = viewy;
                }
           }

      if (fit[j] < minf)
          minf = fit[j];
      }

// sort for selecting best
for (inc = 1; inc <= POP_SZ / 9; inc = 3 * inc + 1) ;

for ( ; inc > 0; inc /= 3)
     {
     for (i = inc + 1; i <= POP_SZ; i += inc)
          {
          vf = ptrf[i];
          vm = ptrm[i];

          j  = i;

          while ((j > inc) && (ptrf[j - inc] < vf))
                {
                ptrf[j] = ptrf[j - inc];
                ptrm[j] = ptrm[j - inc];

                j -= inc;
                }

          ptrf[j] = vf;
          ptrm[j] = vm;
          }
     }

// display best machine
```

```
if (((g % raoc.GetReptFreq()) == 0)
  || (g == raoc.GetTestSize())))
    {
    buffer << "\r\nGeneration " << g
           << "\r\n---------------\r\n";

    pop[0]->DumpStructure(buffer);

    buffer << "       Fitness: " << fit[0] << "\r\n";
    }

// exit, if it's time
if (g == raoc.GetTestSize())
    break;

// fitness scaling (linear normalization)
if (raoc.GetFitScale())
    {
    fit[0] = raoc.GetFitLinBase();
    i      = 1;

    while ((i < POP_SZ)
           && (fit[i-1] <= raoc.GetFitLinDec()))
        {
        fit[i] = fit[i-1] - raoc.GetFitLinDec();
        ++i;
        }

    for (; i < POP_SZ; ++i)
        fit[i] = raoc.GetFitLinMin();
    }

// elitist selection
newpop[0] = pop[0];

// reproduce new members
rw = new RouletteWheel<double> (POP_SZ,fit);

if (rw == NULL)
    {
    buffer << "Memory allocation failed\r\n";
    return;
    }
```

```
        for (j = 1; j < POP_SZ; ++j)
            {
            i = rw->GetIndex();

            newpop[j] = new EvolvingFSM<char,ViewSz,char,MoveSz>
                                        (*(pop[i]));

            if (newpop[j] == NULL)
                {
                buffer << "Memory allocation failed\r\n";
                return;
                }

            if (devgen() < raoc.GetMuteRate())
                newpop[j]->Mutate(2,raoc.GetMaxState());
            }

        delete rw;

        // copy next generation and repeat!
        for (j = 1; j < POP_SZ; ++j)
            delete pop[j];

        memcpy(pop,newpop,POP_SZ *
sizeof(EvolvingFSM<char,ViewSz,char,MoveSz> *));

        ++g;
        }

    // delete buffers
    for (j = 0; j < POP_SZ; ++j)
        delete pop[j];

    delete [] pop;
    delete [] newpop;
    delete [] fit;
    delete [] td;

    // restore window text
    SetWindowText(wdw,"Forge");
    }
```

```
//-----------------------------------------------------------
//  program FOR Genetic algorithm Experimentation (FORGE)
//-----------------------------------------------------------
//
//      forgeta.cpp      v1.00
//
//      Travelling Artist Problem by genetic algorithm,
//
//-----------------------------------------------------------
//  Copyright 1995 by Scott Robert Ladd. All rights reserved.
//-----------------------------------------------------------

#include "windows.h"  // Windows definitions
#include "forgeres.h" // resource constants
#include "strstrea.h" // strstream definitions
#include "iomanip.h"  // stream manipulators
#include "string.h"   // memory management functions
#include "randdev.h"  // uniform random deviate generator
#include "roulette.h" // RouletteWheel class
#include "bool.h"     // ANSI-like 'bool' class
#include "taoptcfg.h" // configuration dialog box

//------------------------------
// Test Travelling Artist Problem
//------------------------------

typedef size_t CityChrom[10];

size_t TAFindCity
    (
    const CityChrom c,
    const size_t city
    )
    {
    // note: no safety catches for out-of-range cities!
    size_t i = 0;

    for (;;)
        {
        if (city == c[i]) return i;
```

```
            ++i;
            }
        }


void TestArtist
    (
    HINSTANCE inst,
    HWND      wdw,
    strstream & buffer
    )
    {
    buffer << "Travelling Artist Problem\r\n"
              "-------------------------\r\n";

    // create configuration and verify it
    TAOptConfig taoc(inst,wdw);

    if (!taoc.GetValidity())
        {
        buffer << "Cancelled\r\n";
        return;
        }

    // data arrays
    static const size_t CSZ = 10 * sizeof(size_t);

    const size_t POP_SZ = taoc.GetPopSize();

    static const char * cityName[10] =
        {
        "Alamosa  ", "Cortez   ",
        "Creede   ", "Durango  ",
        "Gunnison ", "Lake City",
        "Montrose ", "Pagosa   ",
        "Salida   ", "Silverton"
        };

    static const double distance[10][10] =
        {
        {  0.0,220.0, 90.0,155.0,133.0,123.0,182.0,
        89.0,105.0,141.0},
        {220.0,  0.0,135.0, 55.0,173.0,117.0,124.0,122.0,222.0,
        85.0},
```

```
{ 90.0,135.0,  0.0, 92.0, 69.0, 34.0, 95.0, 56.0, 98.0,
  57.0},
{155.0, 55.0, 92.0,  0.0,145.0, 84.0,116.0, 68.0,184.0,
  54.0},
{133.0,173.0, 69.0,145.0,  0.0, 60.0, 72.0,125.0, 70.0,
  91.0},
{123.0,117.0, 34.0, 84.0, 60.0,  0.0, 61.0, 76.0,106.0,
  33.0},
{182.0,124.0, 95.0,116.0, 72.0, 61.0,  0.0,134.0,137.0,
  66.0},
{ 89.0,122.0, 56.0, 68.0,125.0, 76.0,134.0,  0.0,142.0,
  73.0},
{105.0,222.0, 98.0,184.0, 70.0,106.0,137.0,142.0,
  0.0,139.0},
{141.0, 85.0, 57.0, 54.0, 91.0, 33.0, 66.0, 73.0,139.0,
  0.0}
};

// display parameters
buffer << "\r\n      Population: " << taoc.GetPopSize();
buffer << "\r\n       Test Size: " << taoc.GetTestSize();
buffer << "\r\n      Report Freq: " << taoc.GetReptFreq();
buffer << "\r\n        Show Best: " << taoc.GetShowBest();
buffer << "\r\nOper Probability: " << taoc.GetOperChance();

if (taoc.GetMutation())
    buffer << "\r\n        Mutation: " << taoc.GetWeightM();

if (taoc.GetInversion())
    buffer << "\r\n       Inversion: " << taoc.GetWeightI();

if (taoc.GetPMX())
    buffer << "\r\nPart Match Cross: " << taoc.GetWeightP();

if (taoc.GetCX())
    buffer << "\r\n Cycle Crossover: " << taoc.GetWeightC();

if (taoc.GetOX())
    buffer << "\r\n Order Crossover: " << taoc.GetWeightO();

buffer << "\r\n     Fitness Base: " << taoc.GetFitLinBase();
buffer << "\r\n     Fitness  Dec: " << taoc.GetFitLinDec();
buffer << "\r\n     Fitness  Min: " << taoc.GetFitLinMin();
```

```
buffer << dec << "\r\n";

// create working buffers
CityChrom * pop = new CityChrom [POP_SZ];

if (pop == NULL)
    {
    buffer << "Memory allocation failed\r\n";
    return;
    }

CityChrom * newpop = new CityChrom [POP_SZ];

if (newpop == NULL)
    {
    buffer << "Memory allocation failed\r\n";
    return;
    }

double * fit = new double [POP_SZ];

if (fit == NULL)
    {
    buffer << "Memory allocation failed\r\n";
    return;
    }

// pointers for shell sort
CityChrom * ptrp = pop - 1;
double    * ptrf = fit - 1;

// define variables
size_t g, i, j, k, l, n, s, t, p1, p2, inc;
double vf;
char buf[64];
CityChrom vp;
RouletteWheel<double> * rw;
RandDev devgen;

// create roulette wheel for operator selection
double operwt[5];

if (taoc.GetMutation())
    operwt[0] = taoc.GetWeightM();
```

```
else
    operwt[0] = 0.0;

if (taoc.GetInversion())
    operwt[1] = taoc.GetWeightI();
else
    operwt[1] = 0.0;

if (taoc.GetPMX())
    operwt[2] = taoc.GetWeightP();
else
    operwt[2] = 0.0;

if (taoc.GetCX())
    operwt[3] = taoc.GetWeightC();
else
    operwt[3] = 0.0;

if (taoc.GetOX())
    operwt[4] = taoc.GetWeightO();
else
    operwt[4] = 0.0;

RouletteWheel<double> ow(5,operwt);

// create initial population with Josephus permutation
for (i = 0; i < POP_SZ; ++i)
    {
    int plist[10];

    memset(plist,0,CSZ);

    s = size_t(devgen() *  8.0) + 1;
    j = size_t(devgen() * 10.0);

    k = 0;

    while (1)
        {
        pop[i][k] = j;
        plist[j]  = 1;

        if (k == 9)
            break;
```

```
            for (l = 0; l < s; ++l)
                {
                do  {
                    ++j; if (j > 9) j = 0;
                    }
                while (plist[j] == 1);
                }

            ++k;
            }
        }

// main program loop
g = 0;

while (1)
    {
    // display progress in app header
    wsprintf(buf,"Forge (loop: %u of
    %u)",g,taoc.GetTestSize());
    SetWindowText(wdw,buf);

    // fitness testing
    for (i = 0; i < POP_SZ; ++i)
        {
        fit[i] = 0.0;

        for (j = 1; j < 10; ++j)
            fit[i] += distance[pop[i][j-1]][pop[i][j]];
        }

    // shell sort in preparation for linear normalization
    for (inc = 1; inc <= POP_SZ / 9; inc = 3 * inc + 1) ;

    for ( ; inc > 0; inc /= 3)
        {
        for (i = inc + 1; i <= POP_SZ; i += inc)
            {
            vf = ptrf[i];
            memcpy(vp,ptrp[i],CSZ);

            j  = i;

            while ((j > inc) && (ptrf[j - inc] > vf))
```

```
                    {
                    ptrf[j] = ptrf[j - inc];
                    memcpy(ptrp[j],ptrp[j - inc],CSZ);

                    j -= inc;
                    }

            ptrf[j] = vf;
            memcpy(ptrp[j],vp,CSZ);
            }
        }

    // report information
    if (( g == taoc.GetTestSize())
    || ((g %  taoc.GetReptFreq()) == 0))
        {
        buffer << "\r\nGeneration " << g << "\r\n";

        buffer << "Best: " << cityName[pop[0][0]];

        for (i = 1; i < 10; ++i)
            buffer << "->" << cityName[pop[0][i]];

        buffer << "\r\n";

        for (i = 0; i < taoc.GetShowBest(); ++i)
            {
            buffer << setw(5) << fit[i] << ": ";

            for (j = 0; j < 10; ++j)
                buffer << setw(2) << pop[i][j];

            buffer << "\r\n";
            }
        }

    // exit, if necessary
    if (g == taoc.GetTestSize())
        break;

    // fitness scaling (linear normalization)
    fit[0] = taoc.GetFitLinBase();
    i      = 1;
```

```
while (1)
    {
    if (fit[i-1] <= taoc.GetFitLinDec())
        break;

    fit[i] = fit[i-1] - taoc.GetFitLinDec();

    ++i;
    }

for (; i < POP_SZ; ++i)
    fit[i] = taoc.GetFitLinMin();

// automatic elitist selection
memcpy(newpop[0],pop[0],CSZ);

// generate new population
rw = new RouletteWheel<double> (POP_SZ,fit);

if (rw == NULL)
    {
    buffer << "Failed to allocate roulette wheel\r\n";
    return;
    }

for (i = 1; i < POP_SZ; i += 2)
    {
    // get parents
    p1 = rw->GetIndex();

    do {
        p2 = rw->GetIndex();
        }
    while (p2 == p1);

    // duplicate parents
    memcpy(newpop[i],   pop[p1],CSZ);
    memcpy(newpop[i+1],pop[p2],CSZ);

    // skip rest of loop if no operator picked
    if (devgen() > taoc.GetOperChance())
        continue;

    // pick an operator
```

```
switch (ow.GetIndex())
    {
    case 0: // mutation
        for (n = 0; n < 2; ++n)
            {
            // pick indexes
            j = size_t(devgen() * 10.0F);

            do  {
                k = size_t(devgen() * 10.0F);
                }
            while (k == j);

            // swap city indexes
            t = newpop[i+n][k];
            newpop[i+n][k] = newpop[i+n][j];
            newpop[i+n][j] = t;
            }

        break;

    case 1: // inversion
        for (n = 0; n < 2; ++n)
            {
            // pick indexes
            j = size_t(devgen() * 9.0F);

            do  {
                k = size_t(devgen() * 10.0F);
                }
            while (k <= j);

            // calculate length
            s = (k - j + 1) / 2;

            // reverse codes
            for (l = 0; l < s; ++l)
                {
                t = newpop[i+n][k];
                newpop[i+n][k] = newpop[i+n][j];
                newpop[i+n][j] = t;

                ++j;
                --k;
```

```
                    }
                }

            break;

        case 2: // partially matched crossover
            j = size_t(devgen() * 9.0F);

            do  {
                k = size_t(devgen() * 10.0F);
                }
            while (k <= j);

            // swap cities
            for (n = j; n <= k; ++n)
                {
                if (pop[p1][n] != pop[p2][n])
                    {
                    s = TAFindCity(newpop[i+1],
                        pop[p1][n]);
                    t = newpop[i+1][n];
                    newpop[i+1][n] = newpop[i+1][s];
                    newpop[i+1][s] = t;

                    s = TAFindCity(newpop[i],pop[p2][n]);
                    t = newpop[i][n];
                    newpop[i][n] = newpop[i][s];
                    newpop[i][s] = t;
                    }
                }

            break;

        case 3:
            // cycle crossover
            j = size_t(devgen() * 10.0F);
            t = pop[p1][j];

            while (1)
                {
                newpop[i][j]   = pop[p2][j];
                newpop[i+1][j] = pop[p1][j];

                if (newpop[i][j] == t)
```

```
            break;

        j = TAFindCity(pop[p1],newpop[i][j]);
        }

    break;

case 4:
    // order crossover
    j = size_t(devgen() * 9.0F);

    do  {
        k = size_t(devgen() * 10.0F);
        }
    while (k <= j);

    if ((j == 0) && (k == 9))
        {
        memcpy(vp,newpop[i],CSZ);
        memcpy(newpop[i],newpop[i+1],CSZ);
        memcpy(newpop[i+1],vp,CSZ);
        break;
        }

    if (k == 9)
        n = 0;
    else
        n = k + 1;

    // shift and fill
    do  {
        while (1)
            {
            s = TAFindCity(pop[p2],newpop[i][n]);

            if ((s < j) || (s > k))
                break;

            // shift members
            if (n == 9)
                l = 0;
            else
                l = n + 1;
```

```
while (1)
    {
    if (l == 0)
        newpop[i][9] = newpop[i][0];
    else
        newpop[i][l-1] = newpop[i][l];

    if (l == k)
        break;

    if (l == 9)
        l = 0;
    else
        ++l;
    }
}

while (1)
    {
    s = TAFindCity(pop[p1],newpop
    [i+1][n]);

    if ((s < j) || (s > k))
        break;

    // shift members
    if (n == 9)
        l = 0;
    else
        l = n + 1;

    while (1)
        {
        if (l == 0)
            newpop[i+1][9] =
            newpop[i+1][0];
        else
            newpop[i+1][l-1] =
            newpop[i+1][l];

        if (l == k)
            break;
```

```
                        if (l == 9)
                            l = 0;
                        else
                            ++l;
                        }
                    }

                if (n == 9)
                    n = 0;
                else
                    ++n;
                }
            while (n != j);

            for (n = j; n <= k; ++n)
                {
                newpop[i][n]   = pop[p2][n];
                newpop[i+1][n] = pop[p1][n];
                }

            break;
            }
        }

    // delete, copy and loop
    delete rw;

    memcpy(pop,newpop,10 * CSZ);

    ++g;
    }

// delete buffers
delete [] fit;
delete [] newpop;
delete [] pop;

// restore window text
SetWindowText(wdw,"Forge");
}
```

LISTING A.10   FORGETST.CPP COMPONENT
TESTING MODULE FOR THE **FORGE** PROGRAM.

```cpp
//-----------------------------------------------------------
//  program FOR Genetic algorithm Experimentation (FORGE)
//-----------------------------------------------------------
//
//      forgera.cpp      v1.00
//
//      Evolving robotic ants
//
//-----------------------------------------------------------
//  Copyright 1995 by Scott Robert Ladd. All rights reserved.
//-----------------------------------------------------------

#include "windows.h"   // Windows definitions
#include "forgeres.h"  // resource constants
#include "strstrea.h"  // strstream definitions
#include "iomanip.h"   // stream manipulators
#include "string.h"    // memory management functions
#include "randdev.h"   // uniform random deviate generator
#include "roulette.h"  // RouletteWheel class
#include "bool.h"      // ANSI-like 'bool' class
#include "float.h"     // floating-point dimensions
#include "fsm.h"       // finite state machines
#include "raoptcfg.h"  // configuration dialog box

//---------------------------
// Test evolving robotic ants
//---------------------------

void TestRoboticAnts
    (
    HINSTANCE inst,
    HWND      wdw,
    strstream & buffer
    )
    {
    buffer << "Evolving Robotic Ants\r\n"
              "---------------------\r\n";

    // create configuration and verify it
    RAOptConfig raoc(inst,wdw);
```

```
if (!raoc.GetValidity())
    {
    buffer << "Cancelled\r\n";
    return;
    }

// display parameters
buffer << "\r\n     Population: " << raoc.GetPopSize();
buffer << "\r\n      Test Size: " << raoc.GetTestSize();
buffer << "\r\n      Min State: " << raoc.GetMinState();
buffer << "\r\n      Max State: " << raoc.GetMaxState();
buffer << "\r\n      Max Moves: " << raoc.GetMaxMoves();
buffer << "\r\n  Mutation Rate: " << raoc.GetMuteRate();
buffer << "\r\n";
buffer << "\r\nOutput Symbol Wt: " << raoc.GetWeightO();
buffer << "\r\n   Transition Wt: " << raoc.GetWeightT();
buffer << "\r\n    Add State Wt: " << raoc.GetWeightA();
buffer << "\r\n Delete State Wt: " << raoc.GetWeightD();
buffer << "\r\nNew InitState Wt: " << raoc.GetWeightN();

if (raoc.GetFitScale())
    {
    buffer << "\r\n";
    buffer << "\r\n    Fitness Base: " <<
    raoc.GetFitLinBase();
    buffer << "\r\n    Fitness  Dec: " <<
    raoc.GetFitLinDec();
    buffer << "\r\n    Fitness  Min: " <<
    raoc.GetFitLinMin();
    }

buffer << "\r\n";

// data arrays
const size_t MoveSz = 3;
const size_t ViewSz = 3;
const size_t StatSz = raoc.GetMinState();
const size_t POP_SZ = raoc.GetPopSize();

char MoveSet[3] =
    {
    'A',     // ahead
    'L',     // left
    'R'      // right
```

```
    };

char ViewSet[3] =
    {
    'F',     // sees food
    'E',     // sees empty square
    'C'      // sees a cliff
    };

static const size_t GridLen = 40;
static const size_t GridWid = 11;

static const int MasterGrid[GridLen][GridWid] =
    {
    {0,0,0,0,0,1,0,0,0,0,0},
    {0,0,0,0,0,1,0,0,0,0,0},
    {0,0,0,0,0,1,0,0,0,0,0},
    {0,0,0,0,0,0,1,0,0,0,0},
    {0,0,0,0,0,0,1,0,0,0,0},
    {0,0,0,0,0,1,0,0,0,0,0},
    {0,0,0,0,0,1,0,0,0,0,0},
    {0,0,0,0,1,0,0,0,0,0,0},
    {0,0,0,0,1,0,0,0,0,0,0},
    {0,0,0,1,0,0,0,0,0,0,0},
    {0,0,1,0,0,0,0,0,0,0,0},
    {0,0,1,0,0,0,0,0,0,0,0},
    {0,0,1,0,0,0,0,0,0,0,0},
    {0,0,0,1,0,0,0,0,0,0,0},
    {0,0,0,0,1,0,0,0,0,0,0},
    {0,0,0,0,1,0,0,0,0,0,0},
    {0,0,0,0,1,0,0,0,0,0,0},
    {0,0,0,0,0,1,0,0,0,0,0},
    {0,0,0,0,0,0,1,0,0,0,0},
    {0,0,0,0,0,0,1,0,0,0,0},
    {0,0,0,0,0,0,0,1,0,0,0},
    {0,0,0,0,0,0,0,1,0,0,0},
    {0,0,0,0,0,0,1,0,0,0,0},
    {0,0,0,0,0,0,1,0,0,0,0},
    {0,0,0,0,0,0,0,1,0,0,0},
    {0,0,0,0,0,0,0,1,0,0,0},
    {0,0,0,0,0,0,0,1,0,0,0},
    {0,0,0,0,0,0,0,0,1,0,0},
    {0,0,0,0,0,0,0,0,1,0,0},
    {0,0,0,0,0,0,0,1,0,0,0},
```

```
    {0,0,0,0,0,0,1,0,0,0,0},
    {0,0,0,0,0,1,0,0,0,0,0},
    {0,0,0,0,0,1,0,0,0,0,0},
    {0,0,0,0,1,0,0,0,0,0,0},
    {0,0,0,0,1,0,0,0,0,0,0},
    {0,0,0,0,0,1,0,0,0,0,0},
    {0,0,0,0,0,0,1,0,0,0,0},
    {0,0,0,0,0,0,1,0,0,0,0},
    {0,0,0,0,0,0,0,1,0,0,0},
    {0,0,0,0,0,0,1,0,0,0,0}
    };

static const int Offset[4][2] =
    {
    {  0, -1 },
    {  1,  0 },
    {  0,  1 },
    {  -1, 0 }
    };

static const int Lturn[4] = { 3, 0, 1, 2 };
static const int Rturn[4] = { 1, 2, 3, 0 };

// variables
int Grid[GridLen][GridWid];
size_t n, i, d, j, k, inc;
int viewx, viewy, x, y;
char move, view, buf[64];
double vf, minf;

EvolvingFSM<char,ViewSz,char,MoveSz> * vm;

RouletteWheel<double> * rw;

RandDev devgen;

// FSM_TranData<char> td[3][3];
FSM_TranData<char> (* td)[MoveSz] = new FSM_TranData<char>
[StatSz][MoveSz];

if (td == NULL)
    {
    buffer << "Memory allocation failed\r\n";
    return;
```

```
        }

    EVFSM_MuteWts wts =
        {
        raoc.GetWeightO(),
        raoc.GetWeightT(),
        raoc.GetWeightA(),
        raoc.GetWeightD(),
        raoc.GetWeightN()
        };

    // allocate buffers
    EvolvingFSM<char,ViewSz,char,MoveSz> ** pop
        = new EvolvingFSM<char,ViewSz,char,MoveSz> * [POP_SZ];

    if (pop == NULL)
        {
        buffer << "Memory allocation failed\r\n";
        return;
        }

    EvolvingFSM<char,ViewSz,char,MoveSz> ** newpop
        = new EvolvingFSM<char,ViewSz,char,MoveSz> * [POP_SZ];

    if (newpop == NULL)
        {
        buffer << "Memory allocation failed\r\n";
        return;
        }

    double * fit = new double [POP_SZ];

    if (fit == NULL)
        {
        buffer << "Memory allocation failed\r\n";
        return;
        }

    // pointers for shell sort
    EvolvingFSM<char,ViewSz,char,MoveSz> * * ptrm = pop - 1;
    double * ptrf = fit - 1;

    // create an initial population of FSMs
    for (j = 0; j < POP_SZ; ++j)
```

```
        {
        for (n = 0; n < StatSz; ++n)
            {
            for (i = 0; i < ViewSz; ++i)
                {
                td[n][i].NextState = size_t(devgen()
                                    * float(StatSz));

                if (i == 0)
                    td[n][i].Osym = 'A';
                else
                    td[n][i].Osym = MoveSet[size_t(devgen()
                                        * float(MoveSz))];
                }
            }

        pop[j] = new EvolvingFSM<char,ViewSz,char,MoveSz>
                    (StatSz,&td[0][0],ViewSet,MoveSet,
                     size_t(devgen() * float(StatSz)),wts);

        if (pop[j] == NULL)
            {
            buffer << "Memory allocation failed\r\n";
            return;
            }
        }

size_t g = 0;

while (1)
    {
    // display progress in app header
    wsprintf(buf,"Forge (loop: %u of %u)",
                g,raoc.GetTestSize());

    SetWindowText(wdw,buf);

    minf = DBL_MAX;

    // fitness testing by examining the trail
    for (j = 0; j < POP_SZ; ++j)
        {
        // reset fsm
        pop[j]->Reset();
```

```
fit[j] = 0.0;

// initialize search grid
memcpy(&(Grid[0][0]),
       &(MasterGrid[0][0]),
       sizeof(Grid));

// start at beginning, in center, heading south
y = 0;
x = 5;
d = 2;

// do the moves
for (k = 0; k < raoc.GetMaxMoves(); ++k)
    {
    // eat any food found in current location
    if (Grid[y][x])
        {
        fit[j] += 1.0;
        Grid[y][x] = 0;
        }

    // look ahead at next location
    viewx = x + Offset[d][0];
    viewy = y + Offset[d][1];

    // looking past end of grid -- done!
    if (viewy == GridLen)
        break;

    // what does the ant see?
    if ((viewx < 0)
    ||  (viewx >= GridWid)
    ||  (viewy < 0))
        {
        view = 'C'; // cliff
        }
    else
        {
        if (Grid[viewy][viewx])
            view = 'F'; // food
        else
            view = 'E'; // empty
        }
```

```
                // get move from state transition
                move = pop[j]->Transition(view);

                // apply move
                switch (move)
                    {
                    case 'L': // turn left
                        d = Lturn[d];
                        viewx = x + Offset[d][0];
                        viewy = y + Offset[d][1];
                        break;
                    case 'R': // turn right
                        d = Rturn[d];
                        viewx = x + Offset[d][0];
                        viewy = y + Offset[d][1];
                    }

                if ((viewx >= 0)
                && (viewx < GridWid)
                && (viewy >= 0))
                    {
                    x = viewx;
                    y = viewy;
                    }
                }

        if (fit[j] < minf)
            minf = fit[j];
        }

    // sort for selecting best
    for (inc = 1; inc <= POP_SZ / 9; inc = 3 * inc + 1) ;

    for ( ; inc > 0; inc /= 3)
        {
        for (i = inc + 1; i <= POP_SZ; i += inc)
            {
            vf = ptrf[i];
            vm = ptrm[i];

            j  = i;

            while ((j > inc) && (ptrf[j - inc] < vf))
                {
```

```
                    ptrf[j] = ptrf[j - inc];
                    ptrm[j] = ptrm[j - inc];

                    j -= inc;
                    }

                ptrf[j] = vf;
                ptrm[j] = vm;
                }
        }

    // display best machine
    if (((g % raoc.GetReptFreq()) == 0)
      || (g == raoc.GetTestSize())))
        {
        buffer << "\r\nGeneration " << g
                << "\r\n---------------\r\n";

        pop[0]->DumpStructure(buffer);

        buffer << "      Fitness: " << fit[0] << "\r\n";
        }

    // exit, if it's time
    if (g == raoc.GetTestSize())
        break;

    // fitness scaling (linear normalization)
    if (raoc.GetFitScale())
        {
        fit[0] = raoc.GetFitLinBase();
        i      = 1;

        while ((i < POP_SZ)
                && (fit[i-1] <= raoc.GetFitLinDec()))
            {
            fit[i] = fit[i-1] - raoc.GetFitLinDec();
            ++i;
            }

        for (; i < POP_SZ; ++i)
            fit[i] = raoc.GetFitLinMin();
        }
```

```
// elitist selection
newpop[0] = pop[0];

// reproduce new members
rw = new RouletteWheel<double> (POP_SZ,fit);

if (rw == NULL)
    {
    buffer << "Memory allocation failed\r\n";
    return;
    }

for (j = 1; j < POP_SZ; ++j)
    {
    i = rw->GetIndex();

    newpop[j] = new EvolvingFSM<char,ViewSz,char,MoveSz>
                               (*(pop[i]));

    if (newpop[j] == NULL)
        {
        buffer << "Memory allocation failed\r\n";
        return;
        }

    if (devgen() < raoc.GetMuteRate())
        newpop[j]->Mutate(2,raoc.GetMaxState());
    }

delete rw;

// copy next generation and repeat!
for (j = 1; j < POP_SZ; ++j)
    delete pop[j];

memcpy(pop,newpop,POP_SZ *
       sizeof(EvolvingFSM<char,ViewSz,char,MoveSz> *));

++g;
}

// delete buffers
for (j = 0; j < POP_SZ; ++j)
    delete pop[j];
```

```
delete [] pop;
delete [] newpop;
delete [] fit;
delete [] td;

// restore window text
SetWindowText(wdw,"Forge");
}
```

BIBLIOGRAPHY

Cormen, Thomas H., Charles E. Leiserson, and Ronald L. *Rivest. Introduction to Algorithms*. McGraw-Hill, 1990.

Darwin, Charles A. *On the Origin of Species by Means of Natural Selection* (sixth London edition). Thompson & Thomas, 1906.

Davis, Lawrence. *Handbook of Genetic Algorithms*. Van Nostrand-Reinhold, 1991.

Eigen, Manfred, and Ruthild Winkler. Laws of the Game: How Principles of Nature Govern Chance. Princeton, 1981.

Eldredge, Niles A. *Time Frames: The Rethinking of Darwinian Evolution and the Theory of Punctuated Equilibrium*. Simon & Schuster, 1985.

Ellis, Margaret A., and Bjarne Stroustrup. *The Annotated C++ Reference Manual*. Addison-Wesley, 1990.

Emmeche, Claus. *The Garden in the Machine*. Princeton University, 1994.

Fogel, David B. *Evolutionary Computing: Toward a New Philosophy of Machine Intelligence*. IEEE Press, 1995.

Goldberg, David E. *Genetic Algorithms in Search, Optimization, and Machine Learning*. Addison-Wesley, 1989.

Knuth, Donald E. *The Art of Computer Programming, Volume 1: Fundamental Algorithms*, second edition. Addison-Wesley, 1973.

Knuth, Donald E. *The Art of Computer Programming, Volume 2: Seminumerical Algorithms*, second edition. Addison-Wesley, 1981.

Knuth, Donald E. *The Art of Computer Programming, Volume 3: Sorting and Searching*. Addison-Wesley, 1973.

Koza, John R. *Genetic Programming II: Automatic Discovery of Reusable Programs*. MIT Press, 1994.

Krebs, Charles J. *Ecology: The Experimental Analysis of Distribution and Abundance*. Harper & Row, 1985.

Ladd, Scott Robert. *Applying C++*. M&T Books, 1990.

Ladd, Scott Robert. *C++ Templates and Tools*. M&T Books, 1995.

Langton, Christopher G., Ed. *Artificial Life II*. Addison-Wesley, 1992.

Langton, Christopher G., Ed. *Artificial Life III*. Addison-Wesley, 1994.

Press, William A., Brian P. Flannery, Saul A. Teukolsky, and William T. Vetterling. *Numerical Recipes in C: The Art of Scientific Computing*, second edition. Cambridge, 1992.

Sedgewick, Robert. *Algorithms in C*. Addison-Wesley, 1990.

Stroustrup, Bjarne. *The C++ Programming Language*, second edition. Addison-Wesley, 1991.

Tattersall, Ian. *The Fossil Trail: How We Know What We Think We Know About Human Evolution*. Oxford University Press, 1995.

Wilson, E.O. *The Diversity of Life*. Belknap-Hardvard, 1992.

Zadeh, Lotfi, and Janusz Kacprzyk. *Fuzzy Logic for the Management of Uncertainty*. Wiley, 1994.

INDEX

U

Uncertainty Principle, 64

uniform random deviates, 39-40

    RandDev class for, 40-44

W

Watson, James, 3

windowing, 16

Z

Zortech, 52, 60

Genetic Algorithms in C++

Source Code and Applications Disk
Copyright © 1995 Scott Robert Ladd. All Rights Reserved

This disk contains the complete source code from the book Genetic Algorithms in C++. All required files are in the root directory of the disk; just copy the files into a directory on your hard drive, and you're ready to compile.

The source code was tested with Borland C++ 4.5 and Microsoft Visual C++ v2.0; the FORGE application is compatible with 16- and 32-bit Windows environment (including Windows 95).

The FORGE16.EXE file is a 16-bit, Windows 3.1-compatible program. It was compiled with Borland C++ version 4.5.

The FORGE32.EXE file is a 32-bit, Windows 95/NT-compatible program. It was compiled with Visual C++ version 2.0.

Included on this disk are project files for the Borland and Microsoft compilers. The code may need minor changes to compile with newer versions of the Borland and Microsoft compilers.

An Author's Note on Distribution:

Okay, I know reality: Somebody's going to post this source code on the Networks or put it on some user group disk. PLEASE DON'T. The reason we have copyrights is to protect an author's ability to profit from his or her creations; without protection for intelectual property, people such as myself probably would not write these books.

Here's my bottom line: Feel free to distribute the compiled application, so long as you modify the "About" box to clearly note my original copyright and your subsequent changes—that way, we each get credit for our work.

If you plan to use this software as part of a commercial application, please contact the author via M&T Books for an appropriate license. You wouldn't want somebody stealing your work, would you? I've got three little girls and a wife to feed!

Thanks, and enjoy!